LAND OF WATERS

LAND OF WATERS

*Explorations in the Natural History
of Guyana, South America*

Ro McConnell

The Book Guild Ltd
Sussex, England

The Book Guild Ltd.
25 High Street,
Lewes, Sussex

First published 2000
© Ro McConnell 2000

Set in Times
Typesetting by
Acorn Bookwork, Salisbury, Wiltshire

Printed in Great Britain by
Bookcraft (Bath) Ltd, Avon

A catalogue record for this book is
available from the British Library

ISBN 1 85776 458 7

*To Richard who took me there,
and to the many who made this such a
unique and happy time.*

CONTENTS

ILLUSTRATIONS

PREFACE

For six years from 1956–62 my husband Richard McConnell and I lived in Guyana, then British Guiana, affectionately known as BG. How had we come to be there? Richard was appointed to direct the Geological Survey which was making a new geological map of the whole country and I accompanied him. As a biologist I had spent many years studying Africa's great lakes before I married Richard and we went to live in the Kalahari in 1954. I was sad to leave Africa, but what better move for a fish ecologist than from the Kalahari desert to the 'Land of Waters'? The African adventures are not part of this story, but this explains how I came to BG steeped in African ecology, fascinated by problems of tropical biology – such as the origins and evolution of the very diverse fauna and flora, coexistence in complex communities, seasonality where no winter ever comes – and continually surprised and delighted by the similarities and differences between the African and South American tropics.

Here was a whole new world to explore, especially exciting as relatively few studies had been made in BG. This book, based on our travels and analyses of notebooks and collections brought back to the British Museum (Natural History) in London, where work on these has continued for many years, gives a picture of BG as it was some 40 years ago, before it became the independent country of Guyana in 1966. Many studies have now been made in neighbouring countries by specialists well equipped with modern aids we did not then have (such as special cameras, computers, keys to identify fauna and flora) and with the great advantage of working in multidisciplinary teams, as for example on the Amazon, so there is now a vast literature on biology in neotropical regions. But so much remains to be discovered that there is still a place for an explorer–naturalist, and there is an added urgency to record conditions before the unique habitats are destroyed. The interior of Guyana is now threatened as never before, as since the 1980s huge areas have been handed over to foreign logging companies and others mining bauxite, gold and diamonds, which is leading to the sad degradation of many of the rivers and having profound effects on the lives the indigenous Amerindians.

My thanks go to the many friends who helped with *Land of Waters* especially the late Richard McConnell, Bertie Allsopp and members of the Fisheries Department. In the Rupununi, Tiny and Connie McTurk and Maggie Orella offered boundless hospitality and information, as did Bill and Daphne Seggar at Kamarang. The late Jack Holden very kindly took me to the NorthWest, and the late Vide Graham helped with some identifications. For encouragement to publish these travels my especial thanks go to Peggy Varley (nee Brown) and Gordon Howes who both read many drafts. Gordon Howes also drew the delightful black and white illustrations.

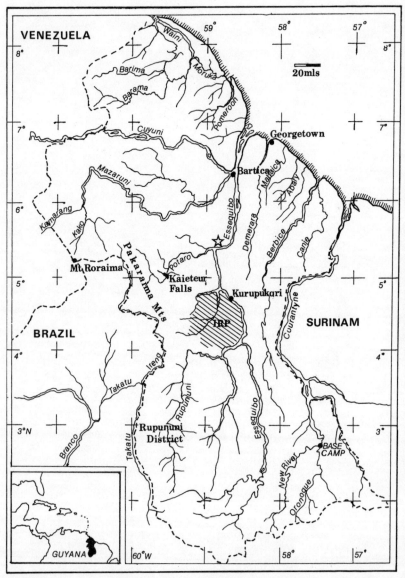

Map 1 Guyana showing sites mentioned in text. Hatched area denotes Iwokrama Rainforest Project. Star denotes Omai goldmine

xiv

1

The Land of Waters

Between the Orinoco and the Amazon, on the north-eastern Atlantic coast of South America lies Guyana, Land of Waters. The American Indians ('Amerindians') who have inhabited this country for thousands of years were said to have called it this for it is a land of great rivers pouring from the heavily forested interior to the sea and water savannas of the low-lying coastal land connected by a complex series of cross channels, a land that is flooded for much of the year. Much of the hinterland is still relatively unexplored, a romantic land which inspired Conan Doyle's 'Lost World'. Clouds meeting the high table-lands condense over the forest and conspire to make it difficult to get air photographs. However the coastal strip carries an expanding modern civilisation.

Flanked by Venezuela to the west and Surinam (formerly Dutch Guiana) to the east, the 83,000 square miles of Guyana extend 600 miles southwards from the 270 mile long coastline to the Brazilian border (see Map 1). The land surface rises from below high tide level – the coastlands being impounded behind a sea wall – to the 9000-foot tableland of Mount Roraima where the borders of Guyana, Venezuela and Brazil meet. The country is so varied that it carries a fauna and flora typical of much of tropical South America, so the results of studies which can be made with relative ease in Guyana are applicable over a much wider area. The forests are continuous with those of the Amazon, the savannas with those of Venezuela and Brazil. As befits its position just north of the equator (8° to 1°N, 57° to 61°W) the temperature is very uni-form, generally around 80°F (27°C) throughout the year, but

1

trade winds keep the coastal areas pleasantly cool and healthy. The coastal regions have two rainy seasons a year yielding about 90 inches of rain, the main rains from April to August and short 'Christmas' rains in December–January, with great variations in the amount of rain and duration of the rains from year to year. In the south the savannas generally have annual rains from May to September, with some 58 inches of rain. The distribution of the rainfall seems even more important than the amount of rain in controlling the vegetation. In the forests it rains on about 200 days in the year and the soil is washed through continuously. On the savanna plants have to withstand waterlogged soils for part of the year and being dried out for the other half, the soils being very leached and deficient in mineral salts.

South America is an immensely old land. The Precambrian rocks of the Guyana and Brazilian shields, the bare bones of the land, are among the oldest rocks in the world, dated by radioactive mineral methods as more than 2000 million years old. Once part of Gondwanaland, which included Africa, Antarctica and Australia, South America became separated from other land masses of the world, an isolation that allowed its own peculiar flora and fauna to diversify with incredible richness. Towards the end of the Pliocene, two million years ago, when the formation of a land bridge between North and South America led to some traffic between the two continents, many North American mammals, including the carnivores, gained access to South America. Then came *Homo sapiens*. Now the increase in human population threatens to change the whole continent very rapidly.

South America, unlike Africa which was rich in hominids from the earliest days of their evolution, had been relatively little affected by man – perhaps the least affected of all the continents except the polar regions. Although highly complex civilisations arose in the Andes, archaeological evidence suggested that in north-eastern South America small tribes wandered in the vastnesses of the forest, numbers kept down by the difficulties of the environment. But in modern times came the population explosion, mainly of immigrant peoples, and malaria control had led to a population bulge of people just attaining child-bearing age when we were there. Also the outside world was realising that South America was one of the last remaining parts of the world to be developed, so that very rapid changes were to be expected. Forests have now been devastated in many parts of the continent and since the travels described here vast tracts of Guyana forest are being cleared at an ever-increasing rate while mining operations are now polluting many of the rivers. So the need is urgent to understand how to make the best use of this land before it is changed and destroyed.

We found that BG was also known as the 'land of six peoples'. How had they come to be there? Since 1678 European settlers had brought Africans from West Africa to work the sugar plantations, and after the 1838 abolition of slavery they brought indentured labour from India and islands off Portugal (mainly Madeira) from 1841, and in 1853 from China. The descendants of these Indians were known in BG as 'East Indians' to distinguish them from the indigenous Amerindians, who tended to remain in the hinterland. Amerindian numbers plumetted, but in the 1950s thanks to modern medicines their numbers were increasing again.

Guyana's Amerindians represent nine peoples of three distinct language groups: the Caribs, the Arawaks and the less numerous Warao. When Europeans arrived there may have been as many as 160,000 Amerindians living along this Atlantic coast (from Venezuela to French Guiana), diverse peoples stimulated by differing environments into societies adapted to making the most of local resources. In the coastal mangrove and swamp forests the Warao, 'boat people', based their society on fishing and seafood, ate palm starch, spent much of their life in dugout canoes and were little involved in agriculture. Further inland and along the rivers the Arawaks developed agriculture based on cassava (manioc) that grows well on poor sandy soils. The Wapishana in the southern Rupununi savannas are of Arawak stock, whereas the Makushi who inhabit the northern Rupununi savannas are of Carib stock (hence different local names for Rupununi fishes).

3

The Caribs who had been a vigorous people dominating trading and were feared as warriors and raiders gave their name to the Caribbean but were then almost wiped out from the West Indian islands. Relatively pure-blooded Caribs still lived along the upper Barama river in Guyana, though their culture was increasingly affected by contact with other peoples. The Carib-related Akawaio and Patamona were based in higher country as on the Mazaruni and Potaro rivers. The forest-dwelling Wai Wai lived and hunted in the extreme south on the borders of Brazil. These societies were woven together with a network of trading alliances, through the maze of waterways and forest trails. Their interrelationships with one another and the encroaching peoples from the outside world were ably summarised by Colchester (1997) (see Chapter 13). Amerindians are excellent naturalists, born of the need to spend long hours in close association with their natural environment when hunting, fishing and collecting food, but it was clear that much information could be lost as the outside world encroached.

Guyana, until May 1966 British Guiana, is the only English-speaking part of South America. The history of the settlement of the three Guianas (Dutch, French and English) was very complex. The first men from the outside world to glimpse this country were the Spaniards on Columbus's third voyage in 1498; Pinzon who discovered the Amazon in 1500 was the first to sail along the whole coast. South America with its legends of El Dorado, the city of gold, drew many men to explore it. The Spaniards made settlements in the northern part, now Venezuela. The English came too, Walter Raleigh among them, on expeditions in 1594 and 1617, when they explored part of the Orinoco delta in small boats; Raleigh lost his son in the adventure. The Spaniards did not settle in the area which later became British Guiana, as it was thought that this country was not as rich as other parts of South America and that the Indians were hostile – though the Dutch making their first voyage there in 1598 reported meeting small English vessels up the rivers which were evidently trading among the Indians. The first British to attempt to settle in the Guianas, in

4

1604, went further south-east, to the area later to become French Guiana.

The Dutch were the first to colonise BG, the Dutch West India Company establishing a base at Kyk-over-al, a small island in the Essequibo river in 1616. They also settled Berbice, 100 miles to the east, and the intermediate Demerara colony was an offshoot from the Essequibo colony. European wars led to these colonies changing hands several times before they were finally ceded to Britain in 1814, 17 years before they were united into one country in 1831. Many Dutch names survive in Guyana. During the various negotiations Dutch Guiana (Suriname) to the east was kept by the Dutch at the expense of 'New Amsterdam', as Manhattan Island in North America was then called, the rich sugar-growing lands of Guiana then being infinitely more prized than the cold barren island which later became part of New York. So do times and values change.

In the 1950s BG had one of the highest rates of population increase in the world, an explosive increase which had followed the almost complete eradication of malaria in the ten-mile wide coastal strip where most of the population lived. The eradication was achieved after 1945 by spraying the house walls with DDT to destroy the malaria-carrying mosquitoes. In 1965 it was estimated that 90% of the total population of 620,000 people were living on 1/25 of the surface area of the country, at a density of 170 people per square mile, compared with less than one per square mile in the Interior. This coastal population was a very mixed one. The descendents of those who came from India (who made up about 45% of the total population at the 1951 census) lived mainly on the sugar- and rice-growing lands of the coast. Those of Afro-Guyanese origin (some 37% in 1951) predominated in the towns, intermingled with Chinese, Portuguese and other peoples. Only the Amerindians (7%) kept away in the Interior. So Guyana had become home to peoples of many distinct origins all using English as a common language.

The coastal alluvial plain was heavily cultivated. Sugar, grown mainly on large estates belonging to companies, and rice, grown mainly on a peasant-cooperative system, were the most important crops, though there were a few coconut groves and other attempts to diversify the agriculture. Livestock – goats, sheep, cattle and donkeys – wandered almost everywhere on the coastal plain. A belt of white sand which seals these coastal lands from the heavily forested interior was covered by a thin forest of 'wallaba' (*Eperua* spp.). This all too easily becomes desert if the trees are cut, so the sands restrict the inland spread of agriculture. Bauxite, aluminium ore, one of Guyana's main exports, was mined from below the white sand. Ocean-going steamers sailed 60 miles up the Demerara river to load the ore and carry it to Canada for processing into aluminium. Inland of the white sand belt lies the dense high forest, stretching mile after mile covering 85% of the country. This forest was inhabited only by a very sparse population of Amerindians and a few prospectors, known as 'pork-knockers', seeking gold and diamonds in the rivers. These were colourful personalities who could withstand the hardships of life in the bush, many of them of African descent came from the West Indian islands such as St Lucia. The forest stretches to the foot of the scarp over which the famous Kaieteur Falls drop a sheer 800 feet into the gorge below. The Pakaraima mountains culminate in Mount Roraima, a 9000-foot high tableland, the 'Lost World' of Conan Doyle, where the border of Guyana meets those of Venezuela and Brazil.

In the south-west, separated from Brazil by the Takutu river in the Amazon drainage, lie Rupununi savannas where cattle were ranched. Although so far from the sea, these savannas are only about 300 feet above sea level (a contrast with many of the African grasslands which are more than 3000 feet above sea level). During the annual wet season these savannas flood extensively and two great drainage systems, the Amazon and the Essequibo, are then in contact. Water flows north via the Rupununi river to the Essequibo and west via the Takutu, Rio Branco and Rio Negro to the Amazon, and certain fish species have, it seems, been able to cross this divide. Except in these savannas, roads in the interior of Guyana were virtually non-existent in the heavy forest cover and many rivers make it very difficult to build them. Access to the Rupununi from the coast was at that time (1950s) only possible by air, a two-hour flight in the old Dakota planes flown by BG Airways. Formerly river boats had been used, but this entailed hauling the boats up many rapids and the journey might take a month. There was a cattle trail, but this was rarely used since the development of air transport; much later (1990s) this became a road.

As map 1 shows, a series of great rivers drain the country from south to north. Innumerable creeks wind their way through the forest to fill these rivers, and great areas of forest become flooded at the wetter times of year. Near the coast the land is so flat that the rise and fall of the tide may be felt 100 miles or more upriver, and vast areas along the creeks are flooded. Savannas near the coast are mainly 'water savannas', grass or sedge (cyperaceous) swamps, too wet for forest except for stands of ite palms (*Mauritia flexuosa*). Floating mats of vegetation (watermeadows) spread out over swamps several feet deep, the cleared areas rich in water lilies. Small rivers run parallel with the coast. From the air the influence of the strong tidal drift to the north-west along the coast can be seen building up spits parallel with the coast, deflecting the mouths of many of these rivers to the north-west. These small rivers connecting various river systems enable small flat-bottomed boats to go from one river system to the next without going out to sea. Near the river mouths are mangrove swamps, the true (red) mangrove (*Rhizophora mangle*) with its stiltroots and viviparous young, growing along the river banks where there is the pull and suck of the current as tides ebb and flow, and the so-called black mangrove or courida (*Avicennia nitida*) on the wave-washed shores along the open coasts outside the river mouths and in the muddy estuaries. Flying into Guyana from the island of Trinidad which lies to the north-west, the plane crosses the mouths of the Orinoco which disgorge the river's rich brown waters into the sea. Perched high above in the plane one can see the extremely sharp interfaces between the muddy brown water, outlined with a vivid band of green where plankton thrives on the nutrient salts brought down by the river, and the clear blue of the open sea. From the plane it all

7

looks so static, even the cloud shadows dappling the muddy waters, so one is not aware of the speed with which these interfaces move and the turmoil of life associated with them, brought home to me later when back at my old job of fisheries research, trawling in the sea below (see Chapter 12).

The delights of the natural history of the mighty rivers and forests of South America were first brought to the outside world in classic books by pioneer naturalists. The Orinoco system was described in the *Personal Narrative of Travels to the Equinoctial Regions of America* by Baron von Humboldt (1852) in three volumes from his 1799–1804 explorations with the botanist Aimé Bonpland. The Amazon system by Alfred Russell Wallace in *A Narrative of Travels on the Amazon and Rio Negro* (1853) and by his entomological companion Henry Walter Bates, who stayed on in the Amazon for eleven years, in *The Naturalist on the River Amazons* (1863). Accounts of early explorations in what has now become Guyana include the charming *Wanderings in South America* 1812–24, by the eccentric Englishman Charles Waterton, three volumes of *Travels in British Guiana* (1840–44) by the meticulous German brothers Richard and Robert Schomburgk, and *Canoe and Camp life in British Guiana* (1877) by the geologist Charles Barrington-Brown who discovered the Kaieteur Falls. Waterton, a born naturalist and pioneer conservationist, was a marvellous observer, happy to spend hours sitting in trees watching birds. In Guyana he delighted in the beauty of the country and forests; he was interested in everything he saw – the great diversity of bird life, caiman and other reptiles and strange mammals such as sloths and vampire bats, the details of Indian life. On his first visit to Demerara in 1812, to visit family estates, he travelled up the Essequibo River to reach the 'inland frontier of Portuguese Guiana' (at Fort Joachim on the Brazilian border – now in the Rupununi District), with 'the chief object to collect a quantity of the strongest wourali', the deadly blowpipe dart poison curare prepared by the Makushi Indians, with which he then experimented on its effects. Despite the great discomforts of the long sea voyages, and the fevers he endured for which his main remedy was bleeding by leeches, he was attracted back to Guyana on three further journeys, returning to England with zoological curiosities.

In 1912 the distinguished American ichthyologist Carl Eigenmann published the account of his fish-collecting travels to see the effects of the very high Kaieteur Falls on the Potaro river on fish distribution. In the 1920s William Beebe organised a biological research station in Guyana, on the Mazaruni river near Bartica, where he and his colleagues from the New York Zoological Society studied a square mile of forest in considerable detail. Beebe's books give a picture of a time when many birds and other creatures now lost, or scarce, were abundant. For instance the horned screamer or mahooka (*Anhima cornuta*), a large bird formerly so abundant along the coastal rivers that it gave its name to the rivers Mahaica and Mahaicony in the local Amerindian tongue, is now no longer found there. Many expeditions from overseas institutions (for example the Oxford University expedition described by Hingston, 1932) and the work of the Forestry and other government departments, added greatly to knowledge of the country. One of the chief difficulties for ecological research in South America is the lack of simple keys for identifying the plants and animals, and the large numbers of undescribed species present in the tropical communities greatly complicate the process.

Living in BG for a number of years one could study the seasonal cycle and its variations from year to year, generally controlled by the duration of the rains. The opportunity to study South American fishes after African ones was also most welcome, as in many ways the fish faunas are very similar. These two continents are the homes of the cichlids and characoid (characin) fishes for instance. In other ways they are strikingly different, South America having no cyprinids (carps), the niches occupied by these in African waters being filled by the remarkable adaptive radiations of characoids in South American waters. Again, electric fishes which have evolved in the freshwaters of both continents and fill very comparable niches are from two quite unrelated families of fishes. Many of Guyana's fishes are widely known, either as aquarium fishes,

9

or from traveller's tales, or from zoological textbooks. There is a flourishing trade in fishes for tropical aquaria, mostly to North America but also to Europe. Everywhere one was struck by the convergences of evolution and in the plant world too – so much so that colour photographs taken in the Rupununi savanna country of Guyana, with its granite kopies, could be mistaken for similar country in Zimbabwe, though the families of plants contributing to the flora are totally different. But again there were striking differences, for example the South American savannas lack the great herds of hooved animals characteristic of African plains. Interest in these biological problems: the extent of seasonal changes; the comparative ecology of closely related species; similarities and differences between the South American and African tropics, ran as a connecting link through our years in BG.

Richard, whose department was making a new geological map of the whole country, travelled widely, camping in remote parts while visiting geologists on their field trips. I sometimes went too, but also became involved with fish and fisheries again, working in cooperation with Fishery Research Officer Bertie Allsopp. The fisheries laboratory was situated at the back of the very beautiful botanic gardens in Georgetown. Shortly after we arrived in BG I had the good fortune to go to the Rupununi savannas with Bertie and Dr C.F. Hickling, the Fisheries Advisor to the ODA (UK Overseas Development Administration), and to stay at Karanambo ranch with Connie and Tiny McTurk. Fishes are very important in the lives of the people of these savannas; they had been little studied scientifically, but everyone was interested in them as a source of food and there was a huge fund of local knowledge about them. Tiny McTurk, an excellent naturalist, was an invaluable help, and it was obvious that this would make an ideal centre for ecological studies where Amazon and Essequibo faunas are in contact. The annual rainy season and flood cycle meant that the fishes were likely to have a well-defined breeding season here, which might make it possible to determine how fast they grew. But the first need was to find out just what fishes lived here, then to return at different times of year to see how they

10

behaved round the year. Meanwhile the research ship RV *Cape St Mary*, originally built for fisheries research off West Africa, had come to BG for two years to survey trawling possibilities on the continental shelf. There was no biologist with the ship, so for the second year of the survey I became their biologist, which entailed going to sea and learning about a whole new fish fauna (Chapter 12).

On the geological trips we generally travelled by air to some remote river pool, where we were met by a geologist in a small plank boat, known locally as a ballahoo, and taken up or down river to camp. Landing on river pools was made possible by the amphibious nature of the six-seater Grummon Goose plane which could put down wheels and waddle out on land when occasion demanded. These flights gave excellent views of the forest canopy through which poked the great cauliflower-like tops of exceptionally tall trees. At one time we used a small helicopter; it would have been interesting to land on the trees, but said to be impossible as the helicopter needed an air cushion below it, and anyway it would blow the leaves off the trees. (Many years later such a system was used to explore the canopy fauna and flora in a neighbouring country.) Often there were vivid patches of flowers on widely scattered trees; purple and yellow seemed to be the fashionable colours, and macaws, always in pairs, red and blue or yellow and blue according to the species, would fly below us. The geological camps provided splendid opportunities to wander in the forests and see animals that one did not normally encounter while busy with fishing nets. On the whole the mammals in this part of South America are extremely elusive. Invertebrates, such as the many kinds of ants, termites and hymenoptera, and their curious nest structures are much more readily visible than the vertebrates – except for the birds whose calls rang out loud and clear over the forest.

This was our home for six very busy years. In more sober moments I was working as a research officer with results described elsewhere, but it was also easy to be lost in contemplation of the complexity of it all – of the life of the mudflats, rivers, forests and savannas – akin to that state of watchfulness

11

when alone in such places so well described by W.H. Hudson in *Far Away and Long Ago*. A seeing-out-of-the-corners-of-the-eye participation, sitting motionless by the hour, just watching and absorbing ... the behaviour of fiddler crabs in mud with their periscope eyes ... the squabbles in the heronry, noisy wing-flapping youngsters clamouring for food ... shoals of fish in gold water ... spiders' eyes gleaming green and bright on the rocks at night ... hearing the swish of fish-eating bats scooping small fish from the water surface, until one almost felt what it must be like to be a crab, periscope eyes pushing up through the mud, or to hop hop along the surface of the warm sea like an escaping foureye fish. As a scientist 'facts' came first and much time was spent in the fish market to see what contribution fish could make for the rapidly rising human population, but here I can relive the delights of the half-way world of the mudflats, the towering forests and the open sunny savannas.

2

Wildlife Encountered in our Travels

What animals would we meet in our wanderings? Information had to be gleaned from many sources: we did not then have Kricher's useful *A Neotropical Companion: An Introduction to the Animals, Plants and Ecosystems of the New World Tropics*, published 40 years later. But we did have many indigenous creatures living in the small zoo in Georgetown's botanic garden where we got to know them as individuals. In 1997 Guyana's known land vertebrates were listed as 1200 species, including 198 mammal species, 728 bird species, 137 reptiles, 105 amphibia, and over 6000 known plant species of which 100 are forest trees of commercial interest, but many more species probably – certainly among the fishes – remain to be discovered and named.

After the open plains of Africa with their vast herds of game the savannas seemed very empty of wild creatures. We might see an occasional deer bounding into a thicket, or a fox trotting along the track, or if very lucky a giant anteater, and armadillo holes showed that more hidden creatures were present. Stanley Brock in *Hunting in the Wilderness*, based on his life in the Rupununi savannas at this time, commented that many of the creatures here – capybara, collared peccary, coatimundi and others – cannot stand the direct rays of the sun and may die if they cross the open savanna by day. This helps to account for the paucity of mammalian fauna on the savannas compared with the plains of Africa, and as the savannas have become enlarged by human activities the islands of shade have been reduced, decreasing the range of these species.

Mammals

Most of Guyana's mammals live in the forest, in the leafy world where they are difficult to observe. Very little was then on record about their habits in the wild, though there have since been many studies made in neighbouring territories. Many creatures are nocturnal, whereas people are diurnal and often fearful of going into the forest at night, in case 'kanaimas' – those widely believed-in jumbies – catch you. Nevertheless the Amerindians were excellent naturalists with a large fund of information on the animals, many of which also appeared in their folk tales, and which needed to be gathered as much of it will disappear. The animals themselves are fast becoming less plentiful and much harder to find since the advent of the gun, the opening up of the interior and the rapid increase in human population.

The most exciting zoologically were those lumped together in the order Edentata, the 'toothless ones', the sloths (Bradypodidae) and armadillos (Dasypodidae) – though both of these have well-developed teeth, and the anteaters (Mymecophagidae), for apart from a few species that have spread north, South America is unique in possession of these groups of mammals. They represent very old groups; living species are few and all rather small, but many giant fossil forms are known.

Another distinctive neotropical group comprises the guinea-pig-like rodents, of which the waterhaas or capybara (*Hydrochaeris hydrochaeris*) is the largest rodent in the world, adults weighing over 200 pounds. Then there are the diurnal agoutis (*Dasyprocta* spp), the nocturnal paca or labba (*Agouti paca*), tree porcupines with prehensile tails (*Coendou* spp) and a species of the well-known domesticated guinea pig in its wild state (*Cavia* sp), among many others. In the absence of large herbivores, these rodents have filled the grass-eating niches in South America.

The ancestors of these neotropical groups (the 'primary endemics') must have been in South America before the continent became isolated from other land masses when Gondwana-

14

land fragmented in the late Mesozoic more than 100 million years ago, when the age of reptiles was nearly over and early mammals were diversifying. The long isolation of the continent, lasting some 70 million years throughout the Tertiary, gave the mammals, both marsupials and placentals, opportunities to diversify to all manner of bizarre new forms. The fossil record tells of many now extinct: of marsupial carnivores, of five extinct orders of ungulates, of huge armadillo-like creatures such as *Glyptodon*, and many kinds of ground sloth from bear size to the giant elephantine *Megatherium*. The New World platyrrhine (flat-nosed) primates differ so markedly from the monkeys of the Old World that it is probable the two groups descended separately from Eocene times from fossil lemur or tarsier-like lineages. There is no evidence that primates existed in South America before the continent became isolated, yet Oligocene fossil primates are known from Patagonia, which suggests that they got to South America by island-hopping from North America. Some of the racoons and other mammals may also have arrived in this manner.

A comparatively brief two or three million years ago, the post-Pliocene connection with North America allowed animals to pass between North and South America across a narrow land bridge. Some South American creatures, such as the nine-banded armadillo, spread northwards, but more of the highly organised North American ones pushed southwards. These included the present-day carnivores. The large spotted jaguar (*Panthera onca*) and plain-coated puma or mountain lion (*Felis concolor*) remained more or less unchanged in form from North America to southern South America. Others gave rise to new species, secondary endemics, in South America, species of fox (*Dusicyon thous*), bushdog (*Speothos venaticus*), the coati (*Nasua nasua* – which may have arrived by island-hopping), the kinkajou (*Potos flavus*), the grison (*Galictis vittata*), the tayra (*Eira barbara*) and the giant otter (*Pteronura brasilienis*) among others. The *Neotropical Rainforest Mammals* field guide illustrates many of these species (Emmons & Feer, 1990).

Some even-toed ungulates also moved southwards over the bridge – the peccaries, two species of which, the white-lipped

15

Three-toed sloth *(Bradypus tridactylus)*

Tree porcupine *(Coendou prehensalis)*

Kinkajou *(Potos flavus)*

Spider monkey
(Ateles paniscus)

Opossum
(Didelphis marsupialis)

Tamandua
(Tamandua tetradactyla)

Aboreal mammals

Coati *(Nasua nasua)*

16

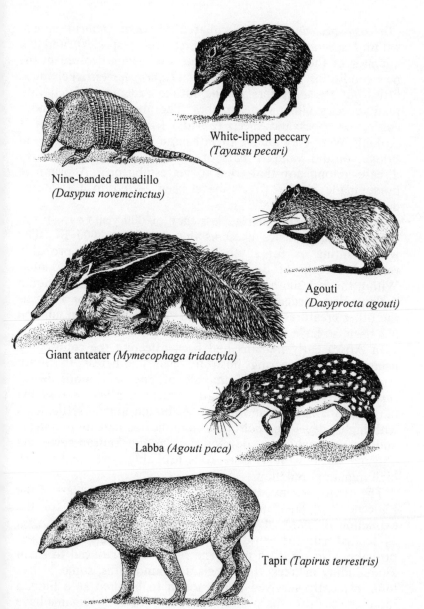

White-lipped peccary
(Tayassu pecari)

Nine-banded armadillo
(Dasypus novemcinctus)

Agouti
(Dasyprocta agouti)

Giant anteater *(Mymecophaga tridactyla)*

Labba *(Agouti paca)*

Tapir *(Tapirus terrestris)*

Terrestrial mammals

(*Tayassu pecari*) and the collared (*Tayassu tajacu*) spread without speciation over a wide area (relict species), and the ancestor of the deer, different species of which evolved in the new conditions. The odd-toed tapir (*Tapirus terrestris*) changed little, but the ancestors of the ratlike rodents radiated into many species filling varied niches. The absence of indigenous cattle, antelopes and sheep (bovids) from South America is striking. Were they unable to withstand conditions on the land bridge, or did vampire bats or some other organisms carry disease among any that tried to get established? A primitive horse made it, for fossils have been found in Pleistocene deposits.

Humans probably arrived less than 50,000 years ago. From archeological evidence it seems that by about 8000 BC they were hunting as far south as Mexico, and they probably reached the tip of South America some 3000 years later. Within the last 200 hundred years came the gun, which should perhaps be regarded as an invasion by a new predator as far as the other creatures were concerned. As the human population has risen, so have the numbers of guns.

In Africa early humans had been affecting the country by using fire and clearing bush for aeons, whereas in South America there were no hominids of any kind until *Homo sapiens* arrived probably in rather small numbers across the narrow Panamanian land bridge. Although human settlements with highly developed cultures – complicated irrigation systems and massive buildings – developed along the Andean spine, the Guyana shield with its poor soils probably never had a very high human population.

The carnivores invading South America after the start of the Pliocene, and later man, were probably responsible for the extinction of many of the large animals, but climatic changes, associated with the world-wide effects relating to the Ice Ages, probably also played a part. The sloths were reduced to small kinds hiding in trees, though giant groundsloths, some 20 feet long, evidently survived long enough to be used as a human food source in southern South America, for their remains have been found in a partially walled-up cave associated with

18

human artifacts. The giant armadillos became extinct too, only relatively small species now surviving.

Climate changes must also have affected the fauna. Pollen analyses showed that the pluvial periods so well-studied in Africa also affected South America, and refugia in dry epochs have now been identified. Floods which have been much more extensive in the past would have encouraged the evolution of prehensile tails, for even now many species have to retreat up the trees in very wet periods. Many of the monkeys, porcupines, kinkajou, tamandua and pygmy anteaters all have prehensile tails. Other creatures, even jaguar, also retreat up trees when the forest is flooded. Most South American animals can swim well, even sloths and deer. The prehensile tails vary in form fitted to function. The naked tail of the tamandua is twisted around the branches; the highly prehensile tail of the spider monkey with a naked ventral surface is used to hang from branches; the porcupine is unique in having a prehensile dorsal surface to the tail which is twisted around small branches from below.

The waters too have their mammals. The manatee (*Triche-chus manatus*) lives in the rivers and goes down to the sea (see Chapter 3). The manatee that appears in the Rupununi Amazon drainage in the wet season must be the Amazonian species (*Trichechus inunguis*). Here too the pink Amazon river dolpin (*Inia geoffrensis*) comes when the water is high. Porpoises or dolphins played at the mouth of the Demerara river; we also saw them up the Courantyne river 70 miles inland from the sea but where the tidal effect is still felt. Were these *Sotalia guianensis* the long-beaked river dolphin recorded from this part of the world? Small dolphins of several *Sotalia* species are found along the coast and ascending the larger rivers. Otters were still fairly common in the rivers though hunted for their skins: the waterdog *Lutra* (*L longicaudis*), very like the otter found in North America and Europe, and the giant otter or saro (*Pteroneura brasiliensis*), with very short legs, a flattened wide head, and tail with lateral flanges.

Sloths are represented in Guyana by the unau or two-toed (*Choloepus didactylus*), and the ai or three-toed (*Bradypus*

19

tridactylus). The 'toes' are really great claws on the front legs by which they spend almost all their lives hanging upside down from the branches. Both kinds have three claws on the hind limbs. The shaggy greenish-grey two-toed is the larger, weighing some 11–18 pounds with a rather pointed dog-like face. The smaller (4–9 lbs) three-toed, grey and black with shorter smoother hair, has a head that is the barely enlarged stump-end of the mobile neck, and a comical flatter yellowish-buff face set in darker hair which gives it the appearance of a mediaeval choirboy; the male has a distinctive black patch outlined with orange on its back between its shoulders. It has a plaintive cry when distressed. The three-toed was fairly common throughout the forested area, being found chiefly in the secondary growth of old clearings, feeding mainly on congo pump tree (*Cecropia*). The two-toed was found in the Rupununi district and a more general feeder; both species are entirely herbivorous. Sloths are reputed to have green algae living in grooves in their hairs, which must assist concealment among the leaves; the captive ones did not look very green but apparently they lose their algae in zoos. Sloths can move fairly quickly through trees if they need to do so and they swim quite well. In the zoo the two-toed would lie together in a cluster, showing occasional signs of bad temper when one of the pile moved. One limb was moved at a time, giving an impression of controlled strength. The three-toed was more amiable and active, and it makes a good pet.

The armadillos are another family of Edentates with teeth; indeed the giant armadillo has nearly 100 teeth, more than any other mammal, though the teeth are simple pegs. Armadillos are rather pig-like creatures though much smaller and covered with horny scutes. When provoked they are reputed to roll into a ball, but the zoo-kept ones were always too fat to do so, and in the field they ran away and dug into the ground. Stanley Brock, a Rupununi naturalist, told me only the three-banded can roll into an impregnable ball. Armadillos are mainly nocturnal, highly adapted for burrowing which they do at tremendous speed, digging into the hard earth with their stout claws. The giant one (*Priodontes maximus*) is a species of the equatorial forests living along rivers, but smaller species were often found on sandy soils. The one most commonly seen was the nine-banded (*Dasypus novemcinctus*) which ranges to Texas; this is less nocturnal and a poor burrower, taking refuge in termite hills and ant nests during the rains when the ground is flooded. One we watched feeding in white sand wallaba bush near Atkinson airfield was rooting in fallen leaves, quite oblivious of our presence, for although the ears are large the hearing is not acute. We watched mosquitoes buzzing around it, concentrating on the soft places between the rings of its body armour. Amerindians look for mosquitoes at the entrance to an armadillo hole to see if it is inhabited and worth digging out. In the Rupununi we once chased a nine-banded by night and caught its tail. It moved very fast and tried hard to dig into the ground but struck a rocky patch, so two of us were just able to hold it. When we roped it for later examination it showed a Houdini's ability to slip its bonds, giving pig-like grunts – almost tiny roars – when handled; the fore-feet claws are huge and the large ears fold flat against the head. Nine-bandeds are known to have an abnormally long gestation period (some 260 days) due to delayed implantation. There are normally four young, all the same sex, two sets of identical twins derived from a single fertile egg, a unique procedure among mammals. Armadillo flesh is well-liked by the Amerindians, although the armadillo's scavenging habit and the fact that it burrows in graveyards make some of them unwelcome food. They are mostly scavengers or insect feeders. As they trot along regular tracks to feeding and drinking places they are easy to trap. The carapaces are used as containers. Pumas are also said to be very fond of them.

Guyana has four species of anteater. The giant anteater (*Myrmecophaga tridactyla*), was fairly common on the Rupununi savannas, generally nocturnal, sheltering in thick bush at midday. The others are all arboreal and difficult to see: two species of tamandua (*Tamandua longicauda* and *T. tetradactyla*, very similar in appearance) and the tiny pigmy anteater (*Cyclopes didactylus*) only rarely seen. A diet of termites or ants

21

has led to parallel forms and habits in unrelated creatures in different parts of the tropics; the pangolin or scaly anteater and the aardvark, both African, have a somewhat similar shape to the South American anteaters, with long sticky tongues for drawing ants up their tubular snouts and stout claws for digging into hard ant and termite nests.

There were generally some half dozen giant anteaters living together in a large run in Georgetown zoo. Grey-black, some six feet in length including the long bushy tail, standing two feet high, they ambled around with a shambling gait as the enormously powerful claws on their front feet, used to tear open brick-hard termite nests and for defence, are tucked away under their feet as they walk. If attacked they rear up and lash out with these claws; it was said that their dreadful embrace and swipes can disembowel attacking dogs, and even puma avoid them. In the zoo they were fed mainly on minced meat and raw egg with a sprinkling of termites and earth, a mixture drawn into their elongated snouts with the foot-long sticky tongue. Amerindians often kept them as pets. The gestation period is about 190 days; they have lived 14 years in captivity.

The arboreal tamandua is much smaller, dog-size, with shorter orange-brown fur, a greyish snout and prehensile tail. One I photographed shinning up a palm tree in the zoo, watched by an excitedly chattering audience of monkeys, had dug into a red ants' nest at the foot of tree but was evidently much bothered by these ants, wiping body and legs vigorously and eventually giving up. These ants did not bother the large anteaters. Tamanduas make a hissing sound and swim well. The little squirrel-sized arboreal silky-coated pygmy anteater was only rarely brought in and difficult to keep alive.

Similar in size and general shape to the tamandua, the tree porcupine also has a long prehensile tail. These New World porcupines (Erethizontidae) probably had a separate origin from the Old World porcupines (Hystrichidae), short-tailed creatures which sometimes ran in front of our lorry in the African Kalahari – and how fast they could run. At least two species occur in Guyana. The common larger one (*Coendou prehensalis*) has long thick spines, the smaller one (*C.*

22

melanurus? seen in the New River camp) has light-coloured spines almost hidden by dark hair. Nocturnal, these amble around in the trees at night and by day sleep in tree holes. They are noisy creatures and can move quite fast, the snapping and cracking of twigs and leaves can be heard a great way away. The beam of a torch catches its red eye. One of the geologists, disturbed one night by continual noises in the tree over his hammock, fired his shotgun up into the tree to disturb the 'bird', and to his great surprise a large and angry porcupine fell right onto his hammock.

Like many nocturnal animals porcupines must leave smell trails, as one could generally smell where they lived. One female photographed in the zoo had a brilliant yellow smear, apparently the secretion of a gland in the middle of its back. These tree porcupines have bulbous noses, like inebriated old soaks, and the small rather red-rimmed eyes complete the picture. Those in the Georgetown zoo were so placed that they were awoken by the last rays of the setting sun, and very cross they looked about it all, despite the delightful meals of pawpaw and mango, banana and pineapple, set before them.

The guinea pig-like rodents may be a compound assemblage of forms. In the absence of ungulates some have pushed into grassy habitats and grown larger than rodents in other parts of the world. The agouties resemble small antelopes in general body form, delicately built, long-legged, with short red-brown chestnut coat, nervous and ready to leap. But unlike antelopes they can manipulate food in their forepaws, having great paw dexterity; they eat fruits fallen from trees and forest refuse, though sometimes they browse. Guyana has four species of agouti, locally called acouri (*Dasyprocta*) and two species of the smaller acouchy, locally called adouri (*Myoprocta*). The latter has a more bristly white-plumed tail and a habit of drumming on the forest floor with the hind legs; it too holds food in its front paws. It is much rarer, but the McTurks had a tame one. The agouties form perhaps the most important round-the-year supply of bush-meat in the Guyana forest. They weigh up to nine pounds and are hunted with dogs, bows and arrows or blow guns or are shot; they are diurnal and

23

mostly found in woods. They never run straight and can make very long jumps from a standing start; they swim well. They have a short shrill whistle, which the Amerindians imitate by blowing a leaf, to call them. They live in small parties and hide in hollow logs or under leaves. Like labba they are covered with sensitive bristles which can be moved by the skin muscles.

The best bush meat is labba, the nocturnal rodent paca (*Agouti paca*) so good that zoo specimens had to be locked up or they would be stolen for food. In Guyana it was said that if you eat labba and drink creek water you are sure to return, a saying which I hope holds true, for it is life in the bush that tempts me there again. We ate a lot of labba over Christmas at Kamarang, where none of us could pluck up heart to kill Patrick the bull, supposed to be the Christmas meat supply for the whole station. The labba is rather more rat-like in shape than the agouties, but grows to over two feet long and over 20 pounds in weight; they are warm brown in colour with rows of whitish spots along their sides. The old males develop grotesque heads, the cheeks becoming blister-like swellings below the tiny bulging eyes, but the snout and head support the most wonderful long strong whiskers, sprouting all round the snout and the oblong mobile nostrils which are moved as a unit with these whiskers. There are also a few stiff hairs behind the eye, which must help the labba to judge the width of holes entered in the dark. Nocturnal, rather solitary creatures they burrow several feet deep near streams and leap into the water or dive into hollow logs when chased. They dig holes and rummage on the forest floor, gnawing at fruits and are purely vegetarian.

Guyana is also the home of a wild 'Guinea pig' (*Cavia* sp). It seems that this common name was a misnomer, for the creature first became known in Europe from specimens from Dutch Guiana (Surinam), and is not found in Guinea, or indeed in Africa at all. But although a species is indigenous in Guyana, the well-known pet (*Cavus porcellus*) probably originated in Peru. In pre-Columbian times this domesticated cavy was found throughout the Andes and probably to the Antilles, where they were kept for meat, for religious ceremonial sacrifices and as pets. The olive-brown native wild guinea pig of Guyana (*C. guiana*) lived in grassy areas on the Berbice and Essequibo coasts but was no longer common.

The capybara known locally as waterhaas, grows to four feet long and two feet high, the size of a pig, and weighs about 150 pounds. They are gregarious semi-aquatic animals, with box-shaped heads, very short ears and a horse-like muzzle; they have no tail. Waterhaas were living in the botanic gardens when these were first made but are now rare near the coast. The spoor of their partially webbed feet was commonly seen along Rupununi rivers where their curious little whistles were heard, but they were shy and difficult to see. They have been much hunted for their flesh and hides, which make excellent leather. They make charming pets; there were two friendly ones in the zoo, until they were given the wrong food by a visitor and died. The females bear half a dozen young a year, in one to three litters; the males have harems of females of various ages and take many years to reach full size. Tiny McTurk said they used to be very common at Karanambo until one year they all died out, as though they had some disease; when plentiful they used to sit toby-jug fashion, with the big ones in front and graded in size to the wee ones at the back. Brock thought they carry and succumb to a trypanoso-miasis-like disease; he added that they die if caught in the sun for prolonged periods when crossing the open savannas as the ponds dry out, though they can run very fast for about 80 yards.

Large herbivores, ungulates, are few in species. The largest mammal is the tapir (*Tapirus terrestris*), a very solid dark brown animal, 3–3½ feet high, 6 feet from nose to tail, weighing up to 400 pounds, the female slightly larger than the male. It is rather like a little horse but on thick short multi-toed legs, almost naked except for a ridge of bristles reminis-cent of a cropped mane along its thick muscular neck – all muscles and power to crash through the thick undergrowth, with its very thick hide clearing away lianas, and providing protection should a jaguar jump on it. It has a long whiffling nose, a very flexible five-inch proboscis of the how-the-elephant-got-its-trunk ilk, and the tubular nostrils are always sampling the air. Tapir are very basic creatures which have apparently remained unchanged for more than 35 million years and are about as primitive as any hooved mammal, though elsewhere their stock gave rise to rhinos. Their present distribution suggests they must have been widespread, but are now confined to three species in South and Central America and one in Malaya. They all live in forests on damp soft ground, where their maple-leaf spoor may be seen (four digits on the forefoot, three on the hind, each toe horn-sheathed) or their sharp whistle heard. They are nocturnal, lying up by day but capable of covering long distances by night, in the Rupununi trekking from forest to the mountains 25 miles away at the start of the wet season. They are semi-aquatic, spending a lot of time more or less submerged. Our Venezuelan helicopter pilot, gazing down on them disporting in the river below, thought he had discovered hippopotami in America. They swim well and fast, and duck if attacked. The McTurks were amused when a caiman attacked one in Karanambo creek, for the tapir let the caiman swim right onto its back, then ducked and escaped into the bush leaving a puzzled caiman on the water surface looking for it. They are very elusive and highly intelligent animals. They feed mainly on foliage and wild fruit; they may live solitarily or two or three together. The young, which have rows of white spots along their sides for the first year, make delightful pets; one brought to the zoo used to follow us around like a dog, sitting on its haunches and gently sniffing the air. The zoo inmates spent much of the day sitting in their large concrete water bath, sampling the air as visitors passed and then submerging as though in disgust. They liked their back scratched and to lick the salt off our arms. At Karanambo where they used to come at night to eat mangoes dropping off the trees round the house, the McTurks actually lured one into the house with a mango trail and photographed it there by flashlight. This considerable achievement proved disappointing as it looked as though it was in a zoo.

The even-toed ungulates are represented by two species of peccary and three of deer. The two peccaries, the whiter collared (*Tayassu tajacu*) and the white-lipped (*T. pecari*), known locally as abouya and kairuni respectively, came from North America and are both widespread in Central America too. They are hunted extensively for food and hides, though they both have a large scent gland on the back which must be cut out before the flesh is eaten. This gland emits a musky secretion by which the peccary can be smelt for a considerable distance. Although both are forest dwellers, the habits of the two species keep them in different types of country and they are never found together.

Peccaries have longer legs than pigs. The abouya, distinguished by its white collar, is relatively small (three feet long weighing 30–45 lbs) and lives in nomadic parties of six to ten individuals. This is the commoner and more widespread species, though not so far-ranging nor so aggressive as the other one; it is the species found in the Rupununi though never seen in the open savanna. The white-lipped kairuni, a larger and far-ranging species, the size of a domestic pig weighing 60 lbs, with a long thin snout for rooting, is the common species in thick forests of the coastal region. Less nocturnal than most forest species, these can be found feeding by day; they are very gregarious and sporadically common in herds of more than 100 individuals. They are dangerous and much feared creatures, truculent with a communal defence and razor sharp canines in the upper jaw, but they are noisy as they crash through the forest. Young peccaries were born in the zoo, one or two at a time, but copulation was so frequent it was not possible to determine gestation periods. The young made a being-sick kind of noise, the mother clapping her teeth at us.

The lack of indigenous antelopes, sheep, goats, cattle (bovids) is one of the most notable features of the fauna. The three species of deer are true deer (cervids), the males losing their antlers and regrowing them every year, the females being hornless. The savanna deer (*Odocoileus* sp) was becoming rare as all the deer were hunted for food. There are no well-defined breeding seasons. They are solitary though family parties of up to five might be seen; they rely on freezing rather than flight for protection. The forest deer or brockets – red brocket

27

(*Mazama americana*) and smaller grey brocket (*M. gouazou-bira*, only 15 inches high, and rather like a duiker in Africa) – were also becoming rare; they are nocturnal sleeping in holes and arbours by day.

South American primates differ from those anywhere else in the world. These flat-nosed monkeys are equivalent to, but only distantly related to, the monkeys of the Old World. Either the two groups diverged at a very early date, or they had separate origins among the lemuroid insectivores. The south American branch diverged to the more primitive squirrel-like marmosets and tamarins, the 'half-monkeys', and the 'hand-tailed' monkeys. The 'half monkeys', which lack prehensile tails, include the douracouli or 'nightape' (*Aotus*), the sakiwinkis with long bushy fox-like tails (*Pithecia*) and bearded sakis (*Chiopotes*) and the little very common squirrel monkeys (*Saimiri*) with long club-shaped (not bushy) tails; these are often called 'sakiwinkis', a good example of the confusion caused by use of common names, as sakiwinki is used for *Pithecia* elsewhere. The hand-tailed monkeys include the many species of ringtailed capuchins (*Cebus*) – organ-grinders' monkeys, the black spider monkey or quata (*Ateles paniscus*) and the howler monkeys locally called baboon (*Alouatta seniculus*). There are no apes in South America. All these Guyana primates are adapted for life in the trees.

Once while bathing in the sherry-coloured waters of a white-sand creek at Atkinson we were visited by a little band of tamarins running through the trees above the pool – black squirrel-sized creatures, bright of eye, chattering to one another, and with the bright golden hands and feet that gave this species the most apt specific name of *Sanguinus midas*. Tamarins have a bushy non-prehensile tail; except for the big toe they have claws instead of nails, which may be a secondary aquisition that enables them to run up the rough bark of a tree, for they are too small to embrace the branches. Diurnal, gregarious, with naked faces and needle-sharp teeth and tusks, they eat green fruits and nuts, also insects, spiders and eggs. Unlike other anthropoids they have two or three young at a time and the father often cares for the young, carrying them

28

all day except at feeding time when he hands them to the female.

In the little olive-green, pink-faced black-snouted squirrel monkeys, the long black-tipped club-shaped tail is not prehensile. These often peered at us through the foliage in gallery forest where they leapt through the branches making continuous creaking noises. The capuchin monkeys, of which four species occur in Guyana, have partially prehensile tails, though furred throughout their length. The long thin spider monkeys, known locally as quata, live in troupes in the tall forest where they feed on leaves, nuts and fruit and never come to the ground. They have the most fully prehensile tails. This tail has a long finger pad on the underside by which they hang, and which is also used as an extra hand. The howlers, which also have a fully prehensile tail with a large naked finger pad, are more ponderous, though they manage to run, gallop and leap though the trees, their copper pelts glinting in the sun against the blue sky.

The spider monkeys live in dense forest and are rarely found in the low-lying coastlands. Their naked pink faces have a mournful expression, so we felt very sorry for them in the zoo. An old female, who looked pregnant continuously for the five years that I knew her, used to shake a visitor's hand through the bars of the cage then smell her hand. This long thin hand was curiously human but almost thumbless, for this species has lost its thumb, a digit unsuited to their progression through the trees, swinging looping curves from bough to bough, the tail being used as a fifth limb. In Central America, where they live in groups of about two adult males, four females with two dependent infants and four juveniles, the females play a more active role in group defence than do the females of howler monkeys.

The howler chorus is a most soul-stirring performance, the great roar kept up for minutes on end by day or night. In Guyana the howlers most commonly seen were red howlers, though a black one is said to occur. In Panama they live in clans, typically of three adult males, eight females, three dependent infants and four juveniles, which range over a territory defended by voice and action against the inroads of neighbouring clans. The males cooperate for clan defence though there seems to be no definite leader, and a female on heat may be covered by several males successively. The voluminous barking roar is given by males, which have a large modified throat box. Young males change clans; we caught one such male in a small sandpaper tree as he was crossing the Rupununi savanna when he fled up this tree, the only available one, at our approach. Howler monkeys do not live well in zoos, they sulk and pine and die. A young one brought to Georgetown zoo was given a guinea pig to keep it company. It used to swing by its tail clutching the unfortunate guinea pig in its arms and should anyone approach it tried to wrap up and hide the guinea pig in a piece of paper. The guinea pig got thoroughly neurotic and had to be exchanged for another one at intervals.

In Guyana the spotted jaguar, known locally as tiger (*Panthera onca*), lives in the forest where it may be arboreal for months in flooded areas, or in prairie scrubland. The plain-coloured puma (*Felis concolor*) lives mainly in savanna areas. Guyana also has the smaller spotted ocelot (*Felis pardalis*), smaller spotted 'tiger cats' (*F. tigrina* and *F. wiedii*) and the uniformly coloured jaguarundi (*F. yagouroundi*). I never saw a jaguar or puma in the wild, though we heard jaguar coughing and saw the spoor in wet mud near Karanambo. The jaguar is a much heavier animal than a leopard. In the fur-coat world its pelt is readily distinguishable from that of the leopard as the jaguar has a spot in the centre of each ring of spots, whereas that of the leopard does not. The jaguar is a good tree climber; puma seem to prefer more open country. Ocelots are tree dwellers for preference.

Among the smaller carnivores, the weasel family (mustelids) here includes the grison (*Galictis vittata*), tayra (*Eira barbara*), and two otters (*Lutra longicaudis* and the giant *Pteronura brasiliensis*) known as water dogs. The tayra is a long slim marten-like creature, the grison more badger-like with a moonlight-silver top to its head.

Racoons (Procyonidae) include the crab-eating racoon

known locally as crab dog (*Procyon cancrivorus*), the coati-mundi known as kibi (*Nasua nasua*), and the kinkajou (*Potos flavus*). Racoons lived in the mangroves on the Demerara river banks. Coatis were common as pets, albeit mischievous ones, their long noses poking into everything. They hunt in small packs, turning over stones and eating insects, birds' eggs or whatever comes their way. The kinkajou is strictly nocturnal, disappointing in the zoo as it was curled up in a tight ball most of the day. But when it did show itself it was an engaging creature with soft curry-coloured fur and beady round bright eyes, its bat-like ears stood out at right angles like handlebars, twisting and swivelling on their axes to catch the slightest sound. It reminded me of the potto I once kept as a 'pet' in Africa, but among the many differences from the potto it has a long prehensile tail, the only carnivore to do so, and is said to be able to climb up its own tail.

The dog family (Canidae) is represented by the fox or South American jackal (*Dusicyon thous*) and the curious rolypoly bushdog (*Speothos venaticus*), a rare species with yellowish short fur, found on the Rupununi savannas. They can be tamed, but one I knew always looked wistfully at the hens.

It was exciting to live in a country with marsupials, restricted mainly to Australia and South America, but one very rarely saw them as they are strictly nocturnal, shy and unobtrusive, which probably explains how they have survived. Some of the South American ones are pouchless; the numerous species here all belonged to the family Didelphidae. The common possum (*Didelphis*), noted for 'playing possum' by shamming dead, occurred in the botanic gardens. It was rather a smelly creature and was sometimes found truly dead on the road. Occasionally charming families of tiny mouse-like opossums, all fitting into a coconut shell, would be brought to the zoo, but spent the day asleep in their coconut shell home.

Of the numerous bats representing over 100 species in Guyana many belong to families exclusive to the New World tropics, among them the vampire bats (Desmodontidae) and fish-eating bats (Noctilionidae). Families represented in both Old and New Worlds include the sheath-tailed bats (Emballo-

31

nuridae) to which belongs the little grey long-nosed river bat (*Rhynchonycteris naso*) so common along the Guyana rivers. Of the bats mist-netted by Dr Petersen, a visiting scientist from Toronto museum, this river bat was often seen on the trunks of trees overhanging the rivers a few feet above the water from where they would flitter away ahead of the boat. I found one inside a large osteoglossid fish arawana (*Osteoglossum*); called water monkey in Brazil these fish have now been filmed leaping six feet from the water taking insects and spiders off trees – was this how this one caught the bat? The fish-eating bats (*Noctilio labialis albiventris* and *N. leporinus*) were first brought to our attention when to our surprise a school reported that bats were catching the small tilapia we had just stocked in their pond. We then found them to be quite common in the botanic gardens, trailing their large feet in the trench water with a sound like tearing silk to catch small fish such as the poeciliids which swim close to the surface at night in these rather deoxygenated waters. Once when I returned to a rotenoned Rupununi stream pool at night to see if any further fish had surfaced, the torch played on bats catching the small floating dead fish, squeaking as they flew. As in other bats their squeaks have an echo-locating function, which probably enables them to perceives ripples. On the Pomeroon river I was blooded by a vampire bat (*Desmodus rotundus*) (described later).

The Bird Continent

South America has been called the 'bird continent' as it has the richest and most endemic bird fauna of any zoogeographical region, with more than 3700 species, of which Guyana has about 700. Waterside birds, herons, snail kites, skimmers and hoatzins are described elsewhere in this book, but there are innumerable other lovely, dramatic and interesting birds, many endemic to South America. Though the fauna lacks many Old World families, the numerous New World groups comprise nearly half the bird fauna and are often very rich in species.

Two orders are confined to South America, the ostrich-like rheas (of which none occurs in Guyana) and the partridge-like tinamous (7 of the 33 species in Guyana), ground dwellers that sit tight in the forest, relying on their camouflage but whose plaintive whistles can be heard early morning and evening. Of the New World vultures (Cathartidae) four species are common in Guyana, sailing high over forest or savanna. The horned screamer (*Anhima cornuta*) was formerly common near the coastal rivers. Guyana has 6 of the 38 species of curassows and guans (Cracidae) including the curassows known as powis or bush turkeys which are very good to eat, and the hannaquoi or little chachalaca (*Ortalis motmot*) which makes such a noise at dawn and dusk.

Monotypic families include such peculiarities as the hoatzin (*Opisthocomus hoazin*), in which the young are hatched with functional claws on the second and third digits of the forelimbs, with which they crawl around in the tree and back to the nest if disturbed (as described graphically by Beebe in *Tropical Wild Life in British Guiana*). The adult has an enormous crop for storing the pimpler leaves on which they feed. The oilbird or guacharo (*Steatornis caripensis*) which David Snow studied in Trinidad caves, was rediscovered in Upper Mazaruni caves; the only nocturnal vegetarian bird, this has a blood-curdling screech, using sounds for echo-location in the darkness of the cave; the young used to be collected for their oil, derived from their palmnut food, which was used for lighting and cooking. The sunbittern (*Eurypyga helias*) feeds on insects and small fish, its beautifully mottled camouflage hiding surprising bright orange patches on the wings, which flash as they fly, frightening predators when displayed like eyes.

Other purely South American bird families include the trumpeters (Psophidae), tall graceful birds like small cranes, producing deep ventriloquist booming notes from their iri-descent black-feathered throats. They make excellent pets and 'watchdogs', mothering any small birds given to them and sounding the alarm when strangers appear – though they abandoned their mothering duties at night when they retired to sleep up a tall tree. Of the more than 300 species of humming

33

Hoatzin (*Opisthocomus hoazin*)

Greater ani (*Crotophaga major*)

Belted kingfisher (*Megaceryle major*)

Snail kite (*Rostrhamus sociabilis*)

Red-fan parrot (*Deroptyus accipitrinus*)

Skimmer (*Rynchops nigra*)

Red-billed toucan (*Ramphastos tucanus*)

Birds

34

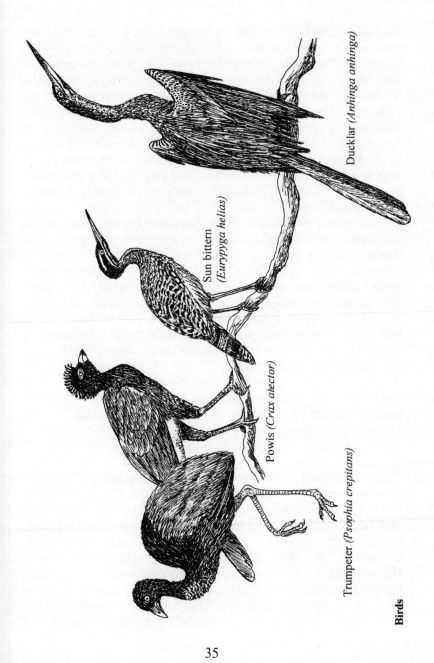

Ducklar (Anhinga anhinga)

Sun bittern (Eurypyga helias)

Powis (Crax alector)

Trumpeter (Psophia crepitans)

Birds

35

bird (Trochilidae), 35 occur in Guyana, and 9 of the 37 known toucans (Ramphastidae), all gorgeously coloured. The jacamars (Galbulidae) resemble the rollers of Africa, and 15 of the 50 manakin (Pipridae) species occur here, where David Snow was studying the dancing males displaying in forest clearings. The fruit-eating cotingids (Cotingidae), of which there are 27 species, include the bellbirds whose notes ring out far and clear over the canopy; the flame-coloured cock-of-the-rock (*Rupicola*) which dances in the sombre green forest on the Kanuku mountains is probably a near relative. At night potoos or wood nightjars (Nyctibiidae) produce curiously haunting noises.

A characteristic of this neotropical bird fauna is that, unlike other parts of the world, over a third of its species are 'suboscines – presong perching birds (Passeriformes) which lack the complex vocal apparatus of true singing birds (oscines). These have undergone two major adaptive radiations: tyrant flycatchers, cotingas and manakins in one group, ant birds, ovenbirds, woodcreepers and some others in the other. Guyana has over 70 species of tyrant flycatchers (Tyrannidae), including the ubiquitous kiskadees of several species, very common even in Georgetown. Some do surprising things for 'flycatchers' – a common one in the botanic garden used to splash down to catch poeciliid fish, and a boatbilled flycatcher caught and ate fiddler crabs on the shore. Guyana has over 40 species of ant birds (Formicariidae), mixed parties of some of which are insectivores foraging together through the forest.

True songbirds include Amerian orials and troupials (Icteridae, 17 species), with many species making hanging nests of grasses resembling those of weaver birds in Africa, as well as cowbirds and grackles. Although this is the only continental bird fauna in which songbirds are in a minority, they are fairly numerous particularly in areas changed by man, such as the gardens in the coastal area. Thrushes sing in the towns. Housewrens often nest right in the wooden houses – their nests are sought after by cowbirds which parasitise them by laying in their nests 'cuckoo fashion'. The South American cuckoos (Culicidae, 12 species in Guyana) are, however, mostly not

36

parasitic, species such as the anis (*Crotophaga*) having communal nests, large dishevelled constructions of sticks in which several families deposit their eggs, the clan sharing the incubation and rearing of young. On a botanic garden island we once saw three anis making a terrific fuss, 'chlonk chlonk' then churring like a sewing machine or a cauldron boiling, kept up for a full minute or so, which made it easy to see how they gained their local name of old witch; was this part of a communal nesting display?

Some groups found throughout the tropics, including parrots, trogons and barbets, are probably relicts, or at least retreating. Some of the endemic groups do not appear to be closely related to any other existing birds. Where ascertainable, affinities are mostly with those of North America, or through North America with the Old World. Although a treeduck (*Dendrocygna viduata*) and a gallinule genus (*Porphyrula*) are common to South America and Africa, and some owls and swallows of Africa and South America seem closely related, these are exceptions. The recent arrival of the cattle egret in South America, described later, shows how there can be some species in common, and the black-crowned night herons are only subspecifically distinct in New and Old Worlds. There are very few direct relationships between the South American and African landbirds, but superficially convergences have led to resemblances between toucans and hornbills, humming birds and sugarbirds, jacamers and rollers, hangnests and weavers.

Exciting and characteristic birds included the humming birds which so often buzzed us as we sat quietly in forest clearings or on a river bank, for the polygamous males have territories and are pugnacious birds, their tiny wings beating at the almost unbelievable rate of 200 strokes a second. They were common in our Georgetown garden, sucking nectar from the red hybiscus flowers. Sometimes we would find a tiny lichen-covered, saliva-glued nest with minute eggs or bumble-bee-sized young. Toucans, with their gorgeous clean-cut colours, called from the tree tops reputedly when rain was coming, or flapped their ungainly way across the rivers with apparent difficulty; they use their long beaks to garner fruits

37

from forest trees and nest in tree holes, the tail folded neatly along the back enabling the bird to fit into the nesting and roosting hole.

Like the weaver birds of Africa, the icterid hangnests have their long bag-like grass-woven nests in colonies, often near a noisy building for they seem to like human company, or in association with marabuntas, those savage wasps, their nest colonies often on the outer branches of a tree with a huge nest of marabuntas helping to protect them from predators. The hangnests and troupials were aggressive birds. Connie McTurk had several 'tame' troupials (orange-backed oriole *Icterus croconotus*) at Karanambo which flew around freely all day into the bush and down by the river, returning to their cages at night. But they had to be caged when visitors were around for the protection of the visitors – as I know to my cost, for one used to fly out of the forest and peck me below the eye, generally when I had both hands full and could not defend myself. We got quite a 'thing' about each other; he used to arrive and wait for me to emerge from under the mosquito net in the morning and from then the war was declared. But I had probably asked for it by encouraging him to display – he would crouch and quiver and sing like a toy musical bird when I moved a finger slowly up and down in front of his face and whistled to him. One I met later in a London Zoo cage also responded to this treatment by displaying. Most of these icterids had vivid black and yellow or red plumage, and many had a cold blue eye which stood out clearly; did natural selection lead to this very obvious and contrasting eye to stop them damaging one another's eyes during their displays?

Longtailed macaws and parrots of many kinds are almost everywhere in Guyana. Flocks of little green red-shouldered ite macaws (*Ara nobilis*) frequented the ite palms of the coastal swamps, and the gorgeous blue-and-yellow (*Ara ararauna*), or red-and-blue scarlet macaw (*Ara macao*), or red-and-green macaw (*A. chloroptera*) flew over the forest, always in pairs. Even when large flocks of parrots and macaws were going to their evening roosts on the islands in the rivers, the flock would consist of pairs of birds, two by two with a very occasional single bird, mute witness to some accident in which one had lost its mate. Many parrots were kept as pets, the little seven-coloured parrot (*Touit batavica*), being one of the most amusing; the large macaws, generally called 'Robert' were rather messy. The Amazon parrots were the best talkers; it was said that if you wanted a good talker you should choose one in which the pupils of the eyes dilated and shrank alternately even when in constant light – which they did to a remarkable degree in some individuals. Many of the pets had quite a large Amerindian vocabulary – one brought back to an English drawing room kept reiterating in makushi 'Girl fetch me an axe', a useful phrase in the bush. Some Amerindians were said to know of a special plant which when fed to parrots made them go bright yellow and increased their market value – until the effect of the food wore off.

Muscovy ducks (*Cairina moschata*) lived wild in the swamps, the drakes much larger than the ducks. Innumerable small brightly coloured tanagers and seed eaters, five kinds of kingfishers and many many others flashed across the scene of our travels. The most haunting spirit of the forest was the screaming piha, greenheart or firebird (*Lipaugus vociferans*), a grey cotingid whose 'pipiyo' ventriloquial call was heard over so much of the forested country (and is now in the background of many television travel films) but it was difficult to see. I never heard its relative the quadrille wren (*Cyphorhinus arada*), another cotingid, so beloved of W.H. Hudson in his book *Green Mansions*.

In the *Neotropical Companion*, Kricher (1997) describes the behaviour of many of these neotropical birds and discusses sexual selection, which makes the pihas scream, bellbirds clang and manakins dance, also the behaviour of the ant birds – some but not all of which follow the ant swarms – and of the numerous bark drillers and probers, woodpeckers and wood creepers, amongst others.

Guyana's Fishes

Compared with temperate regions with their ice-age impoverished faunas, it is a delight to discover the richness of these
tropical faunas, often with numerous very similar species living
together, and often confused by one local name. Hence the
need to use scientific names. Who wants to know about
Guyana' s fishes? For the consumer, the angler and aquarist,
scientific names – the 'fancy names' as a local naturalist called
them – may appear to be an unnecessary complication. Yet
scientific names tell a great deal about the kind of fish, its
general appearance, near relatives and probable habits. They
are also an international language which allows us to compare
the fishes of Guyana with those in other parts of the world and
to discuss them with neighbours in Portugese-speaking Brazil,
Spanish-speaking Venezuela, Dutch-speaking Surinam and
French-speaking Guyane.

Furthermore, if you know the group or family to which a
fish belongs you can guess a deal about its way of life. A
cichlid (pronounced 'sicklid') for example is usually an
orthodox perch-shaped fish with a long spiny dorsal fin, with
the large eyes and bright colours of a fish active by day, a
dweller in still waters, generally with an elaborate courtship
and in which both parents guard the eggs and young or one
parent broods them in the mouth, producing few young at a
time at fairly frequent intervals, generally before or during the
rains. The 'catfishes' on the other hand are mostly nocturnally
active fish (except the little *Corydoras*), drab of colour, with
long barbels, evidently living in a world of smells (tastes) and
vibrations and hiding away by day. The characoids
(pronounced 'karacoids') vary greatly in body form, having
like the catfishes undergone extensive radiations to many
different niches in these waters. They range in size from small
colourful aquarium-sized species such as the pencil fish
(*Nannostomus*) and headstanders (*Anostomus*), to larger food
fishes including the toothless mud-sucking *Prochilodus*, to the
deep-bodied vegetarian pacu (*Myleus*) and morocut (*Colossoma*) in which the strong teeth break up hard tree fruits that

40

drop into the rivers. There are also at least three different lines of predatory characoids: the bulldog-nosed piranha (*Serrasalmus*), whose razor-sharp teeth remove flesh from other creatures with the neat precision of an icecream scoop, and the widely distributed huri (*Hoplias*), the 'dogfish' (*Cynodon* and *Hydrolycus*) and 'fox fish' (*Acestrorhynchus*), which all swallow their prey whole. Yet despite this variation, most characids remain riverine fishes, responding to rises and falls in water level, often spawning at the start of the rains and most of them lacking parental care of their young. The gymnotoid knifefishes are nocturnal, light-shy, fishes, using electrical discharges to orientate themselves, moving as easily backwards as forwards into narrow crevices, aided by the electric field around themselves.

Guyana has many types of freshwater: the rivers and vast swamps of the coastal plain, the extensive estuarine reaches of the rivers, seasonally brackish or fresh; the huge rivers of the Essequibo system flowing mainly through forest, and the inter-connecting smaller forest streams and swamps. In these huge rivers fishes are difficult to catch and many of them migrate over long distances, so it is often easier to study them in tributary streams. Identifying the fish presents difficulties, but in Guyana we were very fortunate in having a large tome on *The Freshwater fishes of British Guiana*, with identification keys, based on Carl Eigenmann's (1912) collecting trip to BG when he travelled up the Essequibo and Potaro rivers to Kaieteur Falls to compare fish faunas above and below this 800-foot high fall, surely an impassable barrier to fish movements.

Eigenmann listed some 360 freshwater fish species from BG, belonging to 27 families. Nearly half of these were characoid fishes (a group shared by the Neotropics and Africa), another third were catfishes of several distinct families, including 'skinfishes' (lacking scales and with long feelers) and 'armoured' catfishes of three groups. The family Cichlidae (also shared with Africa) had 27 species; the Gymnotidae (electric eel) family had 14 species; of the little live-bearing mosquito fish (poeciliids) which frequent the surface waters, some 13 species were then known in BG. Of the sciaenids,

Freshwater flying fish
(*Gastropelecus*)

Baira (*Hydrolycus pectoralis*)

Huri (*Hoplias malabaricus*)

Arawana (*Osteoglossum bicirrhosum*)

Cuti (*Brycon falcatus*)

Stingray (*Potamotrygon*)

Pacu & Morocot (*Colossoma*)

Freshwater fishes

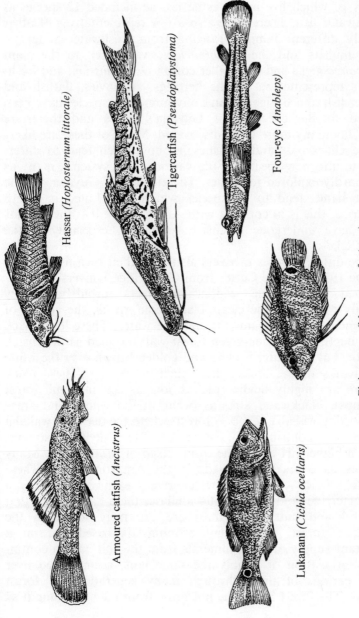

Hassar (*Hoplosternum littorale*)

Tigercatfish (*Pseudoplatystoma*)

Four-eye (*Anableps*)

Flying patwa (*Mesonauta festivum*)

Armoured catfish (*Ancistrus*)

Lukanani (*Cichla ocellaris*)

Freshwater fishes

43

many of which live in the estuaries, he included 12 species as freshwater fish. There were also a few representatives of other widely different families ranging from freshwater stingrays, grey mullets and the *Symbranchus* swamp eel, to the giant *Arapaima gigas* and its smaller cousin *Osteoglossum*, and freshwater representatives of the herrings, anchovies, flatfish and puffer fish. Since Eigenmann's day numerous species have been added to the checklist of Guyana's fishes and there are certainly many more to be discovered. Many of these are likely to be characoids and catfishes, groups which tend to differentiate into new species in the various river systems, many as yet hardly explored for fishes. The cichlids of Guyana, on the other hand, tend to be species widely distributed in South America; this is in contrast with Africa where it is the cichlids that have undergone extensive speciation, especially in the great lakes.

The different types of rivers also have their own fish faunas. In the 1930s George Carter from Cambridge University distinguished between the 'whitewater' rivers turbid with grey muddy water and the clear 'blackwater' rivers, the colour of tea when the sun gleams through the water. These look black with depth, the golden-green forest wall reflected as in a black mirror, but the water is clear and golden brown over the white sandbanks in the areas where such rivers run. These black waters are highly acidic (pH as low as 3.9 in some forest swamps); blackwater streams occur in the white sand areas supporting wallaba (*Eperua*) forest, where the decay of wallaba leaves may contribute to the colour. The whitewater streams have a higher pH and come from mixed or *Mora* forest. Many studies have since been made in the Amazon system where 'white', 'black' or 'clear' water rivers each originate in a characteristic landscape. Water analyses there have shown that mineral and nutrient reserves are extremely scarce in the Amazon forest; its nutrient economy is based not on a constant supply of fresh minerals from the soil but on continuous circulation of mainly the same ions, accumulated over long periods of time, through many generations of forest plants. The forest here does not grow from the soil, using it as a nutrient source, but only on top of the soil whose role is to provide a foothold and water. Such an understanding of the mineral economy of the rainforest gained from limnological studies is of prime importance for the eventual utilisation of the country. No wonder the white sand turns to desert when the forest is cut and its nutrients removed from the system.

In Guyana's forest waters phytoplankton is sparse, but the plankton net choked with fine debris indicated the importance of detritus in production cycles. The seasonally well-distributed 100-inch rainfall far exceeds the water loss by evaporation and transpiration in the very humid climate, so the forest is continually washed by water running from higher to lower ground. The forest soil has only a very thin layer of decaying leaves, a mere few leaves thick, so the soil is very leached.

What of the marine fishes caught off the coast of BG which make up the bulk of fishes in Guyana's fish markets? Our trawl survey took about 200 species representing 70 families. Some of these species occur widely throughout tropical seas. On the whole about 50% belonged to the coastal shelf fauna of the rather muddy inshore water along the South American shelf between Panama and Brazil. But there was also an 'island arc' component of clearwater loving species previously known from around the West Indian islands (see Chapter 12).

3

The Botanic Gardens

The Gardens

Our house in Georgetown was very near the 150-acre botanic gardens in which the fisheries laboratory was situated. To get there entailed a delightful drive or cycle ride through the whole length of the gardens, some 2000 yards, along the red burnt-earth road which ran between waterlily and lotus filled trenches and by the heronry on islands in the lakes. Entering the gardens one was in a world of colour and reflections, bird calls and delectable smells. Masses of orange, red and purple bougainvillea and beds of flowers grew near the gates, lawns spread out on both sides with long vistas and clumps of palms from many parts of the world, and many flowering trees. Away to the left was the small zoo, mainly of the local animals which are so difficult to see in the leafiness of the Guyana forest, then past the manatee pools, till one came to the islands where nine species of herons roosted. Overhead in the trees herons might be breaking off sticks for their nests, for six species of heron nested here. 'Snail hawks' or everglade kites perched by the trenches or dropped to pick up a large apple watersnail (*Pomacea* or *Ampullaria* spp); they also nested on the islands. Kiskadees and other birds called everywhere. If one went quietly one might see a small caiman swimming in the trenches or sunbathing on water lily leaves – the giant red-edged leaves of *Victoria amazonica*, the smaller leaves of *Nymphaea* – or a manatee feeding at the water surface. Beneath certain trees dragonflies with shimmering wings would patrol territories day after day for weeks on end. The cannonball tree (*Couroupita*

47

guianensis) sent out its heavy heady smell from the waxy pink flowers growing off the main trunk, and certain hollow trees always smelt of bats.

There were always new things to see, pseudoscorpions behind the peeling patches of bark on the bluegum trees, wasp nests of varying shapes and sizes, and clusters of pink or green eggs laid just above the water level by the large aquatic apple snails. The trenches reflected the flowering trees, except where the water was carpeted with a pattern of floating plants, blue-green *Pistia* water lettuce, brown-green *Salvinia*, red-green *Azolla*, pierced by yellow-green shoots of water celery. There was also a regular human fauna – East Indian women in cotton dresses with battered straw hats who swept up the leaves, and an old negro oxcart driver, who sat behind two white oxen – one with turned-down horns and a stumpy tail, the other with horns upturned – and descended at intervals to put piles of leaves into his cart. In the evenings and at weekends the garden was frequented by strollers and children playing on the lawns, but by day there were often few people around. Gradually a daily and a seasonal cycle unfolded itself, a cycle that varied from year to year depending on the rains. Always interested in the control of seasonal events in the tropics and the ecology of closely related species, I spent a good deal of time in the botanic gardens studying the herons. There was also the opportunity to study a grand natural experiment here as the immigrant cattle egrets were taking over these heronries.

G.S Jenman, who laid out these gardens, became the Government Botanist and first Superintendent of the Gardens in 1879 (to 1906), when a 150-acre sugar estate was purchased for $50,000 to make them. Jenman loved the gardens that he was creating. He built up a particularly fine collection of palms from many parts of the world which today stand memorial to him. Royal palms, tall talipot palms (whose life ends when the huge terminal inflorescence is produced), stout *Borassus* palms with bunches of red-brown nuts, their fan leaves standing out stiffly and rustling in the wind; others with driptips to their leaves, and the stiff laterally-flattened traveller's palm from

48

Madagascar (*Ravenala madagascariensis*), the bases of their upright splayed leaves holding water for thirsty travellers. He also included indigenous palms, such as the delicate and graceful manicole (*Euterpe edulis*) from the swamps. Jenman thought the manicole the most lovely palm in the world. In 1894 his annual report coming from a more unhurried age comments:

> the numerous clumps of manicole are of surpassing attraction and loveliness, as seen during the hotter parts of the day in the glowing pulsating sun, and the shifting partial shadows of ephemeral cloud and light that play on their trembling foliage, which as with a shiver, sensitively moves with every breath of air that in fitful mood passes through the grove, creating an enchantment in mind and sense of the observer that one feels inclined to rest and linger over, not once in a way, but for hours every day.

It is difficult to imagine how bare the botanic gardens must have been in the early days before the trees, many by our time more than 50 feet high, grew up. Jenman's descriptions of the difficulties of trying to get *Victoria amazonica* established in the trenches bring this home – for these giant water lilies 'could hardly be induced to grow here at all, owing chiefly to the wind, which blew the leaves off as soon as they reached the surface of the water, partly also to the lack of humus and sediment in the newly dug lakes and trenches.'

Jenman's reports are full of scientific interest too. In 1883 he wrote:

> an addition to the flora of the lakes was made this year (1882) worth noting as a matter of local plant history, as it will never again probably disappear from the country, so very favourable are the conditions here to its preservation and wide diffusion, I allude to the sacred lotus *Nelumbo speciosa*. Four or five plants were raised from seed in the autumn of the previous year, two or three of

which perished when removed to the lake through misadventure in planting. However subsequently one became established and spread so rapidly and fruited so abundantly that its eradication would now be a formidable task.

Looking at the lotus-crowded trenches of today it is awe-inspiring to consider what only one or two introduced seeds can do. In the trenches outside the laboratory window the lotus would oust the *Victoria amazonica*, the green spear of the young unrolled lotus leaf piercing the *amazonica* leaf from below, then opening out over it, stealing its sun. But the lotus, a native of India, played a large part in the lives of the immigrant East Indians, being used in their ceremonies of marriages and blessings, the flowers for their beauty, the leaves as plates, the seeds as food. And I once met a girl gathering the unrolled leaves, which she said they spread out on sore legs to draw out the pain. I, too, was always grateful to Jenman for the lotus, their unwettable round leaves flat on the black trench water or lifted clear into the wind to orientate themselves to the sun looking like radio telescopes, or with their lighter under-surface blown back by the wind. Grey-green leaves with a blue-green sheen, in contrast with the glossy red-green leaves of *Victoria amazonica*. Young lotus leaves sometimes lay flat on the water surface, where their unwettable surface would hold drops of clear rainwater with diamond glints, or golden-brown trench water flipped there by a fish or when the trench level was rising. When it rained the silver rain drops, cohering like mercury, spun down to the centre of the raised leaves which behaved like miniature roulette wheels, until the weight of the silver drop at the centre of the leaf bent it over, pouring the drop as libation into the trench, the leaf relieved of its weight then springing back to receive the next one – the jewel in the heart of the lotus. The pepper-pot fruits were such a satisfying shape too, and the perfume which drifted in through the laboratory window from the pink-petalled yellow-stamened flowers was a delightful counteraction to the fish smells. The yellow species, the smaller *N. lutea* native to America, was also

50

introduced here by Jenman in about 1895. The lotus in the trenches around the heronry islands never flowered; they had a very vigorous growth and were said to be a hybrid. The lotus flowers opened by day and closed by night, unlike the water lilies, which became white stars at dusk until mid-morning but then closed till evening. The film makers who filmed part of W.H. Hudson's book *Green Mansions* in the botanic gardens, short of water lilies in the foreground of a pool, took lotus flowers cut short and wired them over the surface of the pool at regular intervals. I have a striking photograph of this botanical phenomenon, taken after they had finished filming for the day.

During the rains there was often a dramatic growth of water plants in the trenches, both of rooted aquatics such as *Victoria amazonica* and of the floating plants such as the water ferns *Salvinia* and *Azolla*, the water cabbage *Pistia* and water hyacinth *Eichhornia*, plants that are being a nuisance elsewhere in the world, for example in the rivers and lakes of Africa. It was attempts to control these plants, which have to be cleared from Guyana's waterways by hand, that led to the search for a plant-eating fish or other creature to help. But to find a fish that will eat water weeds but not damage rice crops when the rice fields are flooded is a problem, so the use of manatees was suggested as these make spectacular inroads into the aquatic vegetation. After the rains the *Salvinia* and *Pistia* would go brown and die back, the floating mat then sinking; presumably this happened when the supply of nutrients was exhausted. *Salvinia* and *Eichhornia*, two of the most troublesome weeds in Africa, are natives of South America, so a search was made by a visiting entomologist to see what controlled them in their native habitat, and whether any insect or other creature could be used for biological control elsewhere. (In the event a weevil was introduced to a lake in Zimbabwe, and is now being used on lakes Kyoga and Victoria in East Africa.) There were two species of *Salvinia* in the botanic garden trenches: *S. auriculata* (believed to be the one causing trouble on Lake Kariba until it was discovered that a previously unnamed species, *S. molesta* was responsible) and *S. radula*. The *Eichhornia* here included

51

E. crassipes, the species responsible for blocking African lakes and rivers (and most recently Lake Victoria).

There was a great variation in seasonality among the plants in the gardens. The cannonball tree (*Couroupita guianensis*) for instance, a native of Guyana, tended to carry some flowers and some of its eight-inch diameter hard woody cannonball fruits at any time of year, but many of the other trees were more seasonal in their fruiting. *Bougainvillea* flowered most colourfully in the dry season, but a number of the most colourful trees flowered before the rains, such as the queen-of-flowers (*Lagerstroemia*) a native of India bearing masses of pink or blue flowers, also the brilliant yellow poui (*Tabebuia serratifolia*) a native of South America (also known as Surinam greenheart). Others flowering at the start of the rains included the saman (*Pithecellobium saman*), also known as the raintree, with its pink pompoms of flower, and the brilliant scarlet flamboyant (*Poinciana*). In both poui and flamboyants the flowers often burst open before the leaves, giving a solid mass of colour. On the other hand the tall longjohn trees (*Triplaris surinamensis*) on the islands only waved their flowers, first yellow then turning copper-brown, against the blue sky in October when the rains were about over, and at a time when the *Peltophorum* were dangling long rich chestnut-red pods, having produced their yellow flowers much earlier. But in this climate not all the trees of a species flowered simultaneously; one flamboyant flowered in August when most of the others had green pods, for example. The kapok or silkcotton trees (*Ceiba pentandra*) in the garden each tended to have their own rhythm; one would be bare of leaves in May, another in August. Many of them produced bat-pollinated flowers about early April and then their large green pods full of fluffy seeds would be ready to burst with the humidity when the first rains came in May or June; but one would perhaps be earlier, another as late as July. This late one did not manage to get its seeds dispersed very well as the weather that year was then too wet for the fluffy seeds to blow around, instead they hung from the tree like wet rags. As there was so much variation from year to year in when the rains arrived, this staggered flowering

52

is probably an advantage to the species, as it means that at least a few of the trees will probably be in the best state to take advantage of the conditions prevailing that particular year. There was also the succession of vegetation in the trenches to be studied. The lotus was certainly a 'grab-it-while-you-can' feeder, growing prodigiously when the trenches were flooded and then fading back more than some of the indigenous plants when the nutrients were exhausted. Was this because it came from a more seasonal climate?

Trenches and Fishes

The drainage trenches of the botanic gardens, like those of the sugar estates, were typically six feet wide and three or four feet deep. The aquatic plant communities in those at Sofia, the experimental sugar research station adjacent to the botanic gardens, were studied by Fanshaw (1952). Many had a *Hydrocleis–Utricularia* community and were covered with floating *Salvinia*, *Azolla* and *Pista*, their unwettable leaves of different shades of green making changing patterns on the surface of the black water, together with the spongy creeping stems of *Neptunia prostrata* (known locally as 'shame-plant', together with *Mimosa pudica* the sensitive plant, for its habit of closing the leaves when touched and at night), and blue flowering spikes of *Eichhornia* water hyacinth. Several species of *Nymphaea* water lilies and yellow-flowered *Pontaderia*, and the white-flowered water gentian *Limnophyton* also floated on the surface: the yellow flowering spikes of *Utricularia* broke the surface and there were submerged beds of *Cabomba*, *Elodea* and *Nitella*, through which aquatic caterpillars ate their way.

These trenches had a rich fish fauna. Some of the fish, particularly the cichlids such as the beautiful lukanani (*Cichla ocellaris*) one of the most delectable fish to eat, and the smaller common or Congo patwa (*Cichlasoma bimaculatum*) and the flying patwa (the flag acara of the aquarium world, *Mesonauta festivum*), and characids such as the wabri (*Pygopristis denticulatus*), were caught by anglers on hooks

53

baited with worms or flour paste. In certain trenches at Sofia we set experimental wire mesh traps throughout the year, but these only took some of the species present, mostly cichlids, including these three species, salmon or sand patwa (*Acaronia nassa*) and very occasional sunfish or pike-cichlids, the long-bodied *Crenicichla saxatilis* (ring-tailed cichlids of aquarists), the male with iridescent blue scales scattered along his body. Characids in the traps included the large predatory huri (*Hoplias malabaricus*) with its formidable teeth, the slender-bodied silver foxfish (*Acestrorhynchus* species, known on the coast as the dogfish, a name reserved for quite different fish in the interior – which shows the need to use scientific names), and the deep-bodied laterally flattened silver *Metynnis* and *Pygopristis denticulatus* both called wabri, vegetarian relatives of the predator piranha.

Serrasalmus species, locally called pirai and in Brazil piranha, the 'cannibal' fish of such terrible reputation, were also taken in the traps, but the species here was *Serrasalmus rhombeus*, black pirai, and not the most virulent species. Their presence here was interesting because they did not occur near the coast when Eigenmann was collecting here in 1908; it seems that they spread into these coastal waters more recently, reputedly in the high floods in the 1930s when they entered the Lama water conservancy from the Mahaica River; they are never found in slightly brackish water. Among the catfish trapped were the armoured hasser *Hoplosternum littorale*, occasional 'sea hasser' (*Hypostomus* spp), and scaleless 'skinfish' khasi (*Rhamdia sebae*), which splashed as it spawned in our fishponds, to which it gained unaided access, at the start of the rains.

When Eigenmann visited the botanic garden in 1908 he examined all the fishes from a trench which had been drained after 20 years. He recorded 23 species of fishes there, of which seven were particularly abundant (five small characid and two gymnotoid species); cichlids were not very abundant. Many of these small characids were still abundant in the trenches and seen swimming near the surface together with poeciliids such as the rainbow fish or guppy *Lebistes* and *Micropoecilia*. The

54

gymnotoids were also abundant though they only emerged from their hiding places by night. Most of these fishes were too small to be retained by the wire mesh of the traps. The cichlids in the traps were often breeding pairs and perhaps entered the traps when looking for a hard surface on which to lay their eggs; in full and lovely breeding colours, the male cichlids are generally larger than the associated females. Among the cichlids ripe fish might be taken at almost any time of year, but among the characids and hasser catfish ripe fish were found mainly at the start of the main rains.

The huri and lukanani feed on other fishes, mainly on cichlids and characids, though occasionally a spiny catfish was found in a stomach despite its spines. In these trenches they overlapped in food habits and both seemed to eat whatever they could get rather than being selective about their fish prey. Huri were found with lukanani in their stomachs, also with smaller huri. The smaller ones sometimes ate dragonfly nymphs or palaemonid shrimps. The salmon patwa (*Acaronia nassa*) generally contained dragonfly nymphs and shrimps, eaten at different meals. This species has a protrusable mouth; is this opened suddenly and the prey drawn in with the inrush of water? Each gill cover has a large eyespot; when the fish is seen from below these look like eyes, but as the fish is often near the bottom one wonders what enemies they could frighten away, or are they used in intraspecific displays as similar opercular spots are used in some other cichlids? The common patwa (*C. bimaculatum*) was here a rather generalised omnivore, including insects and shrimps in its diet along with algal filaments and bottom debris such as fish scales and mollusc shells. The little flying patwa (*M. festivum*) fed mainly on large algae, such as large *Closterium*-like desmids, with some *Cladocera* and bits of plant and bottom debris. Shrimps and the wing cases of bugs were found in the sunfish *Crenicichla saxatilis*, but not many of these fish were examined. Many of these cichlid species are extremely hardy fish and stay alive for half an hour or so out of water, generally with stomachs full of air.

The pirai *Serrasalmus rhombeus* contained pieces of fish fins, generally tail fins, and even fins of others of its own species when these were caught in traps, but they sometimes had insect remains too, and, more puzzling, a bolus of grass roots. This grass may have been something to do with their breeding habits, for some *Serrasalmus* make a kind of nest among plants, and those trapped here were often ripe fish.

The armoured catfish hasser (*Hoplosternum littorale*) also made their nests in the botanic garden trenches in the rains. 'Playing the hasser' and catching them in girigiri dip nets near their nest was a favourite occupation of some of the coastal people, for curried hasser was considered a great delicacy. The hasser male makes a nest of pieces of grass and water weed buoyed up at the water surface by bubbles. One I had in an aquarium produced these viscous bubbles lying upside down below the water surface and working the bubbles into the cut vegetation with his pelvic fins. The male having made his nest is said to induce several females to lay eggs in it. In another species, *Hoplosternum thoracatum*, this seemed to be so, for batches of eggs and young in several stages of development were all collected from a nest under large dead leaves buoyed up by bubbles (see Chapter 8). The behaviour of these *Hoplosternum* catfishes were later studied in great detail in Surinam by Jan Mol (see Ouboter, 1993).

These trenches were like large aquaria in which it was possible to watch the fishes. Flying patwa, the black and yellow flag acara (*M. festivum*), could be seen guarding their young when the water was clear, both in the dry weather before the rains and during the rains. This species is widely distributed in South America and is also a well known aquarium fish; it can be induced to spawn in aquaria, but with some difficulty as it is a shy, weed-eating species. In the wild the mature fish are three or four inches long, the males slightly larger than the associated females. The general body colour is yellowish fawn, darker dorsally, with a striking diagonal black stripe running from the upper jaw through the eye to the extreme tip of the longest ray of the dorsal fin, and with a black spot in a clear yellow ocellus almost on top of the caudal peduncle, like an eye at the wrong end of the fish. The pelvic fins have an extremely elongated outer soft ray of lemon yellow and these, it seems, may be used to signal to the young by special jolting movements.

Between April and June both parents were seen guarding a cloud of young which kept above them in the water. The young were made very conspicuous by the iridescent eye spot and an air bubble in the swim bladder, which shone as though painted with luminous paint. The young in one batch were all the same size, perhaps less than half an inch long; about 100–200 of them which kept together in a ball about a foot in diameter above and following one of the parents. The parent preceded them with special jolting movements of the elongated pelvics, which are held vertically downwards in the water in these brooding fish, unlike the fish when guarding attached young in which the pelvic fins are held horizontally under the body. The male and female parents take turns to lead the young and to drive away any intruding fish, of their own or other species.

Before the young are free-swimming, the parents guarded territory which was only two or three feet long, judging by the distance from their eggs or attached young at which the parents attacked or backed away from other fish of the same species. But when the young were free-swimming the parents guarded the ball of young rather than a special territory, and the whole outfit of parents and young wandered along the trench, under and around submerged plants such as *Pontaderia* and *Utricularia*, to perhaps 10 to 15 feet away. So does the world grow larger for the young. Up to six pairs with free-swimming young and one pair guarding attached eggs were seen together in one trench; there were also shoals of half and three-quarter grown young in the same trench. Predatory lukanani and salmon patwa lived there too, but the *M. festivum* did not seem unduly worried by their presence; they made more effort to chase off members of their own species. The adult patwa swam backwards and forwards with almost equal ease when swimming with the young, which enabled the two parents to travel below their young facing in opposite directions. At dusk the parents and young remained in one place.

One pair watched in May 1957 were first seen guarding what looked like a shaggy slug, one and a half inches long and half an inch wide, on a piece of submerged sugar cane. This turned out to be a quivering mass of tiny yolked young adhering to the cane, probably by special head glands as observed in the common patwa (*C. bimaculatum*). I returned each day to watch them. When it rained and the water level rose I found that the young had been moved nearer to the surface, which might help them to escape the dangers of deoxygenation or predators. They were here for six days, but then, alas, the site was disturbed by cane cutters slashing the vegetation above the trench, so I never knew what became of this family.

In these fish the ocellus on the caudal peduncle is very conspicuous as the tail of the parent is waved gently just ahead of the young. Does this help to orientate the young? When disturbed by a shadow falling on the water the parents fled and the young leapt forward but then seemed to look for the parents; finding the female they stayed with her while the male cruised around until they gained the shelter of the water weeds. When undisturbed the male and female would take turns to peck at the bottom or pick up algae.

In the Rupununi when I later watched lukanani with their batches of young (see Chapter 6), it seemed that the young were orientated by the vivid black and yellow bullseye ocellus on the tail of a each parent. Indeed, the water at this time was so murky that the tail of a quite large parent (a 16-inch long fish) was probably almost all of the parent that the young would be able to see. It is probably significant that so many of these South American cichlids in which the parents guard the young have distinctive tail ocelli, whereas among African cichlids, most of which are mouth brooders, such caudal ocelli are rarely found.

Chemical attraction of the young, about which wc as yet know so little, may perhaps be important too. In the discus cichlid (*Symphysodon discus*) of the Amazon the young attach themselves to the body and fins of the parent (generally the female) and apparently feed on a secretion from the parent's flanks (though the young can be reared in the absence of the parents). And in *Arapaima gigas* the tales of young being fed on 'milk' from the head of the parent may have some basis, for a chemical substance (pheromone) exuded from the head of the parent attracts the young and keeps them close to the parent.

It is always more difficult to study senses that we ourselves do not have to any marked degree. The electric organs and signals in fish such as the gymnotoids form a striking example of this (Chapter 9). It had only recently become possible, with the aid of complicated amplifiers, to turn the tiny very high-frequency electric signals into sounds or flashing lights on oscilloscopes and so detect signals which may be used by the fish to communicate with one another. What senses are we still missing that go undetected? Time senses? Magnetic orientations? It is perhaps hardly surprising that we do not yet know the how and why of so many aspects of animal behaviour, and for example, how migrants find their way.

The Snail Kite

Along the trenches fed the 'snail hawks' or Everglade kites, (*Rostrhamus sociabilis*). which though considered a rare bird is relatively common in Guyana's coastal swamps where it is called the cricketty hawk. One day a visitor, a stalwart of Georgetown's RSPCA, arrived at our Fisheries Laboratory saying 'there is a horrid hawk out there, you should shoot it'. But far from being a 'horrid hawk' which might snatch people's chickens, it is a gentle bird, a kite, feeding entirely on large freshwater snails (apple snails of the family Ampullaridae). Though I later read reports that it occasionally eats frogs, I never saw one do this. It is the only sociable bird of prey, roosting and nesting communally. It also proved a most amusing bird when one got to know the individuals, as they each had a particular feeding territory for much of the year, patrolled day after day from feeding posts, such as one right outside my laboratory window and below which piles of snail shells accumulated. The hawks also had a distinctive vocabulary ranging from a spectacular swearing display at intruders

59

anywhere in the neighbourhood of the nest, to calls to the young signifying that food is on the way.

The northern race of this bird *R.s. plumbeus* is confined by its feeding habits to the shrinking Everglades of Florida; much of the swampland, the home of its food snail, has been drained, and its numbers so reduced that in 1963 only six individuals remained, four males and two females, and great efforts were being made to ensure their protection. The southern subspecies *R.s. sociabilis* occurring in eastern South America and as far south as Argentina is much more abundant but its biology was at that time little known. In July 1953 Haverschmidt counted over 712 snail kites flying across the Nikerie river in Surinam, together with numerous heron species, to an evening roost, but though he noted them carrying nesting material in May 1953 he never located a breeding colony. In Guyana they roosted at the tops of the trees in the botanic garden heronries, all facing into the wind. Their numbers fluctuated with peaks of 45 in December 1957, 35 in December 1959 and 38 in May 1961, and sometimes none at all. They were most abundant when the trenches were low and the snails then easiest to catch, coming to the surface for air and to lay their batches of pink or green eggs (according to the species). In Florida and Argentina snail kites nest socially (when numbers allow this), in small colonies of a dozen or so pairs, very often nesting in bushes only a few feet above the swamp, or even on matted reeds. In the botanic gardens the snail hawk nests were all high in the silkcotton trees, and at the time of these studies never more than two nests were seen at any one time. One pair nested in June 1958, two in September 1959 (a year when they were seen to copulate both in August and December), and in 1961 one pair nested in March and two in September. Thus there was considerable variation from year to year in time of nesting (as among the herons), but on the whole they generally nested late in the rains, which meant that they would be feeding the young as the trench levels were falling and the snails were becoming more readily available.

The male snail kite is a handsome clean-looking slate-grey bird with rump and basal half of tail snowy white, forming a very conspicuous white ring round the hind end of the body. This white ring is shown to maximum advantage during the wing-flapping swearing display at intruders near the nest, and may possibly be used for territory marking. The end of the tail is dark grey-black edged with yellow. The facial skin, legs and feet are vivid orange-red; the long slender, very hooked beak with its overhanging upper bill is black. The female is dark brown flecked with white but also has the white band around the hind end of the body, beyond which the black tail is edged with yellow, and she also uses this white ring in a swearing display, though less forcefully than the male. Her face and legs are bright orange – less red than in the male. The young is like the female but yellower, the very young curry-yellow barred with dark brown, becoming darker as it grows, and with yellow feet; the black yellow-edged tail and white rump develop at an early stage.

Snail kites do, alas, get shot; Quelch long ago reported them to be fat and fleshy and eaten. A wounded one was picked up near the gardens, so we were able to examine in detail the inch-long black curved claws, three directed forwards one backwards, hinged to the yellow legs. Highly mobile claws – like biological prototypes for forceps for handling radioactive 'hot' material by remote control – with which the snails are snatched from the water. The midclaw has a pectinated edge. We were able, too, to examine the long hooked overhanging upper bill which pierces the snail, paralysing its nerve centres so that it lets go of its shell, the much shorter lower bill and the long spoon-like tongue.

Although social in their roosting habits, individual birds had well-defined feeding territories. At certain times of year they would be stationed at 50-yard intervals along the trenches, individuals working the same stretches of trench day after day. This they did by perching on some high spot, a post or tree, or balanced on the tall waving tassels of the sugar cane, watching the trench intently with a dark eye. If they failed to see a snail after five minutes or so, they moved to another observation post perhaps ten yards away and scanned a new bit of trench. The snail picked up in the claws was then carried back to the

61

post, where it was held in one claw and speared with the long bill. This made the snail let go of its shell which fell to the ground, adding to the pile below the post. More than 37 shells, mostly unbroken, all of one species of large apple snail, were counted below one such post. In Florida snail hawks are said to hunt by flying slowly along the marsh grasses, bill pointed down and tail in constant use, and when a snail is sighted they hover over it, then drop to snatch it and carry it off to a feeding post. Feeding varies with the time of day and activity of the snails.

Snail kites also soar and seem to enjoy riding the thermals. One December day a spectacular looping aerial display by a male, high over the silkcotton trees wherein some 35 snail hawks were congregated, ended in the male swooping to copulate with a female on a bare bough, then departing again. At other times they paired on the nest (as in August that same year). In the gardens the nests of rough sticks were all high in the silkcotton trees. Both sexes incubated and cared for the young, which grew remarkably rapidly, their 'weep weep' call fast developing into a wheezing scream demanding food. In Guyana only one or two young were produced at a time, the difference in size between them showing that hatching must be asynchronous. In Florida and Argentina three or four young are said to be usual; thus they obey the general rule that the lower the latitude the lower the number of young per brood (as in the herons). The male snail kite was particularly active in bringing food for the young; he would perch some way from the nest to deshell and degut the snail, taking them only the solid part (the long guts falling down into the undergrowth) and calling to the young that food was on the way. As the young grew they clambered away from the nest but they were still fed, and the wheezing cry was then of value in showing where they were, for instance when one fell to a much lower branch and could not get back again. We watched their first rather unsteady flights. In Florida and Argentina they start to fly about 23 days to a month after hatching.

One could tell when the snail kites had young for the male would come to meet me as I heron-watched round the islands, perching near me, twisting his head and turning his body to face me as I moved, flapping his wings showing the white ring right round the hind end of the body and swearing loudly with his 'crecky-crecky' cry. The wing-flapping swearing he would keep up for minutes on end, and repeat it at intervals, staying with me until I moved on perhaps an hour later. The female sometimes took over the protest from another perch if I moved some distance, but she was not so persistent, she did not wing-flap so much and her cry was different. We also noticed that her cry changed when the young were freely flying. So distinctive was this swearing display that looking back through field notebooks I can see when they must have had young in earlier years before I recorded their nests. The local name cricketty hawk was said by Quelch to derive from the name cricketty for the snail on which they feed, but it is so onomatopoeic of their call that surely the large snail must have come by its local name via the snail hawk rather than the other way round.

Manatees in the Garden

Manatee

63

In the 1950s very little was known about the biology of manatees, and any zoologist living with them, watching them day by day, helping to dissect any that died and even bottle feeding a young one, had especial opportunities to learn something new, as they are very restricted in distribution and becoming rare. In the New World manatees are found from Florida to Brazil where they are represented by two species *Trichechus manatus* from Florida through Mexico and the West Indies to the Guianas and *T. inunguis* in the Amazon and Orinoco rivers. The Florida manatee *T. m. latirostris* is now considered subspecially distinct from the Guyana species; recently these have been much studied (see O'Shea, Ackerman & Percival, eds, 1995). Both species now seem to be mainly freshwater dwellers though *T. manatus* was formerly abundant throughout the West Indian islands. It was from these islands that these manatees were first reported on Columbus's first voyage:

the admiral (Columbus) affirmed that he had thereabouts seen three mermaids that rais'd themselves far above the Water, and that they were not so handsome as they are painted, that they had something like a human face and that he had seen others on the Coast of Guinea.

These Coast of Guinea mermaids would have referred to the third living manatee species, *T. senegalensis*. found off West Africa, and which is, perhaps rather surprisingly, evidently closer to *T. manatus* than is *T. inunguis* the Amazonian species.

By Columbus's fourth voyage in 1502 the manatee was well known to them:

the Spaniards at this Time found a new sort of Fish, which was a considerable advantage to them; though in those parts there is much variety. It is called Manati, in shape like a skin used to carry wine in, having only two feet at the shoulders with which it swims, and it is found both on the Sea and in Rivers ... the Females bring forth young like Cows and have two dugs to give suck...

The buccaneers used the manatee as a meat supply, commenting ... 'these fishes have a sense of hearing extremely acute in so much as in taking them the Fishermen ought not to make the least noise, nor row, unless it be very slightly.' To consider the manatee a fish was (and still is) most useful in Catholic communities as it means that the meat can be eaten on Friday fast days. But the manatee, a warm-blooded creature bearing its young alive and giving suck is of course a mammal. Together with its only near living relatives the dugongs and the probably extinct seacows, it is placed in the order appropriately named Sirenia. These are all herbivores, the only truly aquatic mammals to be so since the other two orders of mammals which have taken to the water, the seals and the whales, both feed on animal food, the former being carnivores eating much fish, and the latter using mainly invertebrates such as krill shrimps and cephalopods.

The dugongs appear to be more marine in habit; they are found off the coast of East Africa and across to the Australian tropics. Steller's seacow, a huge creature growing to 35 feet long, once lived in the cold Bering Sea, whereas the manatee's range north of Florida seems to be limited by cold. About 70 years after Steller's seacow was discovered and exploited as a meat supply it probably became extinct, a warning of how rapidly this can happen.

In all the Sirenia the forelimbs have become paddles. The hind limbs have been completely lost or reduced to a vestigial skeleton hidden in the body wall, and the body is propelled by a large dorsoventrally flattened tail. Sirenia have no close living relatives but fossils are known. It seems that they have affinities with elephants in characters such as teeth growing forward along the jaw, and they have the heaviest bone structure known.

The Guyana manatees that we studied were all *T. manatus* from the coastal rivers. The range does not overlap with that of the Amazonian species *T. inunguis*, as far as is known, but occasionally a manatee would be found in headwaters of Amazon tributaries in the Rupununi district of Guyana in the flood season – one was seen there just before my visit (see

Chapter 7). This would probably be *T. inunguis* the Amazonian species and in very wet years it seems that it might be possible for one to cross the drainage divide here, though I did not hear any reports of them in the Essequibo drainage side of the Rupununi district.

The search for a weed-eating fish led the Fisheries Officer Bertie Allsopp to resurrect the idea of using manatees to clear trenches and keep them free of weed. With great energy he arranged the collection of some manatees from the Abary and Cainje rivers and tried them out in trenches around the fisheries laboratory at the back of the botanic gardens. We also hoped to learn more about their biology by having them at close quarters. Manatees had been living in the botanic garden lakes for more than 60 years, but although William Beebe wrote in 1922 of seeing one 'fondle its young' there, in recent years there was no evidence that they had bred in the gardens. Was the young seen by Beebe the result of introducing an already pregnant female to the gardens (like the appearance of a young one in our trenches one December day) or did the manatees mate in the gardens when the lakes were deeper and less disturbed by visitors? Several manatees were kept in Georgetown's waterworks ponds where they controlled weed growth successfully. We were told that manatees had been tried for weed control in BGs sugar estate trenches some 60 years previously but the experiments had been discontinued as the punts carrying the sugar cane, pulled from along the towpath by straining mules, had 'bumped' the manatees and damaged them. Furthermore the manatees had been found much too good to eat by the sugar estate workers. So the idea of using them as giant mowing machines had been abandoned.

But our trials were very promising. A manatee could clear 26 square yards of floating vegetation in three days, even up to 15 square yards in 24 hours (according to my measurements). They took both floating and submerged vegetation, all except the remarkably spiny stalks, leaves and flower buds of the *Victoria amazonica* water lilies, which then floated out in solitary state untouched. The manatees ate so quickly that soon the problem was to find them food. In zoos they needed

66

some 100 pounds of green stuff a day – and preferred lettuces. In the trenches they got constipated, expelling gas bubbles from the anus. (Would this gas affect their hydrostatic ability?) But they did clear the trenches most effectively, a job that took a lot of labour and was not a pleasant task. So in Guyana it seemed that there could be a minor industrial revolution with the aid of the manatee. This raised a moral problem, should one suggest anything that would put people out of work when there was already so much unemployment on the coast?

Water weed control presents problems throughout the tropics. Bertie sent a note to the scientific periodical *Nature* on the use of the manatee for weed control. This was picked up by *Time* magazine who wrote to us for the facts, but before they could have received them from us they produced a good story. And so the news went round the world and soon letters were pouring in wanting manatees. Lake Kariba, the new lake on the Zambezi in Central Africa, was at that time spectacularly choked with floating weeds, mainly *Salvinia* a South American plant. Was the answer to stock the lake with manatees? We very soon had a report (completely erroneous) via South Africa that manatees were already being used to clear the Kariba weeds. Thus do rumours spread. Even the Royal Irrigation Department Thailand requested, on its beautifully embossed notepaper, one male one female manatee.

But manatees, it seems, do not breed very quickly. Indeed, the amount that they eat makes it obvious that they could not breed like rabbits, for they would soon eat themselves out of house and home – though it was true that very little work had then been done on how productive weed growth in tropical swamps and rivers really is. From zoo specimens it seems that female manatees are some eight to nine feet long before they breed. And how fast do they grow? Nobody then knew. The gestation period is at least 152 days and generally only one young is born at a time. (Recent research indicates female Florida manatees reproduce at four years old, average three years between births and may live for 59 years, O'Shea et al 1995).

In Guyana the young will be about three and a half feet long

67

and weigh some 40 lbs at birth. One not much larger than this was brought to us in May 1959 with the story that it had been taken in a pinseine fishing net at the mouth of the Essequibo river and its mother had 'disappeared' (? = been eaten). We put him into a large stone trough in the fish shed, where he tried to suckle the corner of the trough, wrinkling up his short snout to do so. The pectoral teats of the manatee are in the angle of the mother's flipper – the corner of the trough presented such an angle to the baby, and the rough stone was not, I suppose, too unlike her skin. His short snout wrinkled back into his head, his tiny 'milk bristles' on his mobile upper lip working away as he sucked, and every 50 seconds or so he opened his nostrils for a short breath of air. So we tried to bottle-feed him. What was the composition of manatee milk? No-one knew. The question prompted answers such as that 'tiger's milk is chemically the best substitute for human milk' but this did not help us. We had once had a baby elephant to feed in Uganda – it had followed a local African to his hut when the parents were chased from the gardens – and this little one regarded the brown barn door as its mother until a lorry came by and it then wanted to follow the slowly-moving lorry. We had given it milk enriched with butterfat but when the little elephant died it was found to be choked with fat. We did not want the same thing to happen to the manatee. Only later did we learn how rich seal's milk is in fats. The teat was also a problem. A 'cleft palate' teat was suggested and we came to use a rubber tube with a laboratory clamp clip.

To anyone who is bottle-feeding a mermaid I would recommend a large plastic bag. We sat him in one upright between my knees. Linton, for this was by now his name, sucked away contentedly at the bottle, his mobile upper lips with their little bristles embracing the bottle. He had soft hairs on his head and occasionally he paused to give little burps. Like an adult manatee when out of water on the river bank, he kept his nostrils closed most of the time, even in air. Then every few minutes he would open his nostrils and inhale deeply, his little body changing shape and bulging outwards as he did so. As he finished his bottle his tiny eyes set in their sphincter-like

68

muscles would gradually close. The baby proportions were so different that he could bring his flippers, with their three flat nails, in front of his mouth, a feat impossible in the adults in which the flipper only extended about as far forward as the eye.

Linton seemed to start to eat *Cabomba* water weed so we put him into a trench with an adult pair of manatees. Alas, he was found dead one morning with a great weal across his back as though he had been hit by a board. The watchman had been there all night and it seemed probable that one of the large manatees had knocked the baby with its tail, with which it can give a formidable blow. We later read of a case in a zoo where a male had killed a young one. After Linton died we took him to B.G. Airways to weigh him in his plastic bag. Very few of the passengers awaiting the call to extinguish their cigarettes noticed that instead of more orthodox luggage a small manatee was on the scales. He weighed 35 lbs. The hospital was kind enough to X-ray him. He had no vestige of hind limbs, but the hand-like skeleton of the flipper had five complete digits. All our manatees had three flat nails on each flipper, whereas the Florida ones are reported to have five. One of our two larger male manatees also had hard almost nail-like patches on the end of the tail.

The only young born to our manatees was to one belonging to the botanic gardens but parked in our trenches as the botanic garden staff were on strike. This was in December 1959 and possibly the birth was premature as the result of moving the mother, for the baby remained attached to the mother for some time hidden under her tail. The mother was an eight feet ten inches long manatee from Cainji. I was not there at the time but was told that she went up into the shallow water at the end of the trench when giving birth.

Do manatees have definite breeding seasons or are the young born at any time of year? This possibly premature birth was in December and a young one was born to manatees stocked at Wales sugar estate in December 1961. A suckling manatee said to be three feet long was taken in the Abary river in October 1961 and Linton was caught in the Essequibo estuary in May

69

1959; these suckling ones may have already been a few months old. The only mating reported was in January 1955, when the Abary river was in flood. More than this we did not know.

The birth of a Florida manatee had been described and the author said that the mother, prodded by the male to do so, took the baby to the surface on her 'shoulder', kept the baby on her back completely out of water for 45 minutes. She then submerged until all but the baby's nose was under, then she rose again. This she repeated at a gradually increasing tempo for about two hours. Then the baby was ducked completely but she rose very quickly, each time staying under a little longer for another two hours. This female was estimated to weigh 850 lbs (which means she must have been about eight feet long) and the baby to weigh 40 lbs. Another baby was reported to be 39 inches and 63 lb at birth. In this case the mother was said to slip a flipper under the baby and raise it out of the water every three to four minutes and the male then did likewise; they continued to do this for about a week.

Many people are now studying manatee behaviour in Florida. Observations on breathing in wild baby manatees there showed that they surface for air much more frequently than do the adults – more than 60 times an hour, whereas our adults in Guyana came up perhaps every five minutes or so, and large adults can apparently stay under for about 12 minutes. They come up for 30–60 seconds and take two or three breaths. When anyone was around they came up extremely quietly and without more than the nostril apertures breaking the surface – making just two round holes in the surface film.

I never saw a manatee suckling her young, although some descriptions suggest that the habit of suckling the young upright may account for the mermaid legend. One author said of the young that neither cow nor calf surfaced while nursing; the female lay quietly on the bottom or fed from place to place on the bottom, another said that his young started nibbling grass after four or five months.

We never saw manatees mate in our trenches and, indeed,

70

the whole crux of making use of the manatees to clear weed and whether this will help to save them from extinction turns on whether they will breed in the waters into which they are introduced. Do they need deeper water for mating? Or shallows, or more seclusion? Or what? The only 'eyewitness' account of mating is reported in a footnote by Bertram (1963:58) from the Abary river. Here it seems that mating occurred in extremely shallow water (six inches) and one pair was 'completely out of water', about 35 miles up the Abary river in January 1955 when the river was in flood. Events were said to occupy two and half hours in full morning sunlight. The report said that when first seen a school of 14–16 manatees were disporting themselves in the river and gave the impression of fighting among themselves; later they moved into the shallows and mated lying on their sides.

It is luckily quite easy to determine the sex of the manatee, even in newborn ones, for stocking purposes. In the female the genital orifice is set far back and close to the anus, whereas in the male the orifice with its penis is much further forward, close to the umbilicus and far removed from the anus; the testes are enclosed in the body (as in elephants). There are also differences in body shape. The female is thicker in body, particularly towards the tail; here the male is slimmer and his more pointed tail has a more obvious central support. In adult males the flippers also look more 'elbowed' and he sometimes seems to have a slightly longer snout – though this may be a function of size for many of our males were larger than the females. The tail and flipper structure suggested that these may be so developed to hold the female during mating. But individuals varied in shape and in how they floated in the water. The laboratory staff gave them all names associated with some characteristic, such as 'Sammy-stop-along-top', for the manatees varied a good deal in behaviour too. Most of them would lie completely inert on the bank when seined from the trench and make no attempt to return to the water, but one male had a habit of suddenly arching his body and with a violent flip of his tail could give a hard knock to a bystander, and a good dousing should his tail bash the water surface.

71

Manatees have a thin epidermis which very easily gets damaged during capture. The wound can be further aggravated by a fungal growth. This often developed at the base of the tail and on the elbows of the flippers. Sometimes manatees were brought in with quite large wounds on their elbows which the men maintained were the work of pirai fish (*Serrasalmus*), though whether this was true or not I did not know. We lost some manatees through these infections. The vets tried various treatments ranging from penicillin injections, applications of athlete's foot ointment, and finally Grisovin tablets taken by mouth, the pill being sugared with a bunch of *Cabomba* water weed. Injections were very hard to make into the thick dermal tissue; a huge needle had to be used and pliers were needed to pull it out again, the patient continuing to lie completely inert despite all this. The athlete's foot ointment washed off easily (it was suggested that one for 'swimmers' itch' might be more appropiate). But the oral treatment seemed effective. One manatee, a female, got stuck in a culvert and drowned; she was trying to follow the slimmer male who escaped through the culvert safely. After dissection we sampled the taste of this unfortunate female. The meat is porklike both in taste and appearance, rather a white meat with a very distinct fat layer.

On dissecting a mermaid the first surprise is the lungs, as these run right back along the body behind the kidneys, almost in line with the genital apperture. This is made possible by the diaphragm running diagonally along the body cavity. A six foot nine inch manatee had lungs some two feet two inches long, with the trachea running almost the whole length of the lung. The glottis had a cunning arrangement whereby the nostril channels, each plugged with a round rod of muscular tissue, are pulled open. When closed the nostrils are two eyebrow-shaped markings on the dorsal surface of the snout; to open them the muscular rods are pulled back to leave two almost circular holes more than a centimetre in diameter. The very long intestines have a blind two-horned caecum, the 'pellet factory' where the neat faecal pellets are prepared. These pellets contained much still green and little-digested material suggesting that the manatee is not a very efficient user of the vast amount of food it eats. But perhaps this one had to eat what it could get out of our trench and would have been more choosy about the plants that it ate in the wild. In the trenches the oval faecal pellets, 4–6 inches long, often floated and gave away the presence of the manatees.

The feeding of the manatee is a fascinating performance. Stiff hairs in the cleft halves of the highly mobile upper lip pull plants into the mouth with a circular motion, rather like a giant slow-motion rotifer in action. Each half of the upper lip has about 15 particularly stiff hairs each about one millimetre in diameter. There are other hairs further up the lip, and the lower lip has a pad in the median line with some 15–20 hard bristles. The soft tongue is not very extensible; there is a hard palate and the only teeth are far back in the jaws. In the baby the lip bristles are much softer – stout ones would presumably make sucking at the teat below the mother's flipper a very ticklish affair. The baby's very extensible snout folds back concertina-wise when it suckles, and its head has many more and very soft hairs.

Manatees are shy creatures which feed mainly by night or at dawn and dusk. However if they are hungry and a rise in water level enables them to reach new grass along the bank they will feed by day. Otherwise they tend to be inactive and to congregate together. During the rains in June 1959 when the water in the trenches was exceptionally clear we had five manatees together in one trench and they would sunbathe during the heat of the day, basking with the arch of their backs half out of the water, floating horizontally just below the water surface, heads and tails submerged except when the nostrils were raised for air every five minutes or so, varying from individual to individual. While sunbasking they all congregated at one end of the trenches, bodies almost touching. Sometimes most of them faced upwind, othertimes they were just in a higgledy-piggledy group. Green algae grew on the submerged parts of their backs. Another 'resting posture' occasionally seen was with the body hanging down in the water, tail below the body, more upright and mermaid fashion. We had a male and female together in another trench and here the male nearly always

73

kept higher in the water than the female and just above her, as though protecting her. Perhaps because of this habit males were easier to catch and far more males were brought to us. Manatees swim with their flippers or if they are going any distances by undulations of the dorsoventrally flattened tail.

Manatees are social, gregarious animals and one wonders how they communicate with one another. The only noise that they were heard to produce was that of expelling and inhaling air. There are reports in the literature of a 'plaintive cry', but I never heard one. Despite the lack of any external ear they seemed very responsive to sounds, such as the banging of a car door, and the ones in the botanic gardens would come for food if one whistled to them. Water vibrations are presumably extremely important to them, and probably also chemical changes in the water for they are said to have well-developed olfactory lobes in the brain. The sparse body hairs are much more abundant on the head (where they appear more obvious as they develop an algal growth on them). The eyes set in sphincter-like muscle are tiny but are kept open under water. Every five minutes or so the nostrils would be held to the water surface, very gently the muscle rods would be pulled back and with a waft of sweet hay-smelling breath, twin round holes would appear in the surface film; the creature would inhale for 3–6 seconds then close the nostrils and sink. They could come up to breathe with nothing more than the nostrils showing at the surface and if people were about they often came up under floating water plants and so were very difficult to see. They would also come to the surface to feed under floating weeds or cut grass, and here a circular movement of the grass towards the mouth would be all that could be seen, the manatee feeding with nostrils closed most of time, just opening them when necessary for breathing.

Although they never emerged from the water to feed, they could pull themselves out a short way on their flippers, the hind part of the body remaining in the water, to reach grass above the trench if they were short of food. In a heavily plant-covered trench they would make a clearing at one place and then eat their way outwards from the cleared area night by night hiding under the plant cover by day. Or sometimes they would make a track along the trench through the plant cover and eat their way outwards from this track.

With the rains the water levels in the trenches varied considerably. One night several of the manatees broke through into some experimental rice plots, a warning of what could happen, for to get a fish or animal to control aquatic grasses but not to eat young rice plants is difficult. One August night when the manatees had cleared their trench of weed there was breakout. They broke down three fences and four of the manatees went off downstream towards the sea. A high old time we had chasing them when this was discovered. The trench systems of Georgetown are extensive and complex. Our chase led us behind the race course and finally alongside the law courts in the centre of the town. Here at last we saw manatee noses dimpling the water surface. But just then the local schools were disgorging their hundreds of youngsters, who all 'helped' by screaming with delight each time a manatee dared to breathe. This made the manatees very elusive and trying to seine them from the trench was an almost impossible job. We had had to pay 70 $WI per manatee and it seemed that this investment would slip quietly into the sea when the koker sluicegates were opened at low tide to let the flood waters away. We never did get them all back. Strangely enough we heard later that three manatees had been drowned in Chinese seines in the Demerara estuary a day or so before this, getting their flippers entangled in the stake nets and so drowning, a very unusual event. Was there to be a manatee concourse in the estuary at this time, that our manatees should break out and bolt seawards these same days? In these thoughts I was perhaps unduly influenced by having worked on eels in England when 'something' (but what?) seemed to affect all the silver eels to move seawards on certain nights; floods and the phase of the moon were part of the eel story (as our work showed), but the eels in our laboratory tanks, where they had no floods, would leap out of these tanks on the same nights that the eels were 'running' in the streams. Very strange. This suggested that they were responding to some factor of which we were not even conscious, let alone measuring. And one only has to work with electric fishes to realise how creatures may be responding to forces of which we are not aware until we have designed instruments to receive and measure them.

Our main manatee collector, who rejoiced in the name of Boop Jeetlall, said that he caught the manatees about 86 miles up the Abary river (see Chapter 10), where they go into the 'creek hand' shallows to feed and then return to the river. In the shallows they were generally seen between 4 and 6 pm. In this flat country the effect of the tides backs up the freshwater and here gives a rise and fall in the river of about one foot, but the manatees never get stuck. During spring tides there was an extra lift and they would move down into deeper waters thus moving some six miles or so up and down river. They were very gregarious; he had caught up to four together, and they frequented certain places, so if you missed them one day you could try again in the same place another day and might catch one. Large manatees were also sometimes seen in the sea off Fort Groyne in the mouth of the Demerara river, where the dolphins used to play, but I was never lucky enough to see one there.

4

Herons and Egrets

In the botanic gardens a great natural experiment was taking place, for the cattle egret or buffback heron (*Bubulcus ibis*), a species recently arrived from another continent, had established itself and affected the indigenous species of herons. How it managed to do this, and the consequences, are of importance, for the cattle egret had only recently invaded North America, where the first arrivals were seen in 1952 and where it is now well-established. The Indian mongoose which now runs wild in these gardens is also an immigrant from another continent, but this was brought by man, reputedly to control snakes.

Between 1956 and 1962 nine species of heron and egret were seen on the islands in Georgetown's botanic gardens, of which at least six species nested there. These islands in the small lakes were covered with dense bush; a few tall trees, silkcotton (*Ceiba pentandra*) and longjohn (*Triplaris surinamensis*), festooned with creepers, rose out of a tangled undergrowth of small leafy bushes, patches of screwpine (*Pandanus*) and mother-in-law's tongue (*Sanseveria*), with patches of mukamuka (the arum *Montrichardia arborescens*) palisade along the water's edge. Hawthorn-like trees (*Pithecelobium unguis-cati*) together with a weeping ash-like tree and a few small palms, rose to a height intermediate between the tall trees and undergrowth; these formed the most popular heron nesting sites. The south-west and north islands were ringed with a strong growth of hybrid lotus which completely filled the trenches, which were the homes of small caiman. The south-east island was surrounded by open water, covered for much of the year with a velvety green carpet of *Pistia*, interrupted at intervals by the

Herons and Egrets

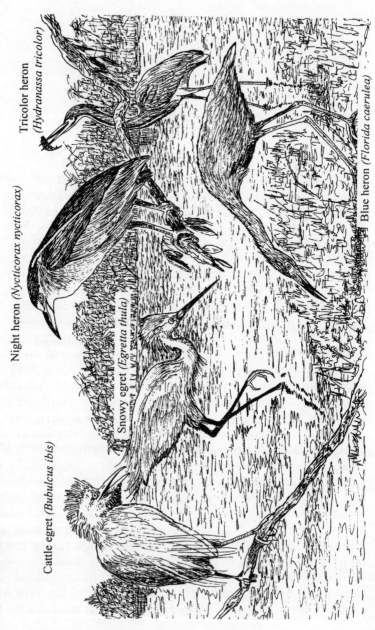

Cattle egret (*Bubulcus ibis*)

Night heron (*Nycticorax nycticorax*)

Tricolor heron (*Hydranassa tricolor*)

Snowy egret (*Egretta thula*)

Blue heron (*Florida caerulea*)

78

huge leaves and spiny flowers of the *Victoria amazonica* water lily, and frequented by jacana spurwings, purple gallinules and the small striped heron (*Butorides striatus*) known locally as chow. Dragonflies, red and brown, hovered or darted over the soft green carpet, and kiskadee tyrant flycatchers rather surprisingly stopped to splash into the wind-cleared patches of open water from which they caught small fish. It was a scene vibrant with life, the warm steamy air full of bird and insect noises, and heavy with the smells of vegetation in the sun, sun on water, flowering trees, and above all, especially in the nesting season, the gullery stench of nesting birds.

During much of the year the island was covered with a squawking, flapping jostling crowd of young egrets of all sizes beseeching parents for food and pecking at encroachers near their nests, the larger young practising wing-flapping prior to flying. In the evening they were joined by myriads more white and blue herons and egrets flying into the roost for the night, many of them young birds from the previous year, not yet in full adult plumage. These had to be content with space in the uppermost branches. High in the silkcotton trees the snail kites gathered to roost, and the last rays of the setting sun caught the ruby eyes of the emerging night herons, large dumpy, nocturnal birds, which leave the roost after most of the smaller herons have arrived back for the night, their silhouettes standing out solidly against the darkening sky, as they sailed forth with odd 'kwoks', serene and slow in contrast with the rapid fluttering of the innumerable small bats which emerged at this time.

Egrets roosted in the garden throughout the year, though the numbers using the roost fluctuated very much, chiefly with the weather, fewer coming at dry times of year. During the drought at the end of 1958, the south-west and north 'islands', no longer real islands as the surrounding moats were so low and clogged with vegetation, were deserted, and only a few (perhaps 100) birds continued to come to the south-east island.

The naturalist William Beebe writing of these botanic gardens in 1922 in his book *The Edge of the Jungle* said that it seemed as if these tiny islands were magnets drawing all the herons in the world, and he described with delight the line on line and party on party of herons tumbling out of the sky and skilfully applying their brakes as they came home to roost. When Beebe watched these herons he found little blue herons (*Florida caerulea*) and little white egrets (*Egretta thula*) dwelling together on certain islands, and that on the other side of the garden in aristocratic isolation, was a colony of the stately white American egrets – *Egretta (Casmerodius) alba* – where they ... 'slept and sat on rough nests of sticks'. Night herons were present too, but he only listed the yellow-crowned night heron (*Nyticorax violaceus cayennensis*).

Forty years later (1957–62) these heronries were as crowded as ever; at the height of the nesting season there hardly seemed to be room for another nest, but the species present had changed. The main change was that the islands had been more or less taken over by the cattle egret or buffback heron (*Bubulcus*) which had invaded Guyana, presumably from Africa or Europe, since Beebe's day. Perhaps associated with this, the numbers of Florida blue and snowy egrets nesting here had declined. Also American egrets no longer nested in the gardens, though a few sometimes roosted here in the non-breeding season; their nearest nesting colony then seemed to be some 30 miles away in the Lama water conservancy. And the black-crowned night heron (*Nyticorax nycticorax*) had replaced the yellow-crowned night heron; between 1957 and 62 only one pair of these yellow-crowned night herons with one young and occasionally single birds were seen in the gardens.

In the annual reports of the botanic gardens, Jenman described how these islands were made by removing the earth around them for building up the central road and thus creating lakes. In 1888 Jenman's report mentioned:

two or three kinds of cranes (= herons) have been among the permanent visitors, especially plentiful during the dry seasons of the past year. Blue hens (= purple gallinule) have been frequent; spurwings (= jacana) and herons have bred on the islands in the lakes; teal ducks have paid occasional visits, as have also curlew and other aquatic birds. In these years, too, waterhaas (*Capybara*) occurred in the gardens as well as crab dog racoons (*Procyon*).

Thus it seems that the heronries became established soon after the islands were created and planted with trees.

There are no records of cattle egrets being deliberately introduced into the New Worlds or escaping from zoos, and it seems probable that the invaders were blown across the Atlantic. In 1957 a little egret (*Egretta garzetta*) banded as a nestling in Spain was shot the following January in Trinidad, so egrets can get across the wide Atlantic ocean. Just when the cattle egret first reached the New World, and why they had not established themselves there sooner, are subjects for speculation, but observations made during this time in Guyana (which have been published elsewhere, in *Ibis*) suggested that man's role in opening up land for stock has been important (see Chapter 10), and also that the breeding habits of the cattle egret, particularly its ability to have two peak breeding seasons a year compared with one in the indigenous herons, have enabled their numbers to build up rapidly.

'Tiger' Long, a distinguished old resident, told me that he first noticed a cattle egret in Georgetown in the First World War, but from some notes of Im Thurn (unfortunately since lost) he thought that they may have been seen in BG before the turn of the century. They were rare until the 1930s when they became established in the backlands behind the coast. Haverschmidt recorded the first one in Surinam in 1946, but in 1947 found them to be quite numerous there. The forest seems to have presented a barrier to their movement inland, for they were absent from the Rupununi cattle country, seemingly ideal for them, until 1961, when we saw the first few there. Once there we predicted that they would increase rapidly, and by 1966 Tiny McTurk reported that they were plentiful around Cajueiro, the outstation of Karanambo cattle ranch.

This cattle egret occurs throughout Africa, southern Europe and tropical Asia and has in recent times also spread to

Australia. White except for traces of buff on the head and mantle, the legs, feet and bill are yellow, but become suffused with pink, making them bright orange in the breeding season, a time when the buff also becomes darker. In Guyana both sexes looked alike, though in parts of Africa the males may be slightly darker in colour. These are the egrets that follow domestic stock, and in Africa the large herbivores, catching insects disturbed by the feeding animals. They are rather restless birds, moving around while feeding. In the heronries they were the 'sparrows', urbane, ubiquitous, noisy, turbulent and quarrelsome. They established their territories merely by raising the buff feathers on crest and mantle and pecking at one another, without the dramatic display of the snowy egret, the calm of the Florida blue heron, or the long snakey neck and formidable bill of the tricolor. The presence of their numbers in the heronries was quite frightening. Should one of the other species be disturbed from its nest, it had to fight back through a milling mass of cattle egrets. In the botanic gardens their favourite nesting trees were the hawthorn-like *Pithecelobium unguis-cati*, bushes of medium height, most nests being between six and twelve feet off the ground. The lower sites were occupied first, later comers having to take higher and more peripheral sites. In these trees nests would be almost touching one another and the birds paired on the nest. I wondered why lower sites were preferred. I once saw a hawk visit one of the higher nests, sitting on the edge of the nest for ten minutes eating an egg, the liquid yellow glistening in the sun on its bill as it raised its head to swallow, while the luckless cattle egret whose nest it was pecked feebly at the hawk's tail, one flap of which knocked it down and kept it away until it could summon up courage to peck again. Perhaps shady sites are also preferred, as birds with nests in full sunlight appeared to suffer on hot days; they stood over their chicks, back to the sun and with outstretched wings, 'wing-shielding' them from the sun, and chortling with open mouth. The young also chortled, with mouth wide open and throat skin vibrating, when in direct sunlight. Outer nests often swayed in the wind.

82

The cattle egret nest here was a rough platform or very shallow cup of sticks on which the chalky blue eggs were laid, generally one to three in a clutch, as in comparable latitudes in Africa. Young cattle egrets are pure white with first a greyish then yellowish beak and dark legs. The shorter beak of the cattle egret with its feathers characteristically projecting further along the lower bill than the upper one, distinguished them from the white young of the snowy egrets and Florida blue herons with which they nest.

The indigenous egrets and herons are beautiful birds. The snowy egret (*Egretta thula*), striking in its immaculate white with jet black legs terminating in contrasting brilliant yellow feet, has a handsome dorsal train, a head crest and a tuft on the breast, all of disintegrated feathers, the aegrettes. The black bill is yellow at the base. It has a distinctive breeding season cry, a deep 'walla-walla-walla', quite unlike the ill-defined squawks of the other herons. Both sexes look alike. When defending its territory it paraded up and down a thin branch, clasping the branch firmly with widely-separated vivid yellow-orange feet – showing them to best advantage – the aegrette plumes raised over its back, throat feathers fluffed out and erected crest tossed over its head, reminding me of a Watusi dancer in Africa tossing his lion's mane headdress, and pecking down at intruders. A real 'I am King-of-the-Castle' display, for the snowy has a fine independence of demeanour, and makes a great show of stamping up and down when establishing a territory. Snowy egrets tended to nest low down, often within a few feet of the ground among the sanseveria and screwpine. The young are pure white and readily distinguished by their dark legs and light feet, though the colours are not as vivid as in the grown birds. There were generally two or three. Family parties seemed to stay together for some time, the parents and grown young later feeding together at the edge of the sea.

The Florida blue heron (*Egretta caerulea*) adult is a uniform slate blue, but in the breeding season the neck ruff of long lanceolate ornamental plumes, and similar plumes on the back and throat, neck and head, become a rich mauve, and the beak becomes brilliantly blue – possibly more so in the male, otherwise the two sexes look alike. For the first year the young are white, distinguished from the snowy egret young by their greenish legs, and from the cattle egret young by the leg colour and shape of the beak. Birds changing from white to blue plumage roosted above the nesting birds in the main breeding season, which suggested that they make this change when one year old and do not breed until two years old. The Florida blues were very quiet unobtrusive birds, raising their mauve neck and back hackles and pecking at intruders only when really disturbed; otherwise they came and went, and established their nests very quietly and discreetly with the minimum of fuss – quite contrary to the noisy bickering of the cattle egrets and the showy display of the snowies. The blues nested in much the same places as the cattle egrets and generally had one or two (rarely three) young. Their quietness and passivity was also shown when feeding, either on the drying mud of the foreshore after the tide had retreated or in the flooded fields, for they are stand-and-wait feeders.

The tricolor (or Louisiana) heron (*Hydranassa tricolor*), a shy, secretive 'lone-snooper', is the most beautiful in colour, a slender, graceful bird. The male was generally larger than the female, though the colours were much the same. The general body colour is dark blue-grey with a dorsal train of hair-like off-white plumes extending beyond the tail, with a white belly and white under the wings – patches of white that flash out from the dark undergrowth as the disturbed bird moves about, for here it was of a more solitary disposition than are the other herons and seemed easily bullied by them. The very long neck is chestnut, with lanceolate plumes on the foreneck, and longitudinal stripes of white and darker colour in the young. The head bears two distinct white plumes ('pendant occipital feathers, a nuchal crest'). The beak is a long vicious jabber, and below the bill there is a bright rufous chestnut patch vividly displayed by a quick skyward tilt of the beak when one bird takes over from the other at the nest. A good example of colour patch being used as part of the language of the species, this was flashed as a signal to its partner that it had arrived at the nest to take over.

Would one have appreciated this by looking at skins of dead birds in a museum? Did this colour patch evolve under the chin because the long dangerous beak was tilted up to avoid damaging the other bird at the nest? When establishing a nest territory the tricolor had a curious display, the bird crouching with bill held vertically skyward, clappering the bill with resounding noise. I later read that in the USA where the display of this species has been studied, the males and females twine their necks round one another and clapper skywards and then nibble headplumes, but here I never saw this ceremony – though I did see them nibbling one another's headplumes. In the botanical gardens the male often made a distinctive 'attraction flight' from his territory (sometimes only a perch on a muka-muka leaf at this stage), a repeated circular flight along the edge of the heronry, made with outstretched neck, and back to his perch, which appeared to be to try to attract a female to visit him. The nests of this species were often solitary, but scattered near the nests of other species, generally rather low down and hidden behind a muka-muka leaf or overhanging tree. But perhaps this was because their numbers were then low in the gardens; in the USA I gather that many of this species would be found nesting together; maybe the attraction flights are not so necessary when there are abundant breeding birds living together. The young, generally two or three, were like the adult in colour though the neck was more striped. Being dark in colour they were in striking contrast with the white young of the other three species; long of neck and beak and bright of eye, with fluffy heads, they regarded the world with a rather suspicious look. They took food from the side of the parent's dangerously long bill, in contrast with the shorter-billed cattle egrets in which the young took the less dangerous beak of the parent right into their mouth.

The night herons which also frequented the islands were large dumpy birds with a short neck and humped shoulders, but a dapper handsome plumage. The commoner black-crowned species, with its well-defined black crown and two long white head streamers, has also a jet-black back above grey wings and a white breast and underparts. The eye is a vivid dark red. The legs are yellow, suffused with pink to become orange in the breeding season. Both sexes are the same colour and size, but the young when hardly smaller than the adults are speckled brown and buff, with their short tails they look rather like owls except for their long beaks. This night heron's cry, a distinctive 'kwok-kwok' which gives them their local name, rings out at intervals through the day when their nests are disturbed by the overactive day herons, and also when they are going out to feed at dusk; it may be heard overhead in the night, at dawn as they return and far out on the mudflats at night. These herons frequented the highest layers of the trees, particularly when roosting, but some nested in the *Pithecelobium* along with the cattle egrets and in the creepers festooning the larger trees. The nests were deep cups and more substantial than those of the other species, often with leaves and mosslike bits as well as thick sticks. They built their nests by day and below certain trees a hail of sticks broken off by the night herons rained down, to the benefit of the cattle egrets which collected them from the ground. The young night herons stayed around the heronry all year; generally there were two young.

The yellow-crowned night heron (*Nyctanassa violacea*), rarely seen in the gardens when we were there, is more slightly built. It is a grey bird with a black face and a distinctive whitish yellow cheek patch matching its yellow crown. The young are speckled like those of the black-crowned night heron but rather greyer in colour. A rare visitor to the gardens was the boatbill (*Cochlearius cochlearius*), a heron confined to South and Central America, but Tiny McTurk told me that many of them nested here 40 years earlier. This is very like the black-crowned night heron in colour but its massive beak is distinctive, as are the broad black plumes on the head and the grey back. The function of the broad slipper-shaped bill is not really known; in Surinam its local name apparently means crab-eater and more recently it has been suggested that this largely nocturnal feeder captures its prey by touch rather than by sight, sucking shrimps and small fish in by rapid beak

86

movements. A heronry was visited in the Rupununi where this species nested together with other herons, along with the American egret (*E. alba*) and grey cocoi (*Ardea cocoi*), and also ducklars (*Anhinga anhinga*) (see Chapter 6). In 1961 to our great excitement one pair of boatbills made a nest in the botanic garden heronry at the beginning of August. Both birds took turns to incubate. The nest was watched closely and visited almost daily for over two months (until October 6), but no eggs ever hatched. Towards the end of this time the sitting birds were getting distinctly restless. Why did not the eggs hatch? Were they addled? One of the pair was a brownish bird, suggesting that it was a young bird. Surely two whole months spent sitting on eggs which never hatched must be almost a record – though in these days of pesticide accumulations causing eggs to be infertile, it may be more common than formerly.

The little striated heron or chow, *Butorides striatus*, which also nests in the gardens, was a more solitary species, the nests being found one at a time, generally low down hidden among the thick tangled greenery and generally near open water round the south-east island. Two or three young were produced at a time. This species varied much in colour, but the body is dark greyish-green with a striated chestnut and white neck and a black cap. The young are dark like the adults. This heron was common along open river banks (such as those of the Abary river, Chapter 10,) where it sits low near the water to fish.

The American egret, which no longer nested in the gardens at this time, is a tall, stately, solitary feeding, statuesque white bird, much larger than the other species here, with a long graceful neck, yellow bill and blackish legs. The deep slender keel gives it a deep V profile in flight as it wheels in to roost. In the breeding season it grows long mantle aegrettes. This species was generally seen feeding in the water savannas where it paddled in rather deeper water and sought food among tufts of aquatic vegetation. In Guyana it seemed to be a freshwater species; I never saw it paddle in the sea (as it apparently does off Florida), though rather surprisingly a few roosted in the mangroves by the sea at Enmore with the other herons. We found them nesting in trees near the Lama stop-off resthouse, and also at Crane Pond in the Rupununi, where it had two or three young at a time.

There are other herons and bitterns in Guyana which we never saw in the botanic gardens. These included the little bittern (*Ixobrychus exilis*) sometimes seen there but which I never managed to see, or to recognise. The beautiful capped heron (*Pilherodius pileatus*), now recognised as another night heron, we saw on the Berbice river; yellowish white, this has a black cap and long white head streamers which gave it a very 'legal' appearance as though attired for a court room. The large and solitary-feeding coccoi heron, *Ardea cocoi*, the most like the heron seen in England, we occasionally saw on the Abary river, and these nested at Crane Pond in the Rupununi where they generally had two young in a brood. The many-coloured agami heron (*Agamia agami*) was reputed to hide away in coastal swamps; I never managed to see it there but one sometimes slipped into the vegetation beside the Rupununi river. Here too a strikingly striped bittern fished as I watched giant arapaima fish rising to the surface below the rocks at Karanambo. Many of these Guyana herons seemed to have ecological equivalents of species in Africa, a lovely group for comparative studies.

The biological year for many species started with the main rains, though the arrival of these varied from year to year. In 1959 they did not start until June, other years they arrived much earlier, in April, or with a false start of heavy drubbing showers in March. By the end of the dry season the heronries would be more or less deserted, but as soon as the first really heavy 'in earnest' drubbing showers came, herons would arrive, particularly the cattle egrets whose numbers were so great that they had no difficulty in finding mates very rapidly, whereas the tricolor herons which were not very common took a long time to find a mate in spite the male's attraction flights. The reaction to the rains in cattle egrets was so fast – within a day or so – that it seemed that the rain itself had a direct effect, triggering nesting activity, not for example via food. Short, sharp, heavy showers (which often did not produce much rain to show in the rainfall figures) seemed to have more effect than more prolonged but gentler rain. So much so that I wondered if the mechanical effect of the drubbing action the rain stimulated the birds; my thoughts flew back to the banks of the Nile in Uganda where African children clubbed termite nests to simulate rain which stimulated the flying termites, those delectable delicacies, to emerge at this time of year.

In the days immediately following heavy rains about April the heronry became active. The cattle egrets and snowies were the first to arrive, closely followed by the little blues which slipped in unobtrusively, then the tricolor. The night herons started later in the rains when the foliage was thicker, which was perhaps related to their bulkier nests, and the shy boatbill last of all. The male herons generally moved in first and established territories. Low sites seemed to be preferred, late comers having to go high in the bushes. Certain bushes were most popular. At times when few were nesting, they all crowded into these few bushes, leaving the rest of the heronry empty – which suggested that mutual stimulation of many pairs is necesssary for successful breeding, as in many colonially nesting seabirds.

In the tropics, where breeding seasons in many creatures are prolonged and ill-defined, attracting a mate in the right physiological state presents greater difficulties than in temperate regions where all the individuals of a species are geared to breed at a definite time of year by the climate.

As I spent hours watching the herons I was more and more impressed with the very different characters of the different species: the black-crowned night herons impassive sentinels, solid and hunch-shouldered regarding me with an immovable red eye; the cattle egrets bustling and fussing themselves in, but once settled sitting very tightly and quietly; the snowies with their very showy performance, their magnificent Watusi warrior dances, yellow feet on black legs widely separated and vividly displayed, and not content with such a showy performance visually, their loud and distinctive 'walla-walla' cries rang out through the heronries. The little streaked herons slid in surreptitiously under the undergrowth, and the tricolor also arrived rather apologetically and was easily disturbed. But the Florida blue just 'happened', it was suddenly already installed, quite the least conspicuous among the shadows of the vegetation, merely raising its hackles and pecking if another heron came too near.

The male herons stake and defend a territory from which they try to attract a female, and here the differences in behaviour between species were most marked. From the female's reactions it seemed obvious that she chose a mate for his site as well as himself, so a good site was very important for an early start in nesting. The cattle egret defending its territory against all corners would become paired when the right signal was given and accept another bird as its mate as suddenly as if a switch had been thrown. The Floria blue sky-clappered, as did the tricolor, and the night herons had a curious snap and hiss ceremony, facing one another with necks fluffed out. The early comers got the best sites, and the influence of numbers on rapid pairing was apparent; late-comers pushed to peripheral and less attractive sites were at a disadvantage.

At this stage the herons were much more agressive to members of their own species than to other species. Snowy egrets displayed more violently against other snowies. This helped the intruding cattle egrets to slip in – a little blue and a cattle egret were seen simultaneously attacking another little blue at one stage. Some birds were displaced from their original territories, and if a pair was turned out, they chose a new site together. Nests were taken over, and even the young turned out.

Both sexes helped to build the nest, though the male did most of the stick collecting while the female remained on the nest platform, receiving sticks from him and weaving them into the nest. The cattle egrets picked up sticks from the ground, numbers of them working together near the heronry; they had to learn how to do it, at first they tried to take live sticks attached to bushes, or two birds would tug at the same stick. From the tree tops came a rain of sticks broken off by stick-

90

collecting night herons when these started to nest. The nests were often within a foot of one another.

The eggs were laid at an interval of a day or so, and brooding started as soon as the first egg was laid, so hatching was asynchronous. In BG one to three eggs and young was the general rule for all these heron species, but at higher latitudes, both north and south, the number rose to five or more eggs. The three young so completely filled these nests, how could they could ever fit in more young? Do these higher-latitude birds build larger nests? David Lack had suggested that this general rule for birds to have larger broods at higher latitudes perhaps reflects the length of day in which parents can collect food for the young. This rule also held for the night herons which fed by night, BG ones having one or two (rarely three) young, those farther from the equator three to five young.

The parents shared the incubation. The returning parent often presented a stick to the sitting bird as part of a take-over ceremony. The nest was often in need of repair from the weight of the sitting birds and tropical downpours; nests were seen to fall away from below the young before they were fully reared, and nests never survived from season to season here, as they are said to do in USA. Instead of bringing a stick, the arriving tricolor gave a quick tilt to its beak, flashing the vivid rufous patch under the chin as it did so.

In the USA the little blue's eggs hatch in 22–24 days, the young are brooded for the first week and make short flights when one month old. In Guyana it took about two months from the time the nest was made until the young left the nest site. Do parents help the young to hatch? A snowy parent was seen to peck an egg due to hatch. In snowy egret families one parent stayed on guard on the nest until the young were quite large – which was seen to pay, for a parent was observed pecking off two cattle egrets lurking round the nests and young. The cattle egrets and little blues left their young unguarded at an early stage, and cattle egret young were turned out of nests by other cattle egrets on several occasions.

On one occasion when a robber pair of cattle egrets turned the young of their own species out of a nest, one of the young fell into another cattle egret nest about two feet below. Its parents, on returning to the nest, chased off the robber's mate, who was then sitting on the nest. They then pecked at the nest sticks but were oblivious of their own young one a mere two feet below it in another nest. The receiving nest already contained three young, two larger and one about the same size as the newcomer. When their parent eventually returned to feed them (surprisingly this was not until an hour later), the newcomer crouched low in the nest while they were being fed. The feeding parent ignored it, but as soon as this parent departed the smallest set about the newcomer, pecking at it vigorously, while the larger young took no notice. At last the runt had another, lower in the peck order, on which to vent its feelings. and the newcomer eventually disappeared.

Feeding the young was an energetic performance and it must often have been painful as the young tugged at the parent while it regurgitated food. Gravity assisted the transfer of food from parent to young, but when the young were nearly full grown they sometimes clambered up twigs near the nest to the highest point to greet the returning parent, and the comic situation was presented of trying to 'gravity-feed' upwards, which they had to learn was an impossibility. Both little blue and tricolor with their long beaks, spilled food out sideways to the young, instead of thrusting them into the mouths of the young, as did the cattle egrets. The young grew fast and the clamour of hungry youngsters, and the smell, increased rapidly, the lower sites becoming plastered with excreta from above, particularly when the cleansing effect of the rain ceased later in the season. During the rains the bushes grew vigorously, supporting the weight of the nests, but at the end of the rains the weight of the birds broke them down. Few nests survived long after the young had started to fly. The growing young spent the time between meals exercising their wings, flapping and squawking with neighbouring young, not venturing far from the tattered nests or nest sites. The pecking they got from other birds when they did so showed there must be strong selection for them to stay put.

When they could flap across to the mainland the young

stood around in 'gaggling gangs' on the grass near the islands, returning to the islands when disturbed. Even at this stage the young cattle egrets kept their feet dry while the young snowies and little blues, both wet-feet feeders, paddled in the rain puddles on the grass. This difference was, it seemed, innate, not learned.

One year a Brazilian hawk eagle (*Buteogallus urubitinga*) took up residence in the gardens and fed on these young, as shown by piles of white feathers on the grass. My vocabulary of noises produced by the night herons was considerably enlarged by the enraged parents of an unfortunate young night heron that was snatched from its nest by this bird. After the nesting season the herons still continued to come back to the heronries to roost, the diurnal herons at dusk, the night herons by day. If the weather was very dry the numbers dwindled. The year that the Christmas rains failed (1958) the heronries were practically deserted at the height of the dry season. But when there were good November rains another wave of nesting started, this time of cattle egrets only, although in about January a few night herons might start, and the odd 'walla-walla' cry of a snowy egret would ring out if the rain had been heavy. But the failure of the aquatic-feeding herons to rear young successfully out of the main rains showed that there must be strong selection for them to breed in the main rains, though their physiology must be elastic enough to take advantage of variations in when these rains start from year to year.

The dry-feet feeding cattle egrets do not compete for food with the indigenous herons with which they roost and nest, which are all wet-feet, aquatic feeders. Humans have undoubtedly helped the cattle egret by opening up new land for them. Also the cattle egrets had two peak breeding seasons a year, in both main and Christmas rains, instead of just one in the main rains as had the indigenous herons. Cattle egrets seemed to be lightly triggered by rain to start nesting, perhaps because they came from a drier country? Now their numbers are high, so they pair quickly and get the best nest sites. When only a few cattle egrets were present here they could probably only nest when indigenous herons were breeding, needing the communal

93

stimulation of their company, but when they became plentiful they could also nest in the short rains when few of the indigenous species were nesting. The results of censuses taken of the nests in the botanic gardens have been described elsewhere (in *Ibis* 1967). Early in August 1959, a year when there was an abrupt start to nesting in all heron species when the rains finally arrived in June after a long drought, the three botanic garden islands carried over 1700 nests, of which nearly 90% belonged to cattle egrets. Of the indigenous species, there were 80 little blue nests, 50 black-crowned night heron nests, 38 snowy, 17 tricolor and 4 chow. By October the young of all species had nearly all left the heronry by day though they returned there to roost at night.

Heavy showers started again in November and very soon cattle egrets started to nest again, first a few, then more and more, and when a rough count was made in December at least 1700 cattle egret nests were seen and no nests of other species – though later in December a few black-crowned night herons started to nest. At the end of December, after very heavy rain, about one dozen snowies, one or two pairs of tricolors and three or four little blues, all developing breeding colours, started to display and establish territories. A few of these then nested and laid eggs, but had difficulty rearing their young. One little blue produced two young but the size discrepancy between these two increased markedly; the larger one then got fed three times running and the smaller one not at all, until the smaller one disappeared. Later the other disappeared too. There is, it seems, strong selection for nesting in the main rains, the time when food for wet-feet feeders is most abundant. The rain also stimulated a gorgeously coloured purple gallinule cock to chase the drabber female round the island, and the snail kite to mate.

The very large number of cattle egrets breeding in December suggested that these were not just left-over birds which had not bred in the main rains, nor just young birds breeding for the first time – though some behaved like virgin birds when mating – but that some individual birds breed twice a year. Without ringing the birds it is impossible to tell whether this was really so. The buff colour was not so intense in cattle egrets nesting at this time as in those nesting in the main rains. As in August these cattle egrets were established on all the islands, but were concentrated particularly in the mid-height trees, where their nests almost touched one another, while the muka-muka sanseveria zones used by other species in August were relatively empty.

In 1958 when the short rains failed the cattle egrets did not nest at all until the rains arrived the following June, a clear-cut example of how important the rains are in controlling breeding in a tropical species, and also how the time of breeding can vary from year to year with variations in when the rains began, ranging from March to June.

These botanic garden observations showed that heron populations build up in wet years, and the cattle egrets particularly when the end of the year rains are heavy. It was very suggestive that the advent of the cattle egret in the USA in 1952 followed a long cycle of wet years in Guyana, indeed the longest wettest cycle since rainfall records started there in 1888. The forest evidently presented a barrier to the spread of the cattle egret inland, for they did not appear in the Rupununi savannas until 1961, and quite probably they spread along the coastal plains northwards.

Observations on the coastal tidal mudflats showed how the herons feed in entirely different ways. The snowy is a paddler at the edge of the sea; it could also be seen paddling in freshwater in flooded fields and trenches at other times, but liked to get its feet wet – and it uses its light-coloured feet to stir up small fish and other food organisms. This species feeds in a small flock and just after the nesting season in small groups of four or five, seemingly family parties with their two or three young. We saw this species chase *Anableps* foureye fish at the edge of the tide, also snowies passing small fish (possibly anchovies) to their young at the nest. The Florida blue had a completely different feeding technique, numbers of them feeding higher up the beach, with a stand-and-wait technique, each bird very still and erect, head held high as though listening for prey. They seemed to eat mainly fiddler crabs, which we could see them catch and swallow. But at Overwagt one February day I watched a blue heron swallow a large (10-inch) 'eel' which it held by the head while it writhed round its beak. It dipped the fish repeatedly in a tidal channel, walking onto the bank quickly after each dip. It took ten minutes to swallow the eel, finally dipping the tail end in water to lubricate it and jerking its long neck to work the eel down its throat – the whole process watched throughout by a very interested little ringed plover. The tricolor heron has yet another completely different feeding technique; a lone snooper, this stalks along the tidal channels, head well down, neck doubled into a long S, beak ready to shoot out suddenly, and the prey is swallowed so swiftly we were never able to see what it was. Does this heron have a special articulation in its neck, as in the darter *Anhinga* which also shoots its neck out suddenly? The black-crowned night herons which also fed on the mudflats only appeared at dusk when the other herons had gone to roost; their hoarse 'kwok' calls came in from near the edge of the sea on moonlit nights or when flying overhead, but what they ate here we never discovered.

5

Journeys to the Interior

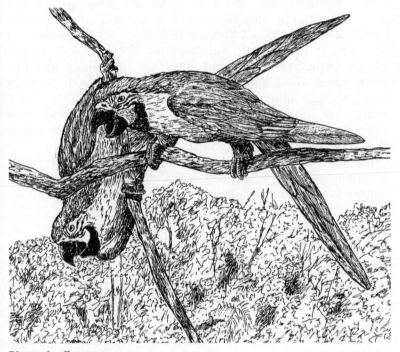

Blue and yellow macaws

When we arrived in Guyana the five or so geologists of the government's geological survey were each based in a different part of the country with a team of local assistants (many Amerindian) to map the geology of that area. As communications were then very poor, they lived very isolated lives. In addition to creating a new geological map of Guyana, Richard McConnell's great achievement was to create a unified geological survey based on Georgetown, from where the geologists spent several long periods in the bush each year. Our early travels were to visit these geologists on location. As there were no roads to the interior, travel was by air or by river.

The planes used were old Dakotas or the small amphibious Grummon Goose which could land on river pools in the interior where there were no airstrips. This landed on water with a tearing sound and could then put down wheels and crawl up a ramp, the crabs scuttling away as it did so. At Georgetown we climbed into the Grummon on the ramp, and the plane then ran down and took off from the wide brown muddy Demerara river, flying low over the canoes and fish 'pens' where the Chinese seine bag-nets were fixed, then up over the neat oblong fields and green canals of the sugar estates, to wilder but still man-altered country, fields and paths, the water conservancy, the white sand with its covering of wallaba bush and on to primaeval rain forest.

The first views that we had of the forest were thus often aerial ones, flying in a small plane or helicopter above the canopy hour after hour, the tops of the trees like a great sea below us, in sun and shadow a multitude of greens. From the air the patterns of vegetation showed clearly, changing with the soil or wetness of the ground, winding rivers and bush with water gleaming through, damp patches with no trees, concentric rings of palm forest, and then the canopy of forest trees. Ecologists need to fly over the country to see such patterns of vegetation, bush islands in dry country, savanna islands in forest, and to muse on the creatures likely to be restricted to these islands. The occasional daring, or hungry, creatures might go beyond the limits of the habitat normal for hundreds of generations of their kind, probably perishing in the encircling type of country, but sometimes a hardy individual or group, with luck, or in years of unusual climatic conditions, would make it across to another island of suitable terrain, introducing new genes into a semi-isolated population. Here in Guyana the forest seemed from the air to be a continuum, with a very abrupt edge to the savanna but there were some bush islands in the savanna country, and riverine bush snaked across the land marking the river beds. However, in the forest the tall trees continued right up to, and arched over, the creeks, for these trees are well-adapted to withstand water-logged soils and flooding. In Guyana some of the tallest trees, such as the mora (*Mora excelsa*) which grows to 160 feet high, occur in swamp forest along the rivers. In the Amazon flooded forest, trees withstand months of flooding, and in neighbouring Surinam air photographs of the man-made Brockopondo lake taken several years after the dam was completed and filled showed many of the trees still alive though only the tree tops projected above the lake surface.

From the air one could see how complex and varied the flora was even in small areas; there may be 200 species of trees within a square mile in these forests. The 'desirable' timber species, such as greenheart (*Ocotea rodiaei*), which grows to 160 feet high but may perhaps take 100 years to do so, are far apart so difficult to extract from among the less valuable tree species. This scattering of individual species showed up well when the trees were in flower, occasional widely scattered trees, or the creepers growing on them, being covered in bright yellow or purple flowers, the yellow flowers visible over long distances to the human eye. But members of a tree species do not flower at exactly the same time; in some species each tree seems to have its own rhythm here where seasonal variations are so slight. So there always seemed to be some flowers and fruits available for the creatures which feed on them, and foraging parties of mixed species of birds would go from tree to tree.

The shape of the tree crowns varies considerably. Some giants project above the general level, throwing long shadows across the canopy in the early morning and towards evening when the sun is low. But the general level of canopy is pretty uniform over much of this land. Was this why no gliding animals have evolved here, compared with the forests of Malaysia where so much forest is on hills? In the high forest of Guyana the trees generally have long clean boles with few low branches.

Many other journeys were made by river, chugging upstream

in an open plank-built 'ballahoo' boat with an outboard engine, hour after hour along wide sunny rivers between walls of high forest. The bends in the river closed the view so that each stretch of water was like a long narrow lake, only opening out as the bend was approached. Down here one had the smell of sun on water, of decaying vegetation and sweet flowers – exotic sprays of orchids hanging from the trees letting out their perfume at a particular time of day – and the sudden cool smell of approaching evening. The forest walls cut out any wind so the rivers were generally calm with the reflections of the tall trees lying deep in the brown-black water, the bush rope lianas hanging from them as straight grey strands, their reflections becoming wriggling grey snakes with the wake of our passing, and gleams of sunlight reflected from the ripples of our wake lighting up the dark undersides of the trees. Leaves and flowers came floating down and often golden pollen dusted the river surface. Some bush ropes ended in a tuft of roots just below the water surface, in which, according to Barrington Brown, the pirai (piranha) often lay their eggs which are then guarded by the parent fish.

The rivers have many rapids and falls, especially in the dry seasons. In the wet season it is possible to travel upriver over many of these, but the stores and outboard engines have to be portaged round some of them, the boat being dragged up on a 'droughing line' rope from the rocks or manhandled round the falls. Many of the rivers have small falls marking the top of the tidally affected stretches; in this flat country these may be 100 miles inland from the sea. Above the tidally affected part, bird life is much more abundant, kingfishers and ducklars (*Anhinga*) testifying to the abundance of small fishes, and swallows dipping to drink as they fly. On our first trip up the Cuyuni we met 'pork-knockers' who work alluvial gold in this area, dragging their boats on log rollers over a smoothed pathway made especially at the side of the falls for this purpose, and on the overland trip to Kaieteur Falls we had to portage round the Amatuk and Waratuk falls.

Bartica – Gateway to the Interior

A first geological survey visit was to Bartica at the junction of the Essequibo and Mazaruni rivers (see map 1), the gateway to the Interior where 'pork-knocker' prospectors stocked up with stores, including dried stockfish and pigtails (from which they may, or may not, get their name) and engaged in 'rum sprees' on their return to town. It is here that boat crews were to be found, the river boats being worked by Boviander folk of mixed African/Amerindian origin. From the air Bartica looked unbelievably tidy, the roads laid out in rectangular blocks, but below it was a jumble of stores and rum shops, the beaches littered with great trunks of greenheart being square-axed into shape by men perched on them wielding axes shaped like those of mediaeval beefeaters, and in great danger of losing their toes. The Essequibo river is here four or five miles wide, and the mile-wide Mazaruni river has already received the Cuyuni waters some miles upstream. The little island of Kyk-over-al, centre of the first colony to be founded in what is now Guyana by the Dutch East India Company over 380 years ago, lies in the Mazaruni near the Cuyuni inflow, but when we visited it only the ruins of a fort were to be seen.

The Bartica area had long been a base for visiting naturalists and scientific expeditions, many from universities in temperate countries, as it was so readily accessible, the timber and gold and diamond mining operations having opened up routes into the then more or less untouched forest. More people probably lived there 50 years before the time of our visit, as the gold was worked out. But although it was one of the better-known areas, the flora and fauna was so rich and varied that only some aspects had as yet been studied, reflecting the interests of the specialists who happened to be drawn to the area. William Beebe was one of the first naturalists to work there; he visited the area in 1909 on his way to the Cuyuni river, and in their book *Tropical Wildlife in British Guiana* (1917) he described visits by earlier scientists to this area. The New York Zoological Society's laboratory, started here in 1917, had to move from Kalacoon House and went to Kartabo in 1921 which was then a centre of research for several years, and from where a square mile of forest was studied in detail. In 1929 the UK's Oxford University expedition made Moraballi Creek, which flows into the Essequibo near Wineperu, their headquarters, from where they studied the life of the canopy, being pulled up to the tree tops in a bosun's chair, as described by Hingston (1932) in *A Naturalist in the Guiana Forest*. Members of this expedition included O.W. Richards the entomologist and his brother Paul the forest botanist, who both became pre-eminent in tropical ecology, the Nicholsons who studied birds, and Hingston who studied spiders and ants. They worked in close collaboration with the Forestry Department, of which a notable member was D.B. Fanshawe who later (1952) produced a very useful review of the vegetation of BG and the different types of forest. Carter's Cambridge expedition from UK in 1930 also worked in the Bartica area, studying the water chemistry of the different types of rivers and creeks. While we were in BG, there was such a spate of visiting scientists, particularly from North America but also many from Europe, that Bertie Allsopp planned to establish a field centre to help with their queries and arrangements. Also Guyana would benefit enormously if the results of all their work could be collated and made available in the country, as the results of expeditions published in widely scattered journals in their home countries were often not available in Guyana. The success of these expeditions depended very much on local help, and the Amerindian field staff was invaluable – able to identify plants and creatures high in the canopy, which visiting eyes not accustomed to the forest can barely see, let alone decipher.

The forest around Bartica was rich in such well-known tropical species as toucans, of which the nesting habits in holes in dead trees were studied by Beebe, and the glorious brilliant iridescent blue morpho butterflies which flapped and sailed through the forest clearings and along the creeks; the flight is very fast and as the underside of the wing is dark the flapping motion gives a curious come-and-go effect. The metallic brilliance may help to protect them from the sun's heat. The best way to catch them was said to be to put out rotten fruit then

102

collect the inebriated morpho from these alcoholic delicacies, but this I never tried. Butterfly migrations were a feature of the Bartica area, streams of yellow ones passing over the river hour after hour.

The 'line' as the road leading from Bartica south to the Potaro river bridge was called, was one of the very few roads in the interior. In places its unique delights included a surface of round logs, known with good reason, as corduroy. Only government vehicles such as the mail lorry and the large ten-ton scammels used by the timber ventures to haul out very heavy greenheart trunks were allowed on the road. And scammels had right of way. But the line penetrated interesting country, rich in birds and butterflies, along a ridge of forest, the trees hung with various kinds of ant and termite nests and the 'pipiyo' calls of the greenheart or pork-knocker bird accompanied the traveller most of the way. We often saw Bartica from the air when en route to Kaieteur, Kamarang or the Rupununi.

Kaieteur Falls

The Kaieteur Falls are one of the wonders of the world and lying remote in the interior of Guyana they were then still completely unspoilt. Here the whole Potaro river plunges over the edge of the plateau 800 feet into the gorge below, a scene of great grandeur and beauty, the restless energy of the waters leaping with upblown spray turbulent against the background of quiet hills on the sunny plateau above the falls, and in profound contrast with the peace of the river winding in the gorge far below. The plateau edge over which the river falls is here curved into a vast amphitheatre. In those days we landed on the river above the falls in the small amphibious Grummon Goose plane, and for departure the plane revved hard, wooshed down the river and took off over the edge of the falls, the land suddenly dropping 800 feet below the plane as it swooped into the air – quite exhilarating! Standing on the rocks at the top of the falls we gazed at the perpetual motion

Swifts at Kaieteur Falls

of the brown water falling in curtains, white gules thrown out into space in four main folds, each white gule of water seeming to fall so slowly into the boiling pool far below, a pool encircled with a double rainbow against the vivid yellow-green background of continuously drenched vegetation far below, from which the foam-flecked river crawled out of the rainbowed pool and down the gorge. The river bends were hidden by forest except for three short stretches, the places from which one could see the wall of water at the head of the river when travelling upriver by boat or on foot.

Kaieteur was still as it was when discovered in 1841 by the geologist Barrington Brown. His book *Canoe and Camp Life in British Guiana* (1877) records that when descending the Potaro river on his geological explorations, he was told by his Amerindian companions in camp one night that the next day they would be coming to a fall 'higher than the trees' around which they would have to walk. The name he gave to the falls, Kaieteur, was the Amerindian name meaning the Old Man falls, for there was a legend that an old man was put into a canoe and sent over the falls. For many years they were officially recorded as 741 feet, but this measurement was made with a barometer and it was discovered that the instrument was affected by the curious climatic conditions in the gorge. Measurements by other means made the falls 800 feet high, one of the highest waterfalls in the world. Away to the west in neighbouring Venezuela a small river at the Angel Falls tumbles 3000 feet from the same geological formation, but this all turns to spray before it reaches the bottom.

At Kaieteur the white gules of water seemed to take about ten seconds to complete their fall; towards the sides of the river the updraft slows down the fall and whips the edge water into spray. This then drops more slowly, carrying an after-image in the eye, like fireworks leaving a vapour trail, and some of it is swept along the slope alongside the falls as mist, keeping the slope green and covered in plants. Behind the falls is a cave in which swifts nest, the white-chinned swifts (*Cypseloides* species) which hawk in the sunlight far below in the gorge. Looking into the cave with binoculars it seemed a veritable hell of white vapours most of the time, but when the mist cleared momentarily one could see green mosses growing there. Lack, in his book *Swifts in the Tower* says that the young swifts here must take their first flight through the falls, and I once saw there a young dead one caught by the leg and dangling in the spray. Far below the swifts hawk in the sun. In the dry season the river flow is much reduced and water lilies grow at the sides of the river above the falls. Watching Kaieteur one felt one should stay there endlessly, like the desert Arabs in Saint-Exupéry's *Wind, Sand and Stars* who, when first shown a waterfall, felt that in deference they should remain there as long as the show was on, until the miracle was over and the river ceased to flow.

There were no buildings to spoil Kaieteur, though talk of 'tourist attraction' and 'luxury hotel' was heard. One special little hut was built for a very special royal visitor, but was then dismantled. The area around Kaieteur had been designated a National Park, then the only one in Guyana. As Kaieteur could then be reached on a day trip in the Grummon Goose from Georgetown, there was no need to spoil the falls by putting a hotel nearby. For those who liked to travel upriver, there was primitive rest house, with the usual hooks for hammocks, at Tukeit at the foot of the escarpment. From here a trail led up through the forest to the top of the plateau.

Both the Victoria Falls, the 'smoke that thunders', over which the Zambezi plunges in Africa, and Kaieteur were discovered from above, by explorers travelling downriver, but it is the approach from below that is perhaps most awe inspiring. Travelling up the Potaro river towards Kaieteur, on rounding a river bend one suddenly sees a wall of water, quite unbelievably high, at the head of the 400 foot wide river. In Africa we once lived near the Victoria Falls, so knew how their appearance changed with the height of river and volume of water going over. Kaieteur has nothing like the volume of water, nor the width of the Zambezi falls. The Victoria Falls now have a road and railway bridge just below them and numerous luxury hotels nearby, and it comes as a surprise to realise that Kaieteur Falls were known to the outside world 14 years before the missionary David Livingstone discovered the Victoria falls in 1855.

Eigenmann's classic study of the *Freshwater Fishes of British Guiana* (1917) arose from his desire to see the effect of this great waterfall on the fish fauna. As he expected, he found that the falls are a complete barrier, the fauna above them being very impoverished and consisting only of species which have got there by the 'back door' from the plateau.

Botanically the Kaieteur Falls park is an interesting area. Tree members of the pineapple family, bromeliads known as *Brocchinia*, grow near the top of the falls. These rather resemble in form the giant lobelias growing on Ruwenzori and other African high mountains, and like them the axils of the leaves hold pools of water. At Kaieteur we found mosquito and tipulid (daddy longlegs) larvae, dragonfly nymphs and frog spawn living in these leaf-pools. I was delighted to be shown the large special bladderwort, *Utricularia humboldtii*, which weaves its way from tree to tree and then produces bladders with which it fishes for tiny water fleas in the pools in the leaf axils; it has a *Marsilia*-like leaf, a purple flower. The sundew *Drosera* also grew on the boggy patches of ground here, trapping insects with long glandular hairs on the leaves. Ferns with special drip tips to their leaves, and mosses and filmy ferns abounded. In a stream crossed on the descent to the rest house at the foot of the gorge we found aquatic cockroaches wandering in and out of the water, to the later delight of a visiting entomologist interested in the wetability of cuticle. At the rest house myriads of Ephemeroptera mayflies came to the light, for it was very dark in the night after the full moon. In Africa this would have been usual, but here in Guyana one did not usually see great numbers of aquatic insects coming round lamps. As we washed our plates in the river by lamplight, water beetles gyrated at the surface, black and yellow millipedes were at the water's edge, and we collected small characid fish (*Creatochanes*) with the dip-net. In the nearby forest early next morning small diptera were dancing below spiders' webs, mad dances, incessant, seemingly faster and faster. One dance taking place in a hollow tree trunk was of midges with tiny bodies and long strikingly coloured orange, black and white legs, below them a long thin spider of very much the same distinctive colours. What was the full story behind this?

Kamarang Christmas

One Christmas we flew over Kaieteur to the plateau country of the upper Mazaruni to visit our friends the Seggars at Kamarang, the centre of an Amerindian reserve where Bill Seggar was District Officer. Among other excitements we had a Christmas picnic jokingly 'diving for diamonds' in the falls at the edge of the plateau. We did not find any – perhaps we were too full of a famous Christmas pudding which had been round the Kalahari with us in Africa and found its way in our baggage to Guyana. Eating it was more of a ritual than a delight, for far from improving with time, as good Christmas puddings are reputed to do, this one had become composted in its wanderings, and I then belatedly remembered that it was probably the one given to us by a vegetarian friend. But we all ate labba, and very good this was. And our Christmas picnic was joined by two otters, who whistled to one another as they worked their way up the rapids, one behind the other diving and humping their glossy black wet bodies over the rocks, watched by a sandpiper. There was later quite a diamond strike here, which led to much development in this area.

We had spent Christmas morning at Danny's village, the community dancing in a large communal hut and drinking piwari (cassiri) out of the large log canoe used specially for making it out of cassava. Danny was an Akawaio, a tribe of Indians of Carib stock studied intensively by Audrey Butt who had lived with them here and written about their Halleluya religion, evidently originating in half-remembered stories brought back from some mission many years ago. David Attenborough had described a visit to Danny's house in his book *Zoo Quest to Guiana*.

At the time of our visit Kamarang consisted of several houses, a store, a hospital and a school. The whole station had been created by Bill Seggar in his many years as District Officer since he and his wife Daphne came here. The buildings were largely built with his own capable hands. Daphne, who shared this lonely station with him, looked after their livestock, cows, sheep, hens. Now they were building an airstrip. For years they had been trying to get a tractor here to help with these jobs. This meant flying one in a chartered Dakota plane to Imbamadei, savanna country where Dakotas could land, some 60 miles up river, then rafting it down to Kamarang. When the tractor finally arrived the Seggars were on leave, and the bright replacement thought, 'We will put it on a raft and catch it as it goes by Kamarang as the river is not wide there'. In the event it went by in the night, unobserved, and straight on and over the falls. Back to square one. But now the airstrip was being built.

The distinguished anthropologist A. Metraux visited this area while we were in Guyana and was amazed at the rapid change in the short time since Audrey Butt had worked there, transistor radios etc invading the district. Since we were there, and the discovery of diamonds, there have been even more drastic changes. Bill had spent much time studying the problems of how best to fit the Amerindians to take part in the modern world and run their own affairs. In the past they had tended to retreat into the forest away from newcomers, though in certain mining districts they were not above renting women-folk out for temporary use, but this retreat is no longer possible. Now Kamarang is the hub of the Upper Mazaruni mining district (see Chapter 13).

'Virgin Territory' – The Geological Survey New River Expedition

The New river in the south-east of Guyana on the borders of Surinam and Brazil, was one of the least explored areas. The country was uninhabited and hardly anyone had been there since the Boundary Commission 25 years previously. The members of this had returned with strange tales of stunted vegetation, and suffered from a mysterious illness said to resemble radiation sickness, hopefully fortelling untold riches from radioactive minerals. But the symptoms were also those of beriberi, and the rice on which they fed had evidently become polished in the sack on the long distance it had to be carried to them. An old inhabitant of Georgetown 'Tiger' Long confirmed tales of stunted vegetation which he had met when travelling up the New river on foot in search of a murderer many year previously.

The New river is joined by its Oronoque tributary before entering the Courantyne river (see Map 1). There was a dispute with Surinam over the boundary here as Surinam maintained the New river is the main Courantyne, the upper Courantyne a tributary. Reading Barrington-Brown's description of his discovery of the New river, in *Canoe and Camp life in British Guiana* (1877), it seems clear that he regarded the Courantyne to be the easternmost river.

A scientific survey was planned to assess the resources of this area, complete with botanist, forestry and agricultural officers as well as geologists, but no funds were forthcoming and no suitable personnel could be found, so this reverted to being purely a geological survey, directed by husband Richard. Organising it in so remote a place was a complicated operation but the Geological Survey had long experience of such bush trips.

First an aerial reconnaisance was made. Fuel had to be sent ahead to Apoteri at the junction of the Rupununi and Essequibo rivers. The amphibious six-seater Grummon Goose was then used, refueling at Apoteri and landing on the river (narrowly missing a submerged tree) at the junction of the New and Oronoque rivers, the site of the Boundary Commission's base camp 25 years earlier. This was now grown over, the only evidence of a former clearing being some enormously tall congo pump (*Cecropia*) trees indicative of secondary growth, The party disembarked on a sandbank in the river and were contemplating wading ashore when a commotion in the water drew their attention to a large catfish which was chopped to pieces before their eyes by pirai. These razor-toothed *Serrasalmus* scooped pieces out of the unfortunate catfish, chop chop

110

chop, the click of their jaws clearly audible, until in a very few minutes nothing of it remained but the large bony head. This discouraged wading ashore!

The survey party eventually consisted of two geologists, Philip Morris and Howard Bateson, good friends, 18 'men' – mostly Amerindians of the Wapishana tribe from the Rupununi who had worked with the Geological Survey for many years – and an Afro-Guyanese boat-builder Mr White. Having built two splendid ballahoo plank boats on the spot, Mr White returned to Georgetown when we flew in at 'half-time' to replenish supplies. It took about seven trips to get all the men and supplies transferred from Apoteri in the Grummon. They landed in the rain and were left on the sandbank, feeling rather forlorn as the Grummon departed. Their first very sensible move was to make some tea, after which they moved across to the base camp site in a rubber dinghy.

The survey party were all in the area for four months. During this time the two boats each travelled 1000 miles, first some 200 miles up the New river and its side streams, then back to base at half-time before exploring up the Oronoque and its side streams to the watershed in the mountains which form the boundary with Brazil. During this trip they saw no-one else. There must be few parts of the world with an adequate water supply so deserted; did this indicate bad soils? They had been asked to look out for clearings spotted from the air, thought possibly to indicate old gardens. But these proved to be places where local whirlwinds had blown down the forest; they found one which had evidently been affected in the last six to twelve months, the trees all snapped off over an area of about ten square miles.

· I was lucky enough to visit this area (31 March 1958) half-way through the survey when supplies were replenished, to see their progress. The geologists had a short-wave radio at base camp so could send occasional messages which we received very prosaically on our phone in Georgetown. Piloted by Johnie Wilson who had flown in the main party, we took off at 6 am from the flat calm Demerara river, circled over the still-

111

sleeping Georgetown and away over the neat oblong sugarcane fields and the water conservancy. It took an hour and a half to fly to Apoteri, where the plane's wheels were wound down and we landed on a rough strip to refuel from supplies sent ahead here. It was a relief to get into the fresh air and lovely to be greeted by bush smells – warm air and wafts of sweetness from some flower hidden in the bush, while 'pipiyo' screaming piha birds called and toucans yapped from across the river. We all helped to refuel the plane, my handkerchief being called into use to strain the petrol. Then on for another very bumpy hour, flying at 1500 feet below cloud and over very knobbly forest-clad hills. This was low enough for us to see the red-winged blue macaws flying in pairs over the forest (we later saw blue and yellow macaws over the New river), also king vultures and a harpy eagle. We crossed the Berbice which, like the Demerara we had seen earlier, was surprisingly small in its upper reaches. A purple-flowering leafless tree, possibly a jacaranda which is native to these parts, and a yellow-flowered tree, possibly yellow poui (*Tabebuia serratifolia*) dotted the green canopy at intervals. There was no sign of any human activity or habitation after we left Apoteri.

The New river was the biggest sheet of water we had seen since leaving the Essequibo. We suddenly found ourselves circling over the base camp, its bright green tarpaulins standing out against the darker green of the surrounding bush – a circle and whoosh of water as we landed on the river, where a brand new grey-painted ballaho, the *Amuku*, was coming to greet us with Philip and Howard, shaved and looking very spruce, Edwards the driver, two Alberts and two other Rupununi Wapishanas all in the boat. The mail and food we had brought with us were very welcome, especially the fresh fruit, vegetables and eggs, since it was impossible to buy any such thing here as there were no local inhabitants. But fishing was good and fresh fish a main element in their diet.

Philip and Howard then joined Richard and Cyril Dixon from the Geological Survey in the plane for a two-hour aerial reconnaisance up the rivers to the Brazilian border mountains. The co-pilot joined me to collect fishes, though he said he

112

preferred a gun and would like to shoot a 'tiger', as jaguars are called in these parts. He added that he had once tried to do biology at school in England, where he had been sent from his Guyana home, but 'could make nothing of it'. A great pity in this country where there is so much biology to be enjoyed. He knew none of the Guyana trees and had not been farther than Bartica before starting his flying career. But he obviously delighted in things mechanical and took to the camp radio and outboard engines.

The friendly camp cook Jo showed us a 'hedgehog' in a small tree above the mess tent where it had arrived that morning and now slept, its prehensile tail gripping the branch. With binoculars one could see long grey hairs hiding the spines, showing it to be the smaller of Guyana's two porcupine species. Near camp we found huge worm casts, made by a giant oligochaete earthworm. Leaf-cutter kushi ants were busy along the path. The orange flower spikes of *Heliconia* gleamed round the camp; lizards clattered through the fallen leaves and butterflies landed on the tree trunks.

There was now such a splendid solid landing place that one felt there should be a flagpole planted there. Log-edged steps led to the river and a section of bush had been cleared to give a view up the Oronoque. In this part of the camp the mess tent consisted of a tarpaulin covering a table and the radio equipment, another tarp under which hammocks were slung, each fitted with a special hammock mosquito net (for in Guyana we never used tents which would have been much too airless). Nearby was the kitchen tarp. Paths led away to the men's quarters and 'all modern conveniences' (here a longdrop). Geological survey camps were made as comfortable as possible as the geologists spent so much of their lives in them – at least two three-month periods each year. Good camp organisation helped the efficiency of the work and everyone to keep healthy. We had young men coming to Guyana on short expeditions who thought it tough to 'live rough' but got ill, then expected to be looked after. But we all had great admiration for the early explorers who accomplished so much with so little equipment – and no radios and planes to rescue them if things went wrong.

113

A party of us went fishing. I had some rotenone fish poison, Albert a bow and arrows – the usual Amerindian way of fishing – and another member of the party produced a vast hook baited with the guts of some fish on a rope like a droughing line thick enough to haul boats up falls. To my slight alarm the co-pilot had managed to borrow a gun. Bush clothed both banks; there was a fairly swift current and the water was too brown to see any fish except near the rocks and in the calm backwaters, where grew patches of blue-flowered *Eichhornia* water hyacinth. The river had risen two feet since their arrival and now covered the sandbank on which their original landing had been made. We put ashore in a small creek where cuti fish (*Brycon falcatus*) with their charactistic black and yellow tails, waited below certain trees to catch the fruits falling into the water. Here too were other characoids, much as in Rupununi creeks, described later. Albert shot at one of the fast-moving cuti, hitting it but not retrieving it; it seemed he would lose his arrow or have to swim for it in his clothes (which we always kept on in pirai-frequented waters), but he cunningly cut a long branch with which he retrieved the feathered end, as usual floating upright, and hooked it out of the water with his bow between wood and string, with a facility born of long practice.

We landed on the rocks at the Oronoque Falls, a lovely spot, to look for pacu, a deep-bodied characoid fish (*Myleus*) excellent to eat, which comes to such places to feed on the podostemaeous water plants growing attached to the rocks. The sun was out and here one could see the fish; a haimara (*Hoplias macrophthalmus*) shot away from under the rock and the distinctive *Exodon paradoxa* and small *Geophagus* cichlids (both known as aquarists' fishes) were common. One of the party caught a large black pirai about 12 inches long on his hook. The co-pilot, fishing for the first time in his life, hooked a haimara but lost it, and then the spoon got stuck. I rotenoned a small pool but the plane suddenly reappeared so we had to return to camp before the full harvest could be collected. I expect the herons we saw fishing there later as we took off from the river reaped the benefit, and the rotenone,

114

which only affects a fish's respiration, would not poison them.

The geologists reported good fishing here, with red and black pacu caught on spoon baits. Haimara were numerous, but not its smaller relative huri common over most of BG; perhaps the two species are mutually exclusive? Black pirai (*Serrasalmus rhombeus*) were very numerous and grew very large – up to half a dozen pounds, but the fiercer red one found in savanna pools (*S. nattereri*) was not seen. Even the Wapishana who love water would not bathe in the river here but stood on the rocks to wash. Large catfish, 'probably scaling more than a hundred pounds and with a mouth like the front end of a pontiac car' had been caught; which of Guyana's many large catfish species were these?

We had an excellent meal of fresh fish before starting the homeward flight. The clouds were higher and we flew at 3000 feet, less good for seeing birds over the forest canopy, but the drainage lines and treeless patches showed up clearly. As we flew north the visibility got worse, but the haze was smoke from burning canefields, for in Guyana they fire the canefields before the sugarcane is cut to remove the 'trash' and make cutting easier. On the seaward side we emerged into sunshine and bright colours as we circled the town; the tide was out leaving yellow-green algae and grey mud glistening where a pinseine fished the edge of the sea. Truly another world. We landed on the Demerara river again, the wheels were wound down and the plane waddled up the ramp. The end of another trip.

We met Philip and Howard on their return at the end of four months and stood them the 'largest possible' steak at the Palm Court, a Georgetown restaurant where one ate out of doors in the warm night to the noisy accompaniment of frogs and crickets. Then they chose 'the same again' to the astonishment of the waiter. They had waited four months for it! While they ate we heard about the rest of the expedition. Apart from their own party they had not seen another soul for the whole trip. There was good soil in the hills but the patches were too few and far between, and along the river much of the land was swamp. The Wapishana members of the party did not like it;

115

they thought the game 'too smart', too difficult to catch though there was plenty of it, and there was too much swamp and far too many mosquitoes. There was a lot of bamboo forest along the upper New and Oronoque rivers, with brazil nut trees poking through (Oronoque is a name for the brazil nut tree). They found the flora quite different from other parts of southern Guyana; the Wapishanas (who had been with Howard in the WaiWai country and were good naturalists) did not know any of the trees. Tough going it was, 'rugged travelling', waterlogged country, 15 miles or so of bamboo swamp and nowhere to camp for two days, and then only a perch two inches above the water. The side-creeks were crisscrossed with tacubas (fallen trees), and while up there the water level fell, so that on the downstream journey they had to drag the boats over tacubas a foot above the water level. The water also fell while they were up the Oronoque and they had to get the boat down an alarming six-foot vertical drop on their return. Each boat carried a geologist, a cook and four men. There was a friendly rivalry between them, the two parties meeting and comparing notes and playing chess in the evenings when they could. 'It is not a place for a man on his own, he would go crackers.' After six weeks or so they lost their appetites (a remarkable feat in these two) and a good deal of weight; travelling in a small boat all day seemed much more exhausting than walking. At night it was surprisingly cold. They were very glad they had taken the Wapishana men, who proved excellent, good in an emergency and their cheerful 'we nearly drowned the boss today – a good laugh' attitude a tonic.

They all commented on the presence of game but that it was remarkably shy – though it never saw man. Perhaps, they thought, this was because predators were so numerous and much in evidence among mammals, birds and fish. There were many jaguars around – one was seen swimming in the river and another shot by one of the men who found it watching him while he was collecting brazil nuts. In the Kanuku mountains too, they said, when you penetrate far in where the game has not been shot it is very shy, much shyer than where it has been shot at and there are fewer jaguar and other preda-

116

tors. In the New river area howler monkeys were abundant, also squirrel monkeys and marmosets, and spider monkeys which fell deadly silent when a harpy eagle sailed overhead. Tapir crashed away and there were plenty of acouries, one of which was seen swimming in the river, and two-toed sloths (one found drinking from the river). Tamadua and porcupines were also seen. In the water otters were plentiful, a brown species with an undercut lower jaw and white bib; they were very selective and fed mainly on lukanani (*Cichla ocellaris*). An anaconda was seen but rather surprisingly no caiman were seen at all. Huge (six-foot) marabunta wasp nests hanging over small creeks were a hazard below which one had to creep; butterflies were abundant. Fish were plentiful and a main item of diet which helped greatly to tempt their faded appetites.

Among the collections brought back, in addition to the geological specimens, were some fish. Also young brazil nut trees, several six-inch tall ones growing out of the little private plant pot formed of the extremely hard outer fruit case. The brazil nuts we buy in shops in Europe grow some 60 or so together, packed like a chinese puzzle into a football-sized very hard woody outer case. This must fall from the top of the 50-foot high tree with quite a thwak – not a tree to sleep beneath! But the case does not break and one wondered how the macaws, even with their strong beaks manage to eat brazil nuts as they are reported to do. Are the nuts softer while still unripe? Some of the nuts germinate inside the hard case, the shoots pushing out through the small hole at the top where the fruit was originally attached to the tree. Gradually one seedling would gain at the expense of the others. We had been asked to collect brazil nuts for analyses as they were reputed to accumulate radioactive minerals, a suggestion that had had a profound effect on export of nuts from Brazil, though a Brazilian mining journal pointed out that their pigs fed exclusively on brazil nuts waxed fat and procreated extensively without mishap.

Rugged travelling (from a geological survey photograph)

6

Rupununi Days I: Karanambo Round the Year

Deep in the interior of Guyana, reached by flying over the forest, lie the Rupununi savannas, separated from the Rio Branco savannas of Brazil by the Takutu river and to the north by its tributary the Ireng. By great good fortune Dr C.H. Hickling, Fisheries Advisor to the UK Overseas Development Administration and an old friend with whom I had travelled on fisheries projects in Africa, came to BG within the first few weeks of our arrival, so Fisheries Officer Bertie Allsopp kindly invited me to fly south to the Rupununi savannas with them in April 1957. We were looking for a weed-eating fish which might help to clear the drainage trenches along the coast of the abundant growth of water plants. We stayed at Karanambo ranch in the North Savannas (see Map 2) with those kind friendly people, long-time residents, Tiny and Connie McTurk. So began a long friendship and working relationship with them in the Rupununi district.

Apart from the beauty of the country and the amusing characters living there, the Rupununi offered special opportunities for fish studies. It had never been explored ichthyologically and the Essequibo river system was here in contact with the headwaters of an Amazonian tributary when the whole countryside flooded each year. Which species crossed the drainage divide? Furthermore, the main rains were annual (May to September), unlike the coastal areas that had two rainy seasons a year, which meant that many Rupununi fishes had a well-defined breeding season geared to the floods. This might make it possible to trace the growth rates of the young fish and determine at what age they started to breed. This is

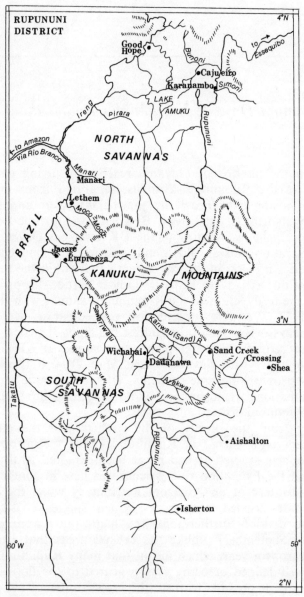

Map 2 The Rupununi District

120

often very difficult to do in natural waters in the tropics, where seasonal changes are too slight for growth checks to show as annual rings on the fish scales – the method most commonly used to determine fish ages in temperate countries – and also where ripe fish are found at any time of year, so it is not easy to determine growth rates by analyses of length frequency curves. Visits to the Rupununi were therefore made at various times of year to see the effects of the seasonal flood cycle on the fishes, and to explore the waters of north and south savannas and the two drainage systems.

The first visit to Karanambo in April 1957 was just before the rains, when many ponds isolated on the dry savanna were seined and most of the fish caught were found to be ready to spawn. To see the growth of young fish resulting from this spawning, this area was revisited in September/October as the floods were withdrawing, and visits were also made to Pirara, Manari and Emprenza on the Amazon drainage side to the west. In December the south savannas were explored. Karanambo was visited again in May 1958 at the start of the rains to see the spawning runs of the fish, and again in November/December when working with a visiting professor Hans Lissmann from Cambridge UK on gymnotoid electric fishes. The final visit to both north and south savannas was in April/May 1961 in a further attempt to see spawning runs, but the rains were very late that year and the country extremely dry. For many subsequent years news of the fishes, floods and fishing were sent to me by my good friends the McTurks and Maggie Orella of Manari ranch, a daughter of H.P.C. Melville, an 1890s pioneering settler of Scottish descent who with two Amerindian wives founded a remarkable Rupununi family.

In April 1957 after several hours of flying in an old Dakota over dense rain forest, the wide savannas suddenly opened out with a glorious view along the Pakaraima mountain foothills. Although some 300 miles from the coast, these savannas are only 3–500 feet above sea level; they form the watershed of the Essequibo and Amazon, their tributary headwaters here in contact in wet years. Lush green with sky-reflecting swamp patches in the wet season, they become parched brown when very dry, with blue distances in the hills. The Ireng river winds its way close to the Pakaraima foothills to join the Takutu river north of Lethem (the district headquarters); the Takutu flows to the Rio Branco, thence to the Rio Negro and the Amazon beyond Manaus.

The Rupununi savannas are divided into north and south savannas by the 3000-foot high Kanuku mountains through which the Rupununi river runs northwards. The north savannas form a wide flat plain rimmed on the north-west by the Pakaraima mountains. It is here in the large swamp area of Lake Amuku that the Amazon and Essequibo drainages were in contact. To the north-east lies the dominating mass of the 2000-foot high Makarapan mountain, visible from almost all over the north savannas, the home of the Makushi Indians of Carib stock. South of the Kanukus the country is hillier with bare rocky inselbergs, smooth grey onion-weathered rocks; with views of Dacroban and Wiwitau rising 1000 feet from the plain, and the three-pronged Shiriri which can be seen from much of the south savannas, regarded as the legendary home of the Wapishana Indians of Arawak stock. The grassland is drained by an intricate network of swamps and creeks lined with ite (*Mauritia flexuosa*) palms, the open country dotted with the gnarled shapes of fire-resistant rough-leaved sandpaper trees (*Curimatella americana*). There are also isolated bush islands of tall forest and from the plane window one could trace the creeks by gallery forest and ite palm swamps. Waiting patiently for the plane were Amerindians mounted on oxen which were at that time used as riding and pack animals. In the wet season one could travel from Lethem on the Takutu to Manaus in Brazil by launch, but before planes were introduced the only way to get to the Rupununi from the coast was to ride up the cattle trail (as vividly described by Evelyn Waugh in *Ninety-two Days*), or to travel up the Essequibo river by boat, a journey which took a month when the water was low and there had to be frequent portages. In the 1950s this was no longer possible as there were no longer any river pilots.

The origin of these savannas was being investigated by a

team directed by Professor Theo Hills of Canada's McGill University to find what had caused the forest to change to savanna. What roles had long-term erosion cycles, climate and man played in their formation? Were these savannas stable, or would they revert to forest if man did not burn them each year? Much of the tough bunchy grass then clothing them was not very palatable to cattle except after it had been burned. Why do these savannas have only one rainy season a year? This is unusual at this latitude; it means that the plants have to withstand great seasonal changes from waterlogged soil in the wet season to drought conditions at other times of year, and the plants also need to be very resistant to fire.

The Rupununi was ranching country, as described in books by David Attenborough, Michael Swan, Stanley Brock. The first cattle had been shipped upriver from Brazil in the 1790s, and by the 1960s the Guyanese herd had grown to as many as 60,000 head. Eighty percent of the annual rainfall, some 55 inches a year, falls between May and August, causing widespread flooding. The soil is so leached and mineral-deficient that the sparse grass supported only 10–20 beasts to the square mile – that is 50 acres were needed to each beast – so the ranches were very large. In the 1950s nearly the whole of the south savannas was run as the Dadanawa ranch which occupied some 2500 square miles of country, grazed by 27,000 cattle and 700 horses, and at that time producing 3000 market-able steers a year. Most of the cattle were descendents of Spanish longhorns, slow-maturing animals, taking eight years to reach peak development and becoming very wild and diffi-cult to catch. To improve the strain, Hereford bulls, zebu bulls (a strain of humped Indian cattle *Bos indica*) and, more recently, Santa Gertrudis (three eighths zebu, five eighths shorthorn) and brahmin cattle had all been introduced. The brahmin were the most promising, being hardy, drought-resistant, fly-resisting, fast-maturing animals, their long legs enabling them to cover the country in search of grass. These Rupununi cattle lived more or less wild, rounded up twice a year for culling and innoculations against vampire bat-carried paralytic rabies, the only endemic and highly fatal ailment here. The cattle were never dipped, as they had to be in East Africa to rid them of ticks. They used to be walked down the cattle trail to the coast, which took about 25 days, but the going was so bad (with frequent stampedes) that losses were seldom less than ten percent. In the 1950s the meat was being flown out on B.G. Airways old Dakota planes. The trail very quickly became overgrown, but has now been converted into an 'all-weather' road to the coast.

Karanambo Before the Rains

On this brief first visit in April 1957, in the company of Fisheries Officer Bertie Allsopp and Dr Hickling, to look for a weed-eating fish, Tiny McTurk, that excellent naturalist, bumped us across the savanna in his old jeep to seine various drying out ponds: Looking-glass pond, the Long pond and ponds near Cajueiro outstation of his cattle ranch. At this time of year these isolated ponds were shallow and several hundred yards in circumference; each lay like a glass reflecting the blue sky, surrounded by parched khaki-coloured grass, the water surface clear except for beds of water plants such as water hyacinth (*Eichhornia*) growing on the downwind side and more or less rooted in the mud. Most of the ponds were only knee-deep and fish could be seen breaking the surface. They held surprisingly large numbers of about 30 species of fish, most of them large and many of them predatory species – presumably all the smaller fishes in ponds with so little cover had been eaten by this time of year. Many fish had empty stomachs or only contained bottom debris – a little mud, grass roots and fish scales; there seemed very little else for them to eat.

Seining is always exciting, a kind of lucky dip. Unless the net is empty ('keep the bottom rope down') there is a great moment when with a splashing and flapping it is finally hauled ashore. Here there was added excitement when the net stuck in the mud, weighed down by a miraculous draught of fishes, as we had to wade in to extricate it before the snapping jaws of the red pirai (the piranha *Serrasalmus nattereri*) destroyed the net. Needless

124

to say we waded in boots and trousers, a very necessary precaution. Amerindian helpers lacking canvas boots wrapped old bits of sacking round their legs as anti-pirai leggings.

The colours of the fishes are so marvellous when they are fresh from the water, but fade so quickly. Here catches included vivid yellow and black lukanani (*Cichla ocellaris*) one the world's largest cichlids and much larger than those seen on the coast. Next to arawana (the osteoglossid *Osteoglossum bicirrhosum* only found here) they were considered to be the best eating fish. Arawana, the large scales giving a pink and green opalescent sheen to their silver bodies, with a large upturned mouth and two black cirri jutting out below the chin, are the closest relatives of the giant arapaima (*Arapaima gigas*), but also seem to provide one of the best baits to catch arapaima. Arapaima also occur here but escape back to the main river from the ponds. Very colourful cichlids included the green, purple-spotted saucer-shaped *Cichlasoma severum*, known to aquarists, and the long elegant *Chaetobranchus flavescens* with two green stripes between eye and upper lip. Characoids included the 18-inch long slender kwan (*Schizodon fasciatus*), the aquarist's banded *Anostomus* with striking vertical black stripes and forceps teeth, the foot-long yacatu (*Prochilodus* sp) round and grey with a vacuum-cleaning mouth lacking teeth, valued food fishes over much of South America, and the large-toothed highly predatory ubiquitous huri (*Hoplias malabaricus*). But most noticable of all were the vivid red pirai, the piranha of terrible reputation in traveller's tales, reputed to reduce men and animals to skeletons within minutes of their falling into the water.

This red pirai (*S. nattereri*) though the most dangerous of several serrasalmonids in Guyana is not as formidable as another species (*Pygocentrus piraya*) found in Brazil, but is capable of inflicting horrible bites and a menace to any wounded creature in the water particularly other fishes, which often showed characteristic lunar-shaped bites from their caudal fins. Red pirai generally live in small schools; they rarely grow larger than about eight inches long, not nearly as large as the black pirai (*S. rhombeus*) which seems to stay in

125

Red Piranha

rivers, the red pirai being the main species in open savanna ponds. Vermilion red on chest and belly, with a bulldog-blunt face, the jaws lined with shearing teeth in a single row but backed by reserve replacements. These teeth remove a piece of flesh with the neat precision of an icecream scoop, leaving no flap of skin to heal over the bite. Several of the Melville family had lost toes when young. The danger from pirai varies greatly with the species involved. The 'piranha' that a friend in later years took me to see on sale in a famous London store for 10 guineas each, was the harmless wahbri (*Pygopristis denticulatus*), which are easier to ship, as *Serrasalmus* tend to bite holes in the oxygen-filled plastic bags used for air shipment. The danger also varies very much with the circumstances. The red pirai were more likely to bite when the water was low, a time when food was scarce. Once they started to bite they seemed to go berserk. Splashing seemed to encourage them to bite, for in these waters most fish were not frightened away by splashing, as this generally signified food falling into the water from overhanging trees.

Pirai have profound effects on fishing methods as they chew up any hooked fish or those entangled in nets and traps, damaging the gear to do so. Amerindians have invented many cunning spring hooks and traps to lift fish clear of the water as soon as they are caught to avoid the ravages of pirai. It proved practically impossible to use gill-nets, a standard way of catching fish in comparable African waters. But they generally did not bite at night, and bringing cattle across rivers where pirai were abundant was best done after dark. Once when flying over the Rupununi a fellow passenger gave a graphic description of trying to get goats across the river far below us by night to avoid the pirai, only to discover that 'goats cannot swim, they behave like inflated wineskins'.

The catfishes were some of the oddest fishes in the seine net. They included three-foot long, black striped tiger fish (*Pseudoplaystoma fasciatum*) with great flat heads and long barbels, and even stranger but smaller long thin ones completely covered in bony armour from head to tail (whip-tailed *Loricarichthys*). The males of these carried a bunch of 100 or so pea-sized eggs suspended from a special elongation of their lower lip. There are innumerable kinds of armoured fish in South American waters, yet apart from the semi-armoured *Syndodontis* none in African waters. Why? Does this signify differences in desiccation problems, or predator pressures, or what, in the two zoogeographical areas?

Many of these fishes grunted as they were hauled ashore, for numerous South American fishes make some kind of noise. Despite their empty guts these fishes were in very good condition with much fat. The check in feeding at this time of year represented a physiological winter to the fish and the scales of many of them showed rings, very like the annual winter growth checks in fish in temperate climates. The females of nearly all the species, particularly the characids, were full to bursting with ripening eggs, almost ready to be laid as soon as the floods come. The body cavities were so distended with eggs that there hardly seemed room for any food in the guts, which were reduced to a string-like tube, and in *Prochilodus* a huge gall bladder suggested that the fast had been a long one. The arawana females contained huge, one-centimetre diameter, orange ova, totalling about 186 in the two ovaries; the male broods the eggs and yolked young in his mouth. The only fishes that had already spawned at this time before the rains seemed to be the whiptailed catfish and some of the lukanani, in both of which the eggs are looked after by a parent.

On other days we explored the river. Tiny shot a stingray (*Potamotrygon hystrix*) with bow and arrow – the fish was lying in the sand in the river shallows, places where by undulating their pectoral fins they dig themselves into slight hollows. These persist for some time and may be used by other creatures – including the visiting biologist Gerald Durrell who thought such a pool a good place to bathe in until he realised it was a stingray hollow. Of the dangers, mostly imaginary, in the Guyana bush, the stingray most often causes trouble. The barbed spine on its tail can inflict what is by all accounts a most painful wound, but the poison is not heat-resistant so the best treatment is to put very hot water on it. Stingrays have a habit of lying just where one has to jump out of a boat to push it over a sand bar, and even the wary Amerindians were often nicked by the barb. The only remedy was to take care, and shuffling one's feet and wearing canvas boots helped, though its barb can pierce such boots. One stingray we speared on a later visit twisted its long tail and jabbed its poison spine at the spear in no uncertain way. The first we caught in April had had its tail and sting cut off, but the wound had healed over; this had two fully formed and nearly-ready-to-be-born young ones inside it which swam when put into a pool. We were most intrigued as we had not then expected stingrays to breed so far upriver.

When we baled out the old boat for river explorations, several armoured catfish (*Ancistrus* spp) were hiding between the planks. The males had numerous tentacles on the snout, the function of which was not known; both sexes had curious hooks on the side of the head with which the fish 'held on' when we tried to drag it out of its cranny.

One day we visited the neighbouring Amerindian village Yupukari, where encouraged by Canon Jack Holden they were

128

reviving an old dance ceremony, a Parashara dance. Such dances were then becoming very rare. It appeared to be an excuse for what in Africa would be called a beer drink, but here was known as a spree. The liquor was parakari, made from the all-important cassava by roasting it then letting it ferment (not by chewing the cassava as for cassiri, another alcoholic drink met at Kamarang). Many of the villagers wore a traditional costume of a cape and sun-burst hat made of ite palm leaves – an all-important plant to the Amerindians which very conveniently lines most creeks on the open savannas, the huge fan-shaped leaves glittering in the sun. Each villager had a 2–3-foot long trumpet made out of congo pump (*Cecropia*) on which he blew producing a booming noise. The trumpets all had some emblem on the end, such as a traditional fish (but one had a small Dakota plane carved from wood). These villagers danced slowly in a circle, chanting and blowing and welcoming the other half of the village representing the 'visitors'. At a traditional dance Tiny said the people would be divided into two lots, the Parashara and the Tukwii humming birds. The Parashara guard the drink and the Tukwii have to fight their way into the house, in the old days breaking down the house. The fellow who could get into the house first stuck his arm into the boats of parakari and became boss of the feast, sharing out the drink. When dancing it is the women who choose their partners.

We were taken into several Amerindian houses to see the woven cane warishis they use as rucksacks for backpacking goods on the savanna, and woven matape long tubes for squeezing the poisonous juices from the cassava, and we sampled cassava and parakari. As usual various pets lived in the house, parrots and waracobra trumpeter birds (*Psophia crepitans*); tortoises as a reserve food supply were penned in one hut. Yupukari also had a church and a school, the latter with bright coloured posters showing peoples in other parts of the world – including one of the River Nile dam at Jinja, Uganda (a surprise as this had been my home for six years!).

At Karanambo we were introduced to kushi leafcutting ants (*Atta* spp), Tiny leading us out by torchlight, for they work

129

mainly at night, to watch the procession of ants, each carrying a large segment of leaf back to the ant-heap nest. Tiny woke us at 4 am (by request) to hear our first howler monkey chorus, a most exciting moment. Later we heard them at many different times of day, but the immense vibrating roar never ceased to be impressive.

What a rush that first Rupununi visit was. As we were taking live fishes with us by air to Georgetown, swimming in thick plastic bags blown out with oxygen, we could not delay – even though we nearly did get left behind in Teddy Melville's bar in Lethem. But as we flew over the parched dusty country, faded khaki with geometrical patterns blackened by fire, the rivers marked by lines of trees above dry beds of sand and rock snaking and oxbowing their way across the flat plain between Essequibo and Amazon drainage, I was already planning to return.

The End of the Rains

It was September when I was again flying over the Rupununi, amazed at the change, delighting in the rich green country below and the views of the mountains now sharp and clear in the rain-washed air, sky and cloud reflections in the vast flooded areas pattened with water lily flowers. We landed in a humid world, rich in the smell of sun on water and lush vegetation. To get to Karanambo we had to leave the jeep and cross by boat through the flooded bush. But the rains were nearly over and the savanna was drying out rapidly.

While the waters were still high we fished around Karanambo to see how the young fish resulting from eggs laid at the start of the rains had grown. Small fishes were everywhere. The mortality of these fishes at this time of falling waters was immense. Here in a flooded field, being fished intensively by herons and egrets, the small seine took over 1000 fishes mostly less than four inches long, young of the year. A pool only three feet in diameter, isolated and drying up in the bush at the edge of the river, yielded eight fish species. Every-

130

where bird tracks in the soft mud told of visits by herons and other wading birds including ibis and the huge negrocop stork (*Jabiru mycteria*). On the rivers kingfishers and terns were having a glorious time, and caiman and otters were very active. Man was also making the most of the seasonal abundance, barbecuing as many fish as he could handle in the fishing camps on the streams down which the fishes were moving from the drying savannas back to the main rivers.

This is the main flowering time for water plants and the air was sweet with the perfume of water lilies, yellow-flowered *Trapa* and blue-flowered water hyacinth *Eichhornia* in the swampy parts of the savanna. In the rivers upright flower spikes of Podostemaceae sprouted out of the bunches of their huge crisp, lettuce-like leaves attached to the rocks. At this time of year the water is crystal clear and the whole country-side seemed to be one huge aquarium full of fishes of all sizes and shapes. Like the Amerindians one could spend long hours perched in the trees overhanging the creeks watching the fishes. Armed with bow and arrows they await large edible species, such as arawana, cruising in from deeper water. Many things give the fish away – widening rings of sunlit ripples sweeping across the bottom of a shallow pool after a fish has just touched the surface, or a break in the golden pollen-dusting the surface of a calm lake. Amerindians were not the only beings perched in the trees watching, kingfishers and herons and even kiskadee tyrant flycatchers take fish. Little river bats which roost in the branches overhanging the river flew out as we climbed the trees, and at night fish-eating bats (*Noctilio*) caught small fishes near the water surface. Imagine swimming in clear creeks full of the tropical fishes beloved of aquarists – schools of striped pencil fish (*Nannostomus* and *Poecilobrycon*), the ubiquitous little cichlid flying patwa (*Mesonauta festivum*) jaunty in gold and black, the colourful but so difficult to catch small characid *Exodon paradoxus*, characterised by two large distinctive black spots on its sides, eating the soap as we washed, and innumerable small silvery characins tickling by pecking at toes.

By day the cichlids and most of the characoids were feeding

actively and the catfishes (except for the one-inch long armoured *Corydoras*) hidden away, together with the gymnotoid electric fishes, under stones or in crevices in the rocks or the innumerable dead stumps and branches which littered the flooded floor of the forested areas. But as soon as dusk fell there was an immediate change-over, the characoids and cichlids hiding away completely motionless – which presumably reduces water vibrations that might attract night-hunting predators – trying to flatten themselves against a rock, above a submerged leaf, or among the prickles of a submerged palm. The catfishes and gymnotoids then emerged from their crevices to feed in the places where the cichlids and characoids fed by day.

In the pools night is a different world, and it must be a noisy one for so many of the night-active fish produce noises, while the gymnotoids communicate by electric signals (see Chapter 9). In the torchlight the colours of the diurnal fishes, now hiding away motionless, are different, and these diurnal fishes are then easy to dip-net. The torch caught golden-red eyes of plecostomine catfishes grazing algae off rocks and logs and the golden eye gleam from large prawns in rocky crevices.

One particularly lovely place, Crane Pond, lay up a small creek from the Rupununi river not far from Karanambo. We first went there one September day when the river was falling fast, the rate of its fall marked by varve-like lines along the sandy banks caused by the regular wind ripple during the day. We had difficulty in getting the small ballahoo up the shallow creek, over fallen tree trunks and under overhanging branches. Shafts of sunlight through the trees illuminated patches of water to a golden brown and lovely fishes swam by. I made fruitless efforts to catch belone (*Potamorrhaphis*) swimming near the bank, and small characids. Hopping out of the boat at intervals and dip-netting among the leaves produced marvellously disguised catfishes, including *Farlowella*, a mere twig of an armoured catfish with a greatly elongated snout, perfect mimicry. The little wire trap set in the creek while we continued up to the pond caught amongst other things an angel fish (*Pterophyllum*). The bag seine caught the very lovely three-spotted headstander (*Anostomus trimaculatus*).

132

Soon the boat would not be able to get up to the ponds as the creek would be too shallow. But we just made it and suddenly came out into a pond covered by a large expanse of the giant water lily *Victoria amazonica*, with its huge leaves and pink and white flowers. What excitement to see this huge and very prickly water lily growing wild. Tiny stopped to shoot (and miss) an arawana with his bow and arrows. We paddled through the trees, disturbing the little river bats, until we came to where the boatbills, large white egrets (*C. alba*) and grey herons (*Ardea cocoi*) were all nesting. Cormorants (*Phalacrocorax olivaceus*) and duckler darters (*Anghinga anhinga*) were nesting here too. All around was life in fantastic abundance, one hardly knew where to look, from the giant water lilies carpeting the water, the leaves crowded together as in the botanic gardens at the end of the rains, to the innumerable nests around and above, now at the end of the rains mostly filled with fluffy balls or gawky young herons or cormorants. The others started to fish for pirai, one of the objects of the trip, using lumps of meat as bait. This was bird-watching with a difference, sitting in the centre of the boat with binoculars while the anglers at both ends of the boat, laughing and chatting away in Makushi, were as fast as they baited their hooks swinging the brilliant vermilion pirai into the boat, where they lay snapping at our feet. These red pirai together with numerous caiman wait under the heronry for any birds that fall in, or for food disgorged when the birds return to feed their young and start to fight. It would not have been a good place to bathe.

The shy boatbills evidently started to nest later in the season than the other herons, when the undergrowth is very thick, for their young were all very small. Most had two young of markedly different sizes, showing incubation is started when the first egg is laid. The shadows lengthened and we had to return. What a day, boatbills, giant water lilies and whip-tailed catfish all in one day. We took a *Victoria amazonica* bud, incredibly prickly, to open in the house in a large basin of water. The flower is white the first day, pink the second, the pink pigment staining the petals until they are deep red the third and final day. By then it was full of a large brown beetle (*Cyclocephala castanea*) hatched within it and its pollinator; these zoomed by us as we lay in our hammocks at night, lights out, hearing Tiny's stories of the old days and river trips.

Fish Retreat, Karanambo

At Karanambo in September 1957 we made various attempts to catch the fish retreating down side creeks to the main rivers as the water receded. We tried a nylon Chinese bag seine and gill-nets set across Karanambo creek, which entailed swimming across the creek as this was still more than six feet deep (with a caiman making a great snoring noise somewhere downstream) to tie the end of the net to a tree. It was dark in the creek beneath the trees, despite odd gules of sunlight thrown onto the water. Small fish (the characid *Ephippicharax orbicularis*) were skittering at the surface, indicating that the oxygen content was low in the dark water. This was perhaps to be expected as so little sunlight penetrated the water and the decomposing leaves would have deoxygenated the creek pretty rapidly despite its flow riverwards. Once the net was set Tiny went to shoot arawana, for we were always hungry, while I dip-netted in the leaf litter at the creek edge. The dead leaves had a remarkably rich fauna of small fishes at this time of year, both small species beautifully adapted to this habitat, such as the small gnarled catfish *Agmus lyriformis*, also *Coydoras* species, scuttling on the bottom, small armoured loricariids hiding away, and dwarf cichlids such as *Apistogramma*, and the young of species found elsewhere when larger and at other times of year which included numerous gymnotoids (*Hypopomus*), characoids (such as *Acestrorhynchus*) and cichlids (*Acaronia* and *Aequidens*). There were often tapir by the creek which crashed into the water, and a musty smell gave away a tree where a porcupine was sleeping by day.

The two-inch mesh gill-net stretched across the creek caught little, for the small characoids and larger fish, swam against it, along it, and then leapt over it in their hurry downstream. I

134

caught a few in the dip-net as they did so. The nylon bag seine we left overnight across the forest creek. About 8 pm we decided to visit it. It was a pitch-dark night but in the creek the torchlight caught what appeared to be a foot-long caiman in the net. When we tried to distentangle it, we suddenly realised that what we had thought was its whole body was just its foreleg – the body extended on and on into the darkness downstream of the net. Tiny went back to the house to get a gun, leaving us in the utter darkness to 'mind the caiman', where two nights previously we had heard a jaguar coughing nearby. After a seeming age Tiny reappeared, shot the caiman and we extracted it from the net. It was an eight-foot long black caiman (*C. niger*). In the morning we found it had walked away. After all this the catch in the net was only three much-chewed skinfish, no good as specimens.

Something always seemed to prevent our getting good specimens from this bag seine. On another occasion we had otters damage it, and a heron in it, and if we did not pick it up before dawn the pirai chewed great holes in it and let out the catch. The same happened with gill-nets of various mesh which we tried several times in the main river. These did produce large deep-bodied pacu (*Metynnis* spp) not caught by other means, stomachs packed with wild guava fruit from trees at the edge of the river, but most of the fish were damaged by pirai, which holed the net while tearing at the fish, making it an expensive fishing method. We could hear the pirai in the net, a 'huhuhu' differing in tone with the different species of pirai, but the sound was made by any size of pirai, even very small ones. So we knew when to take especial care when lifting the net. We later studied the fish retreating downstream in the Amazon drainage.

Water Skaters

In September, from the bushes overhanging the Rupununi river and its side creeks, such as Simoni, myriads of large gerrid-like water skaters (*Cylindrostethus linearis*) poured onto

135

the river surface as the boat passed, disturbed by its vibrations, until the surface of the creek was boiling with them. They had a very marked daily rhythm of behaviour. During the day they climbed up twigs dipping into the water and hung in large clusters, some six to twelve inches long, below the twigs and a foot or so above the water, insect piled on insect, each with head and front legs outstretched, in a loosely packed clump. When disturbed they fountained down on to the water surface, but climbed out again as soon as the disturbance passed; the river was generally choppy with a regular breeze at this time of day. In the evening just as the sun dipped below the trees they poured down and completely covered the wide flat river, which was then always calm, mirroring the sunset sky. Here they skimmed on the river surface, breaking the sunset reflections. At night they were not seen on the river surface, but they skimmed again at dawn on the glassy surface. These clusters were also seen in December and April/May; at the latter time we also saw little ones, suggesting they have a defined breeding season before the rains. But during the onset of the rains they disappeared from the river, then rising turbulently. Where did they go?

Throughout the forested creeks of Guyana large water skaters are abundant, and in the more open savanna creeks smaller species lived. The surface film of Guyana's waters seemed a very busy and populated place, often made visible by golden pollen, supporting many insects (including ants) and hunted over by spiders (some carrying their egg balls with them), well worthy of proper study. And later it was very exciting to find the related skater *Halobates*, the only 'marine' insect, along the edge of the tide in the Essequibo river mouth.

The Start of the Rains

In May the following year (1958) when I revisited Karanambo after the rains had started, the waters were flooding the other way up the creek and out through the forest, spilling over the banks onto the savannas. The fish were then pushing through the bush out into the savannas with the flood. Should the rains start here before the river rises would the fish then push out into the savannas against the current of water draining off the land? But for meteorological reasons it is more usual for the rains to start farther south (and in the Kanuku mountains) so the river generally rises before the rain falls here locally, and the fish moving out into the savannas then move with the flood. Indeed lukanani were said on occasion to leap out on land ahead of the flood. Some characoids (*Prochilodus*, *Schizodon* and *Hoplerythrinus*) that I saw all trying to cross the road to Karanambo airstrip, then acting as a dam to the flood, supported the view that these fish travel with the flood. The fish barely made it, splashing agitatedly across the road in water only 2–3 inches deep in their urge to go with the flood; Tiny said he had seen monkeys catch yacatu (*Prochilodus*) here when the water was very shallow. However, in the main river large red pacu were seen pushing upriver against the flood, their red backs breaking the surface of the now turbulent and turbid water near the river bank. The flood often drops after an initial rise, and many fish and spawn must get stranded. When the flood is rising, swirling in sticks and dust, the water gets very murky. Some of the fish, such as the yacatu, make characteristic noises on their spawning runs, and we could appreciate the value of sound to bring fish together in such murky water. Some Amerindians said that only the males, which are smaller and easy to recognise, make the noise, others that the males make a different noise from the females. A school of nine, from their size all males, sounded like an outboard engine coming upriver; we tried without success to get a sound recording.

Once the water was high the fish were very hard to find and to catch. There was then more time to look at other things. The oligochaete worms were intriguing, fluorescent green/red 'earthworms' about the size of those found in English lawns, but which climbed the trees and were caught some five feet from the ground under the damp bark, and up trees five yards above the rising water when the ground was flooding. They wore saddles at this time of year, their egg cocoons which I

137

was later told they leave in tree tops. As I collected them they tried to escape upwards to the light, rather than downwards as one expects 'proper earthworms' to do.

It was remarkably hot and airless in the flooded bush by the river, and mosquitoes of many kinds were legion. A particularly large black one waved the white tips to his metallic blue legs in the air and had a deeper note than the very high-pitched whine of a smaller browner kind. Long sleeves and trousers, and a hat pulled down over the ears were always a 'must' here, especially along the rivers frequented by the biting blackfly (*Simulium*) known locally as caboura. In the still air sounds carried remarkably well – the moo of a calfbird (the cotingid *Perissocephalus tricolor*), the crack of an arapaima smacking its tail onto the water, the hum of flies, the chirp of a cricket, a fish splash, a woodpecker drumming, a leaf falling. Perfumes, too, hung in the air, the gorgeous fragrance of an orchid – most of which only let out their perfume at a fixed time of day, presumably when their pollinator would be active – against a background smell of flooded earth. Gleams of sunlight filtered through the trees, and fishes breaking the water surface sent tell-tale ripple reflections in ever-widening circles across the carpet of dead leaves on the creek floor. It was here in September that I first met the rattling butterflies (*Ageronia* sp) which rattle loudly as they fly, particularly when two encounter and circle one another; white with black bars on their wings, they had another peculiar habit, sitting head-downwards when they landed on tree trunks. Later I met them elsewhere in white sand bush.

Army ants (*Eciton* spp) scoured the bush floor alongside the creek where the land was not yet flooded. One could hear the sinister patter and rustle of their coming, and insects and other creatures trying to move out of their way. Some of the ants carried pieces of prey – a grasshopper leg, a piece of spider, a large cockroach wing. While watching army ants cross the flooded creek through the intertwined tracery of thin twigs from trees growing both sides of the creek, I found a bridge made of solid ants, their bodies hanging together from a log to a large leaf while other ants poured across the bridge, some carrying pieces of insects. (Hingston pictures such a bridge in *A Naturalist in the Guiana Forest*.) Another May day I found myself right by their bivouac in a hollow tree by the water's edge. Luckily I could claim diplomatic immunity by standing in the water, insulated from the madding crowd, to watch them. The hollow at the base of the tree, from the ground to about three feet high, was almost completely filled with army ants hanging in ropes, some holding eggs or young in the rope, while empty pupal cases littered the ground below the tree base. I went to get a camera and on return found the jungle floor a living carpet of ants fanning out from the bivouac in a triangle, towards the sun and ten yards wide at the advancing end. With a patter and a rustle they advanced over the leaves, a few over trees, but mostly on the ground, cockroaches escaping before them. They then made a rapid advance along the five-yard front along the creek. In spite of a moving carpet of ants now some 15 yards long, the bivouac was still packed with a mass of ants and eggs. Some caught in a plastic pot attacked the pot. When I returned in the afternoon the ants were streaming into the bivouac along an inch-wide lane and there was now a solid mass of ants in the tree with pieces of grasshopper being carried into the mass. The next day we were away all day and the day after this the bivouac was empty. Tiny said that sometimes balls of ants float on the water and may be carried downriver (as I later saw in a TV film of a smaller species of ant filmed on an Amazon tributary). Parties of mixed species of antbirds are associated with these ants, feeding on the insects disturbed by their passage through the forest.

Ants were reputedly used by Amerindians for endurance tests during initiation ceremonies. The particularly large and virulent one-inch long *Dinopneura grandis*, known in Guyana as 'twenty-four hour' ants because the effects of the sting last that long, were fixed into wicker screens and applied to various parts of the body, sting side to the skin, of the initiates. So the ant provides for the Amerindians what the lion does for the Masai in Africa, a test of manhood. What better indication of the relative significance of invertebrates and vertebrates in the two continents?

139

During the rains Tiny took me with him up the Rupununi river towards the Kanuku mountains when visiting his balata bleeders. Balata is a kind of wild rubber bled in the wet season from balata or bulletwood trees (*Manilkara bidentata*, Sapotaceae). Impervious to salt water, balata was once used for marine cable insulation until polyethylene was produced for this purpose more cheaply. So balata was then used mainly for the outer cover of golf balls, and Guyana was then exporting about 65,000 lbs of it a year. A balata tree grows 100 feet high; it may take almost 100 years to reach full size and it can only be bled once every 7–10 years. A bleeder tapped 8–12 trees a day. The latex was dried on trays and might then have to be carried several miles from the forest depot to the river, from where it was taken to depots downriver, weighed and flown to the coast. The bleeding had to be done during the rains. Journeys of many days or weeks might be necessary to get into good balata country.

At this time of year one could travel upriver right through the Kanuku mountain gorge to the south savannas. The balata bleeders travelled upstream in a string of plank-built ballahoo boats, the first powered by an outboard engine towing the others with their rations for weeks cut off in the jungle: rice, salt, sugar, soap and canvas boots, old single-barrel shotguns and bows and arrows. One lot we met had an umbrella up over the boat as it was drizzling. The rain often came rather too violently for umbrellas: a jag of lightning, thunder, swirling cloud, leaves whipped off the trees, birds flying home and Tiny rearranging his hat brim to take the sudden draft, and then the river surface turned to silver-pitted pewter with large cold raindrops. But the showers were generally soon over, the sun came out and we dried off quickly.

There was a great deal to see as we travelled along the river. The wild guavas lining the banks were in fruit, their hard fruits rattling against the wooden boat as it rounded bends disturbing the little river bats. Tall silkcotton trees rained their kapok-clad seeds onto the river surface where they were swept fast downstream. Purple passionfruit flowers floated by, and from the taller trees sprays of orchids in full flower arched over the river framing the view; the deep purple sprays of *Cattleya superba* were very common here – an arch of them barred the way to Simoni lake. Birds were everywhere, herons, kingfishers and cormorants fishing all along the rivers, a glossy purple ani (*Crotophaga major*) drying its purple-green wings, a red-headed woodpecker 'carpenter bird' silhouetted on a dead tree, kiskadee tyrant flycatchers calling and mobbing a hawk, redhead swallows skimming the river surface, a humming bird hanging in mid air over the river joined by a second and flashing to the bank. Pairs of green red-winged parrots screeched out of a tree and across the river, their reflections below them; wisissi tree ducks flew over us ten at a time, whistling as they went, then a solitary large muscovy duck flew over. Caciques were busy weaving their long hanging nests of grass, often in close association with large marabunta wasp nests. Some of these marabunta nests were three or four feet long; Tiny said they are used year after year, even when the river rises more than usual and carries away the bottom half of the nest. Large dragonflies were common, and three feet above the river small mayflies danced in the sun, their long tails streaming.

During the rains we visited Simoni creek, which entered the Rupununi river a mile or so below Karanambo, to look for brazil nuts (*Bertholletia excelsa*) which only grow in certain places. These trees take 15 years or more until they mature and the fruit 8–9 months to ripen. We occasionally saw an iguana lizard on a branch and sometimes pairs of macaws, like the parrots always in pairs, and monkeys including howlers as we passed. Simoni creek and lake were visited again when hunting arapaima in September 1957 (as described later) when the water was very high. But when we returned there in May 1961, a year when the rains were very late, the river was so low that we had to paddle there in a corial, for we could not use the usual ballahoo and outboard; a day of exercise for shoulder-blades but delightfully quiet without the engine. At this time of year the minute young of the large water skaters were very abundant, suggesting they breed seasonally, but tight clumps of large ones still dropped onto the water surface from dead logs sticking out of the river. The river banks were now 15 feet high, sandy cliffs with innumerable bird nesting holes, and stingray hollows on the sandbanks below them. Birds were as much in evidence as ever – large and small kingfishers, glossy ibis, striped bittern, cocoi heron, anhinga, a large brown 'fish hawk', a mangrove cuckoo. But now there were no small characid fish to be seen, unlike the wet season when small fish were abundant everywhere, and one wondered what the birds were feeding on. Simoni lake was now a green pasture with tapir and jaguar tracks in the damp sand at the river's edge, and with cormorants, small white herons, jacana and black vultures. The river was low enough to reveal colonies of a spectacularly flanged clam living in the river bed; Tiny said the Akawaio and Arekuna indians used to come here to collect their shells. Dip-netting in the pools produced small cichlids and tiny flatheaded *Otocinclus* and other lorcariid catfishes.

Simoni creek was crisscrossed with debris from fallen trees, locally called tacubas, for these tropical woods do not rot easily. Holed by woodpeckers and beetles in the air, the boring is continued underwater by mayfly nymphs (of the family Polymitarcidae – a habit I had encountered in Africa where on Lake Nyasa they had been unkind enough to bore through the wooden hull of my boat). In the crevices of the submerged logs we found tiny clams (were these the young of the large ones in the river bed?), small shrimps and dragonfly nymphs, the boring ephemeroptera themselves, then 'nations' of catfishes. Some of the tacuba crevices were packed solidly with fishes, mostly small catfishes but of at least 17 species, many of which had stout dorsal and pectoral spines which they locked across the crevice when we tried to remove the fish; they squeaked loudly as we did so – most of these night-active fishes are very vocal. Certain logs contained many fishes of one species, others had many species packed together; the size of the crevice appeared to be the only limiting factor. Among them smaller purplish pygiid catfish, which do not have fin spines like the others, snaked their way. Were these feeding on the other fishes?

Many of the pygiid catfishes are parasitic on other fishes, having a spiny gill cover with which they are said to snag the gill filaments of other catfish to feed on their blood. To this catfish family belongs the dreaded candiru (*Vandelia*) said to be attracted by urine to enter the orifices of unwary bathers, from which it can only be extracted by surgical means. Rumour had it that the Chinese man running a local store had been so afflicted and the fish extracted by using a fishhook, but to my regret I never met him to ask about it. These fishes, which are a convenient size for bait, could be caught by hanging a cow's lung in the river for they then crawl into the lung passages. I never saw this done – I never seemed to have a cow's lung handy – but I did collect pygidiid catfishes from beneath stones as well as from tacuba crevices.

The ring of cutlass on hard wood as we cut open the logs to collect the fish echoed back from the forest wall. Tiny said Amerindians are aware of this food source and if really short of food will split logs to get these fish, though they are not very palatable. One log six feet long yielded 15 *Ancistrus* armoured catfishes, four of them males with snouts fringed with incredible bunches of branched cirrhi, and 13 skinfishes of two kinds. A large hard-headed skinfish with a 'humhumhum' came from a log almost out of water. Rather surprisingly no gymnotoids were found here; elsewhere a large *Sternopygus* knifefish had slithered out of a log at my feet to my considerable surprise. The only non-catfish here was a sunfish pike cichlid (*Crenicichla*).

Returning upstream the wind had changed and it was a three and half hour paddle with caboura *Simulium* blackflies biting hands and chin as we went. It was very quiet without the engine and we were watched by squirrel monkeys and a tiger bittern, and passed below the large silkcotton where the negrocop jabira stork nested, solitarily in the rains. We had a short stop to cast a spoon for fish as food. As usual I got into a tangle, but Tiny and old Dutch, the fascinating old timer who was with us, caught baira (*Hydrolycus scomberoides*), one of which had a large 'baira beetle', a parasitic isopod, on its tongue. He also caught lukanani, pirai, *Acestrorhnynchus* and 'tigerfish', so we did not have to go hungry.

Fishermen's Fishes

On river trips when we could use the outboard engine we often trolled a spoon or plug bait. These took large predatory fish, many of them excellent to eat. They included the cichlid lukanani, the large black pirai (growing to 41 cm and 2 kg in weight), baira (*Hydrolycus scomberoides*, up to 3.4 kg) said to be the only fish to take a plug bait 'from below', which is perhaps a clue as to how its two extremely long lower canines may be used, moruwe (*Boulengerella cuvieri*), and large skinfish such as parawareme (*Phractocephalus hemilopterus*) remarkable for the abruptly divided black on yellow (or red) colour along the sides of the body, also black striped flat-headed tigerfish (*Pseudoplatysoma*), the whiskerless catfish (*Aegeniosus ogilvie*) and the large jundai (*Rhamdia*) the fat of which Anton the cook maintained caused tummy upsets, though I was never scientific enough to test this.

Flyfishing also took many of these species and arawana, which only feeds from the surface. But as I am notoriously bad as a sport fisherman, I cannot fairly comment on this. Angling in the Rupununi was very good and greatly enjoyed by those who fished here and the fish were certainly excellent to eat, particularly arawana and lukanani. A fisherman from the coast proudly landing his first lukanani here, enormous by coastal standards, was horrified when his Indian companion threw it straight back into the river saying we always put that size back here.

The characoid biara, of which three species were caught here, are very curious elongated silverfish with two huge elongated canine teeth in the lower jaw which actually pierce the upper jaw in some species and specimens. The function of these is not known; there were tales here of these fish being found head downwards around rocks, their tails breaking the water surface, at certain times of year. Is this some special feeding attitude (to get crabs?) or part of their spawning behaviour? Stomachs of those we caught were empty except one which contained fish remains. One was caught in our two-inch mesh gill-net by its long teeth.

144

The moruwe or pirapoka – Rupununi fishes have different local names in the Wapishana and Mukushi languages – (*Boulengerella cuvieri*) with its elongated jaws is another large characoid about which little was known. Young were taken here in September. By day they were very active and hard to catch, but at night they slept at the surface and could be lifted out with a dip-net.

Other characoids commonly caught on the troll included the large black pirai (*Serrasalmus rhombeus*). Up to 2 kg in weight, 40 cm long, smoky grey sides with a golden sheen, blackish head and vermilion iris to the eye, with fearful shearing teeth, they were very noisy, 'huhuhhuing' when caught. Though much larger than the red pirai they are much less dangerous. There was here a neat ecological separation, the red pirai common in savanna ponds but the black pirai confined to rivers. Often there were grass roots in the stomach (did this tie up with nesting habits?). Tiny reported that in the rains when full of spawn they congregated in and around the wild guava bushes growing in the river at Karanambo.

Lukanani, the largest and most beautiful of the cichlids has been mentioned many times. But here at Karanambo we watched them guarding their young when the river was very low in May 1961 Lying on the laterite cliffs – the 'Karanambos' which the Indians say were a raiding tribe turned to rock – from some 15 feet above the water we gazed down on the fish, a kingfisher's-eye view shared by a small green and chestnut kingfisher which landed near me between its plunges. Below us round the rocks and in the small bay were five pairs of lukanani each with a small cloud of young above them. The two parents were of similar size (about 40 cm long). The young, probably several thousand in each bunch, kept in schools about two feet in diameter, the small fish weaving into the school, spreading out and turning back, always above the parents. The school spread by the small fish from the back rushing forwards but the back ones always seemed to be the first to start diving, when at times they all dived and the shoal sank out of sight; the water was too murky to see how they were called down. One shoal moved progressively, another stayed in the same place for a long period; each school seemingly orientated by the parent's tail with its 'bulls eye' black gold-ringed ocellus showing up clearly in the murky water, waved like a flag in front of them. From above, from where the young also got their view, the tail ocellus stood out very clearly; the parent was slanted head-down and the body so big it was obscured in the cloudy water, so all the young could probably see would be this tail. At intervals plops at the surface suggested the second parent was close by. These fish seemed to have no fear of a six-foot long arapaima which rolled over near them when it surfaced to gulp air.

This whole backwater was a most peaceful scene. Jacanas and two glossy ibis were feeding on the yellow-green grass at the river's edge across the small bay, kiskadees called from the bushes above and a hermit humming bird stooped to drink and hummed in my face as we fish-watched. There was often a vividly black and yellow striped tiger bittern (*Tigrisoma fasciatum*) feeding here too. These were the rocks in which electric eels lived and boomed when disturbed.

Arawana and its relative the giant arapaima both have a fairly wide range in tropical South America. There are a few living osteoglossids elsewhere, one in Africa (*Heterotis niloticus*), three in the Malay archipelago and Australia (*Scleropages* species), though fossil forms are known. So these living species are evidently relicts of a group formerly widely distributed. In the Rupununi arawana grew to about 28 inches long and 5½ pounds in weight. The size at different times of year suggested they did not breed until two or three years old. The male carries the yolked young in his mouth. The young are generally spat out when the fish is caught, shot with an arrow. A group of yolked embryos were brought to me, with great excitment, alive in someone' s hat, but they did not bring the parent.

Arawana are beautiful fish which may be seen cruising just below the surface, the two black cirrhi on the protruding lower jaw stretched ahead of them. Do these perceive water vibrations? Amazon studies later showed that these cirrhi help with

146

The Kaieteur Falls, 800 feet high, Potaro River (chapter 5)

Sea defences, East Coast, showing coastal plain below level of very high tides

The Geological Survey headquarters, Georgetown

Geological camp on the New River (chapter 5)

River travel: portage on the Potaro River (chapter 5)

Air travel: the amphibious Grummon Goose plane

Botanic garden trench with *Victoria amazonica* waterlilies (chapter 3)

Botanic garden island heronry (lotus and muka-muka in foreground, chapter 4)

Seine netting a botanic garden trench for electric fishes (chapter 9)

Water conservancy hand-dug canal (chapter 10)

Diving equipment used by diamond prospectors near Bartica (chapter 5)

Tiny McTurk, Dr Hickling, Bertie Allsopp embarking at Karanambo (chapter 6)

Ireng river and Pakaraima foothills from air (chapter 6)

Awaiting plane at Karanambo airstrip (chapter 6)

Rupununi river scene (chapter 6)

Diane McTurk with 'tigercat' and Maggie Orella at Pirara Creek camp (chapter 7)

The 'stop-off' with fish traps, Pirara Creek (chapter 7)

astnet catch from savanna pond (with lukanani, tigercatfish, red pirana, huri)

Seine netting a south savanna creek, Kanuku mountains backdrop (chapter 7)

Yupukari village, with parashara ceremony (chapter 6)

Akwero, Moruca District (chapter 8)

The Waini river below the tidal limit (chapter 8)

Leaving Kokerit, Barama river: distant villagers indicate height of mora trees (chapter 8)

Matthew fishing at Manawarin (chapter 8)

Kitty jetty with pinseine boats and blue heron (chapter 11)

Pin seine staked on tidal mud, near Georgetown (chapter 11)

Young fisherman with catamaran
board and catfish catch (chapter 11)

Parrots at Sandcreek; kept as pets in most Amerindian villages

Georgetown Marine Fisheries HQ with facilities for fishermen (chapter 12)

V Cape St Mary trawl survey: sorting the catch (chapter 12)

Trawl catch mainly of sciaenid fishes with a large manta ray (chapter 12)

Embryo *Pristis* sawfish from inside a large female caught in trawl (chapter 12)

respiration when the water is deoxygenated. These fish feed mainly from the surface and stomachs here contained miscellaneous creatures which might have fallen into the water, beetles and grasshoppers, frogs and even river bats, as well as snails and fish scales. Michael Goulding much later produced a spectacular film of these fish, in Brazil, leaping six feet from the water to take spiders and insects off riverside trees.

We Hunt the Arapaima

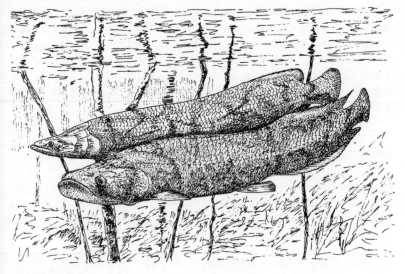

Arapaima gigas

One September day Tiny took me to find an arapaima, one of the world's largest freshwater fish, widely known from an old BG postage stamp, and of considerable zoological interest. Was it on this occasion that we found ourselves up the orange trees picking fruit for breakfast at 3.30 am? For Tiny, Amerindian-fashion, believed in early starts. We set out while Orion was overhead and were chugging along the river to Simoni creek at first light, (5.30 am) when the herons were going out to feed, large water skaters cruising on the glassy surface, and chow, an agami heron and a tiger bittern were already fishing along the river; a caiman left a bubble trail and in the distance a powis was calling and a monkey howling beneath a pink-flecked sky.

Simoni lake was calm, the rising fish making circles in the golden pollen dusting the surface. Despite its large size (6–9 feet long) arapaima like shallow water and the lake-like places at the sides of the river where the giant water lily grows. Here we put out five baits for arapaima, set about 30 yards apart in a semicircle. Each bait was a piece of arawana hiding a 3½-inch long hook attached by six feet of rope to a float. At this stage no line was used, but when a float started to run across the surface, pulled by an arapaima below, the trick was to lasso the float with a stout clothes line on which to play the fish until one was close enough to harpoon it and pull it into the boat.

Other fish were also attracted to the bait and the floats bobbed as pirai helped themselves to it. Fish rose around us while we waited and a large kingfisher, grey with chestnut belly, white collar and barred tail, fished near us, plunging head first into the water. Tiny told of once seeing one of these dive and come up stone dead without a mark on the body, and the Indians with him said it must have met an electric eel. We moved the boat at intervals as pirai nibbled the bait, but no luck with arapaima. About 6.20 am the sun came over the trees and the lake became glassy as the fish ceased to rise. Parrots screeched over and an anhinga and a boatbill joined the fishing party.

About an hour later we moved to another pond, passing a canoe paddled by an Indian man and woman with four children. The sun was remarkably hot by 7.15 am. We trolled as we moved and Tiny landed several lukanani and black pirai; a caiman came out from the bank. *Victoria amazonica* water lilies grew here, though both leaf and flower were much smaller than at Crane pond (where they were well-fertilised from the nesting birds). Here we threw out baits and three arapaima played around us, the hind half of the body with the dorsal, anal and caudal fins appeared as the fish rolled and dived. Their heads were difficult to see but small fish seemed to be playing round the head of one of these. Bubbles of air expelled from below the operculum of the large arapaima came up right by the boat. Tiny said several are generally seen together.

Arapaima are easily seen and heard as they come to the surface and gulp air every eight to ten minutes, turning from the surface with a swirl, showing the large scales along their greenish-gold flanks and sometimes cracking the water with the flat surface of the fins. The gulp and pistol-shot crack were clearly audible for a long way in the bush, particularly at night when there was no wind. So it was easy to detect where they were living.

Suddenly the bait was taken. But this arapaima – which we saw to be a large one – broke free. Then a second bit, this time on lukanani bait. The float ran, was successfully lassoed and the chase was on, the large fish tugging the boat into the bushes at the flooded sides of the river. Round and round we went, paddling frantically to try to keep clear of the bushes, where the line would have become hopelessly entangled and we would have had to cut it. Finally after 20 minutes of energetic struggle Tiny landed it. Even pulling it into the boat was diffi- cult for it was 6 feet 4 inches long with a 3 foot 6 inch girth and 148 pounds in weight. Tiny appeared quite exhausted. It was male, with scarlet red flanks and white belly below the grey-green back. The scales were grey edged with scarlet, the top of the head green, the sides purplish-grey and whiter ventrally. Argulid fish lice ran on the surface of the scales. The fish was blind in the left eye, but the right eye held a white gleam – from the brilliant reflecting layer often found in the eyes of large predatory fishes (generally white, orange or red – memories of orange eyes gleaming in a 95 lb Nile perch, *Lates niloticus*, caught in East Africa, and in sea fishes too). A gleam that strikes terror into the pursued?

Having caught our arapaima we turned homeward, trolling as we went. The red-legged black-winged skimmers (*Rynchops niger*) called 'jack-jack-jack' as we passed the sandbank where they were now nesting. We landed and found a nest with two eggs (Tiny says there are generally three). There were no tern nests yet though great-billed terns (*Phaetusa simplex*) were flying around. Turtles nested here later. The dip-net took not only small characoids and catfish from the edge of the river but buried in the sand, just the tips of their snouts protruding, young glass-like gymnotoids (*Gymnorhamphichthys hypostomus*), not much longer than their name, and almost transparent except for black tips of their tails; I never did find the adult fish.

Back at Karanambo we measured and dissected the arapaima and looked at the highly vascular swim bladder which is used as a lung. This had two red glands along the dorsal surface and a veritable spider's web mat of spongy blood-filled tissue. He was fat and the stomach contained a 10-inch long hun (*Hoplias*), itself a predatory fish. His gill rakers were 3 cm long; the stomach 14 inches long; there were two pyloric caecae and the gut was 92 inches from pylorus to vent. He was parasitised by nematode worms.

Cutting up such a large fish was more like dealing with a cow, and the flesh was red. This was rolled into strips about one inch thick. The fishermen who come to Guyana from Brazil to take back salted arapaima strips rolled round and round a stick, which are put into brine for 10–15 minutes, drained, then spread and rubbed with salt and left in a box or hung out for a few days. In Rupununi villages the long strips of salted fish hanging on a clothes line to dry were often to be seen.

Each jaw had only one row of conical teeth, but there was a toothed patch on the bony tongue, which gives the osteoglossid fish their name, and a large toothed area in the roof of the mouth, inward-curving teeth to stop prey from escaping. These toothed tongues are used for grating cassava and the plant guarana from which Indians make a drink, and the large scales to pluck mandolins. (Shades of the pricelessly rare marine fish coelacanth, which when discovered scientifically was found to already have a commercial use, the Comoro islanders using its scales for roughening inner tubes when mending bicycle punctures.) Arapaima's opercular bones were deeply striated,

150

no use for age estimation, but the scales had clear rings. It seemed probable that the annual cycle of flooding here would leave annual growth rings. This fish had nine clear rings on its scales. Was it nine years old? This was a fairly usual size to be caught from these waters at this time (though in olden days much larger ones were reported). Other skeletons lying around fish camps produced scales with about 11 rings.

In Brazil where arapaima are grown in ponds they mature when four or five years old. They spawn readily in water two or three feet deep among aquatic-plants. Both male and female gouge out a 20 inch hollow in the bottom with chins and fins. Near the old Lethem road, which followed a very old Indian trail, Tiny had pointed out such hollows said to be scooped out by arapaima, the same sites being frequented year after year, the fish waiting until the savannas are flooded before spawning. Brazil studies showed that only a third of the eggs ripen at a time, the other ova being available should the first batch be lost through sudden changes in water level, a very real danger. Even so, an estimated 47,000 eggs are laid at a time, which hatch after five days into 11 mm long larvae and another five days later these swim in groups above the head of the male while the female drives off other fish. The young are not mouth-brooded. Folk tales of the young being fed by milk from the head of the parent must have their origin in a white chemical secretions from the parent's head which induces the young to stay together near the adult; if the parent is killed the young will follow another adult.

Brazil had a closed season for arapaima fishing, but in BG efforts to get a closed season had not then been successful. In consequence Brazilians came over the border to catch, salt them and take them back to Brazil. In Guyana arapaima were only found in the Rupununi system, though they must have originally come from the Amazon side. How long stocks would last with increased fishing pressure was a matter of great concern. Though they grow fast to reach their enormous size, they do not mature for four or five years and need more protection than most of the other Rupununi species many of which may mature in one or two years.

151

7

Rupununi Days II: The Amazon Drainage and South Savannas

Capybara

In September 1957 we moved to the Pirara and Manari creeks in the Amazon drainage. These sunny open savannas away from the Rupununi river were another world, flat as far as the eye could see in one direction and with the blue Pakaraima mountain foothills on the western rim of the plain. To the west lines of bush told of creeks that drained to the Amazon, but on the eastern side of the plain the rivers drained to the

Essequibo. Between them lay pools, channels and swamps full of water in the rains, and the country was all more or less under water in wet years. Recent air photographs showed that the closest contact between the two drainage systems was through channels from the Ireng river north of Good Hope ranch to the ponds near the Cajueiro outpost of Karanambo ranch (the 'Lake Amuku' area), but the contact was very close at several points in both north and south savannas. Lake Amuku drained mainly down the Pirara creek Amazonwards, but long ago the Dutch cut a channel from the lake to the Essequibo watershed over which they could haul their boats. Tiny showed me where this channel had been, now merely a large line in the bisiwisi sedge swamp near the site of the old ruined fort of Sao Joaquim. We fished much in the pools in the 'no-man's land' between the two drainage systems and on Pirara creek draining the vast swamps of the former Lake Amuku. What fishes had crossed this divide?

The Pirara creek flowed through the flattest part of the district. Away from the creek a tree showed up from ten miles away – and there was no tree nearer if the rather wild cattle give chase. The Pirara creek is really a tale in itself, for we camped here with a band of Amerindian and other local fishermen who came here every year to a 'stop-off' pole fence they had built across the river for an annual harvesting of the fishes as they run back to the main river. This is the time of plenty, an annual fish gorge, and those fishes which are not eaten on the spot were hot smoked, 'barbecued' on the site for later use. We all slung our hammocks in the riverine bush beside the creek. Above us in the tops of the trees was an upper storey of hammocks belonging to fishermen trying 'to get away from the mosquitoes' and who shinned up and down the trees silently at all hours of day and night, for much of the fishing was done at night with torches bows and arrows. No wonder the Carib boy scout on a visit to England (Chapter 8) reckoned that English boys could not climb trees – by his high standards! These fishermen were very helpful in sharing news of their catches and showing us their fishes. We were camping here with Maggie Orella and many of the fishermen were her relatives. Diane McTurk was with us too, looking after a small tiger cat, possibly a young ocelot, she had brought with her.

Throughout the day and most of the night fishermen brought in fishes shot by bow and arrow. They tended to select lukanani and said that the biara had already gone downstream – that different species move down at different stages in the withdrawal of the waters. What factors prompted them to go and guided them? I had visited the stop-off two weeks earlier and found large numbers of stingrays that had been shot to remove them before they could endanger the fishermen, but the flesh was not used. When the water fell low enough, traps were fitted into the stop-off fence. These were emptied at intervals and their catches showed that particular species tend to move downstream at well-defined times of day: lukanani were mainly trapped in the early morning, red pirai in the daytime, *Prochilodus insignis*, with its back and yellow striped caudal fin, just after dark, and skinfish by night. Some came in schools, others singly. At this time of year almost all these fishes had quiescent gonads, but their fat stores were fully replenished. Here I saw the only specimen I ever did see of a second species of lukanani, *Cichla temensis* known here as dare or deer lukanani for its dappling of white spots. I collected it although it had a large pirai bite out of its side – and just as well I did so for I never saw another one. This is a species common to the Amazon and Orinoco, but was not yet recorded from the Essequibo system. The most brilliantly coloured fish caught was a large *Geophagus surinamensis* cichlid, resplendent with orange horizontal stripes on a sea-green background; the hind ends of dorsal and tail fins both had light blue spots on a deep red background, pelvic and anal fins decked with peacock stripes on deep red. It produced a grating noise by grinding its pharyngeal teeth.

Watching the fishes above the barrier here one could see how the three-dimensional world is fully used even in water a mere nine inches deep – *Potamorrhaphis* garfish cruised just below the surface, many characids such as matarap (*Creatochanes caudomaculatus*) moved swiftly in midwater, and small

155

Geophagus fed on the bottom. A manatee which had been seen here just before we arrived must have been the Amazonian species *T. inunguis* (see Chapter 3).

To the south the neighbouring Manari creek also flowed Amazonwards. This was a special creek for fish-watching as the water was so clear. Here innumerable small characoid species were all feeding together, dashing wildly towards anything, leaf, fruit, insect or soapsud, falling into the water. When bathing here in September one's happily bare body was tickled by tiny nibbles from numerous small fishes, but on later visits, December and May in the low water before the rains, very few small fishes were left. In these rocky streams the fishes that are so easy to see were tantilisingly hard to catch – almost impossible without the use of fish poison and we were not 'walking with any' to use the local phrase.

In the calf-deep water near an old stop-off on Manari creek shoals of spotted *Leporinus* (*L. granti*) fed on algae off the rocks, with an *Anostomus* of upturned mouth almost upside down in its efforts to scrape the rocks, and small cichlids (*Acarichthys*). Below this the river ran over shallows with *Plecostomus* and *Loricarichthys* catfishes clinging beneath the large stones, little darter-like black-striped *Characidium* in the sandy scrapes between the rocks, and other small fishes swimming in the quiet pools among the grasses at the pool edge. Downstream the river went into a clear pool before turning through large boulders and flowing out as a shallow stream over small rocks. In the deep pool several species of sunfish pike cichlids (*Crenicichla*) lived together and *Cichlasoma spectabile* was caught on a worm-baited hook. As catching fishes among rocks was so difficult, our Amerindian driver Paul improvised a miniature bow and arrow with which he shot a vivid black and yellow *Anostomus* and a large prawn with elongated claws, but missed a gaudy black and yellow *Leporinus fasciatus*, its colours in circular bands around its body. Many juvenile stages of aquatic insects lived under the stones and sponges grew on the rocks.

From Manari we also seined large deep pools near the Takutu river, both in September and December. The largest lukanani

(*Cichla ocellaris*) I ever saw came from this creek; dark in colour, this weighed seven pounds after guts and gills had been removed and like all large lukanani it was a male. These ponds yielded several large Amazonian species of fish not found in the Essequibo system, the 18-inch long golden herring (*Ilisha amazonica*), and the extraordinarily long drawn out biara *Rhaphiodon vulpinus* which looks exactly as though the front end of one fish had been fixed onto the tail end of another; also many large sciaenids (*Plagioscion*), known here as lukanani mother. Why this name? They eat fish but are lukanani found inside them more often than other fish? *Plagioscion* are also found in the sea, but a smaller and purely freshwater sciaenid found here rejoiced in the scientific name of *Pachypops*.

In the clear waters of Manari creek a number of Amazonian species were found which were not recorded from the Essequibo system. The pond and swamp dwelling fishes can evidently more easily cross the divide through the flooded swamp pools in the wet season, but the clear-stream dwellers are less able to do so, and hence are restricted to one or other side of the divide. On the Manari side these restricted species included several *Crenicichla* species, the spotted *Leporinus granti* (replaced by another spotted species, *L. maculatus* the other side of the divide).

There were several surprisingly marine-looking fishes, with mainly marine affinities, the herring *Ilisha*, small *Stolephorus* anchovies, the sciaenids and a flatfish (*Achirus*). A small black and white striped puffer fish (*Colomesus*) found in the stony pools was almost identical with those found in the Demerara estuary swimming so busily around the boat moorings and large ones taken in the trawl from the sea, but they had recently been shown to be different species (*C. psittacus* in the sea, *C. ascellus* in the Rupununi). Then too there were the stingrays, though these belonged to a strictly freshwater family of stingrays. On the Amazon side they were 1000 miles from the sea by connections to the Amazon.

On my first stay in Lethem, some seven miles from Manari, I dearly wanted to visit Brazil; I also wanted to buy a hammock from Figueredo's store on the Brazilian side. Such visits were not officially encouraged. I borrowed a boat, but it was a bumbling heavy object with one very battered paddle. Getting to Brazil was certainly hard work, and just as we had nearly made it and were about to 'touch trees growing in Brazil' reaching out over the river, the wind got up and blew us back to the BG side. Eventually we did make it, and I had many happy journeys with that hammock. My friend Canon Jack Holden had a good party-stopping line: 'When I last swam to Brazil...'.

Lethem was not my favourite place, but it had hitching posts and a certain wild west flavour. Teddy's bar by the airstrip was a great meeting place. Richard first arrived there on Teddy Melville's birthday and had a room half-way between two Brazilian dance bands playing different tunes for the occasion. The government rest house was noted for its flies, but the District Commissioner's house was more friendly; I was once there to see Father Christmas sweating into his complete red coat and white beard as he climbed up a ladder and through a bedroom window, there being no chimney, for the annual Christmas party for all the children. Another time at a convivial wedding reception at Teddy's I received a great swacking kiss and hug from someone I hardly knew with the doubtful compliment that 'of all the loopy folk we get up here, we think you absolutely the loopiest, counting scales on fish'. The day after the wedding old Dutch, a very deaf guest, was still asleep in a chair and some kind person had sewn up his pockets with his goods in them in case he lost anything. I never, alas, saw the fire walking performed here on St John's midsummer day. In the wet season when the river is high one could go all the way down to Manaus from Lethem by launch, and so to the sea via the Amazon, and pink dolphins were occasionally seen here (not only at weddings), evidently the long-beaked platanistid Amazonian river dolphin (*Inia geofroyensis*). Rupununi food, farine cassava dried to a grapenut consistency and jerked dried beef known as tasso, took some getting used to, but we ate a lot of fish. An alcoholic soup of cassava, piwarri, was drunk in the fishing camps.

South Savannas

From Lethem I visited Emprenza, Charlie Melville's ranch, travelling there in a Landrover with Edwina his wife and their children. The road south of Lethem crosses many streams, all tributaries of the Takutu flowing Amazonwards, at each of which we stopped to look for fish. My English training had taught me to creep up quietly, moving very slowly. But no fish were to be seen. Then the children raced up, spat into the water and dropped in leaves and twigs much to my disgust, and immediately fishes of many kinds appeared, attracted by the splashing and prospect of food from above. An amazing number of fish species all dashed at any flower or insect falling into the water, indicating that they were short of food in these streams and very dependent on items from outside the stream, also that many species eat the same food – whatever they can get – at this time of year.

Emprenza was on the Sawariwau tributary of the Takutu where a rock bar across the river, covered with crisp crinkly leaves of podostemaceous water plants in which plecostomine catfishes lived, formed a large bathing pool. Here we set gill-nets and left them overnight, but the catch was only of plecostomine catfishes. We went out at night with torches to dip-net and 'chop' the sleeping fishes. Huri and patwa cichlids were asleep in the rock crannies and the small groups of little corydorid catfishes relatively inactive. Examining the catch next day we were so absorbed that we brushed away a great bovine head which appeared among us, interested in the salt used to preserve any surplus catch, later to discover it was their zebu/Holstein bull, often a rather ferocious creature.

The next day, Sunday, we had a family outing to seine ponds at Jacare (a Brazilian name for small caiman). Charlie Melville's eight children came too, all perched on the family tractor. Travelling with us in the Landrover was Charlie's mother Koko Maria, the charming old lady whose photograph showing her kindly wrinkled face and long silver hair was captured in David Attenborough's '*Zoo Quest to Guiana*'. She was well in her eighties but still enjoyed a day out fishing. At this time of year (September) many of the aquatic plants were in flower, yellow flowers of *Jussiaea* set in their regular *Trapa*-like leaf mosaics, and the dark blue of a *Pontaderia*-like flower, a scene set against the backdrop of the blue Kanuku mountains 15 miles away to the north. Seining here was easy and catches were huge, mostly small young-of-the-year fish: little deep-bodied silver pacu (*Metynnis* spp and *Cataprion mento*), small lukanani, 20 cm long arawana, red pirai, foxfish (*Acestrorhynchus*) of three species, huri, small spiny reckerecki *Acanthodoras* catfishes squeaking away, *Leporinus* and patwa cichlids. We also caught numerous small characoid *Bivibranchia* here, round of body with tightly adhesive scales and a highly protrusible mouth, specialised for sucking mud from the bottom; we caught them here again in December but never found them anywhere else. We returned to camp on the Sawariwau in December the same year (1957) and seined again at Jacare. By then the water was reduced to isolated pools one foot deep. Most of the fishes (except the *Bivibranchia*) were then much larger. The leaves of the podostemaceous plants had died down, but the upright stalks carried their purple blossoms necessary for identifying the species.

We had two camping trips in the south savannas in the dry season (December 1957 and April/May 1961), both trips made in convoy with a geological survey party. Then another short visit to the neighbouring Dadanawa ranch (in the Rupununi watershed) in December 1958. We had some outstandingly lovely camp sites; the main impressions that remain are of camp life with its night noises, and the wide views from the bare granite hilltops which we climbed through sweet-smelling bush. There were always new things to see; a hermit humming bird feeding on the vivid purple flowers of a turkshead cactus almost at our feet, while we in turn were watched by a harpy eagle sailing high overhead; an occasional savanna deer or red brocket bounding for the cover of a bush island; a fox running for a mile at 20 mph alongside the Landrover. We rarely saw snakes, but a beautifully reticulated kamoodi anaconda (*Eunectes murinus*) was in a shallow sunlit pool where I went to wash, and one night the torch picked up a black and yellow

160

banded snake among the leaves carpeting a pool. Kingfishers perched by me and humming birds buzzed as I fish-watched; the large mud nest of an oven bird in the bush by the camp; two little owls standing in the sun outside their armadillo hole burrow at 8 am blinking over their pellets of beetle elytra. And down in the forested creek lived a sun bittern (*Eurypyga helias*) beautifully camouflaged amongst the dead leaves, calling in a plaintive mew – which merged with the whine of the mosquitoes – then suddenly flying off with orange 'eyes' bursting out as the wings unfurled. In April when the savanna was extremely dry the crisp leaves below the trees lining the creeks rustled with every movement of any small inhabitant. Cicadas on the sides of the trees produced monumentally loud steam-engine choruses at exact times of day and at dusk or when clouds obscured the sun. At night, eyes glinting in the torch beam gave away the presence of the flat spiders (*Selenops*) which emerged from crevices to sit on the rocks with their front legs on the water surface feeling for the vibrations of their prey (often small fish). What did they catch? They themselves were so hard to capture.

At night so many creatures woke up. Porcupines crashed into camp, armadillos emerged from their holes on the savanna, fish-eating bats and different kinds of fish were active too. It was hard for a zoologist to waste any time by sleeping. But a hammock slung in the open is the best way to keep in touch with what is going on, even if it was not always possible to discover what creature was making the intriguing scuffling noises below. Crawling insects can sound quite loud in the stillness of the night when there is no wind, the ground is dry and littered with crisp leaves. Spider's eyes shine curiously large and bright in the torchlight, showing up from a very long way away. The taste of powis bush turkey was enhanced by eating in the open air – under a full moon so bright that it dimmed the normally brilliant Southern Cross, which the Makushi Indians say is a powis being shot by a hunter.

On the December 1957 trip seine netting savanna pools produced many fish species, and it was on this trip that the gymnotoids were first watched feeding by night in the clear river pools. This was at a particularly lovely camp site on the Rupununi-draining Sand Creek, near a bare exfoliated hill with marvellous views over the grassy plains and bush-lined creeks away to the north to the blue and sunlit Kanuku mountains, and a few miles away to the east the huge, bare rocks of Wiwitau rising 1000 feet above the plains. At this time of year grass fires crawled in a thin red line across the plains leaving blackened patches and attracting caracara birds of prey and swallowtailed flycatchers to the insects escaping from the fire; smoke silhouetted the ite palms at sunset, and the fire left red trails at night. On the bare rock hills grew barrel cacti, two inches to a foot high, their shallow root systems spreading over the rock and into the cracks, collecting water from a wide area; many were topped with fluffy knobs containing a few bright pink flowers which were visited by humming birds. In the small patches of thorn bush on the rocks nightjars rested by day.

We camped again on the sandcreek in May 1961, this time by a large pool used for swimming, but always with one eye open for a resident caiman with a charmed life which watched us from the bank. Nearby were several ponds with strikingly different types of water and vegetation; one cloudy with clay and few plants, the next crystal clear with an abundant flora. Why the differences? A visiting botanist was amazed at finding so many species of bladderwort (*Utricularia*) for example in such a small area. Such local differences contribute greatly to the variety of habitats in a small area, probably one of the factors which helps to explain how so many fish species can coexist in one area. In December many of the aquatic plants had been in flower, but by April they were nearly all dead and shrivelled, and even the jacana 'lilytrotters' were reduced to walking on the stony stream bed.

The south savannas have fewer large ponds and pools than the north, and since the river flows northwards the river here dries up into very small pools in the dry season. The small size of these dry season refuges probably limits the fishes able to live here throughout the year, for only small fish – mainly small species – were found in these upper reaches in the dry season. In the sunny stony pools of the open savanna streams algal-scraping fish thrived, such as the characid *Parodon* scraping the rocks by day and plecostomine catfishes by night. There was an amazing variety of these armoured catfishes; by day they hid under the stones, the pupil of the eye contracted to a narrow 'C' by a special flap. Many had hooks on a moveable preoperculum on the side of the head with which they held themselves in crevices when any attempt was made to pull them out. Many were gaily spotted and coloured.

The deeper pools shaded by trees were inhabited by cuti (*Brycon falcatus*), fast-moving fish which lived in small or large schools of similar-sized fish, the redtail (*Chalceus macrolepidopterus*), solitary or in pairs, and the smaller matarap (*Creatochanes caudomaculatus*). The overhanging trees dropped fruit and flowers into the pools, each splash dashed at by many of the fishes, and also made a leaf litter over the sand and between the rocks, which was rich in small water beetles and fishes such as the three-line pencil fish (*Nannostomus*) and dwarf cichlids. In the bays at the edge of the pool aquatic insects such as slender *Hydrometra* water measurers and large gerrid water skaters strode across the surface, whirligig beetles gyrated and spiders ran. On the rocks just above the water level the cast skins of dragonfly nymphs were left, showing where they had crawled out of the water and emerged as adults at night, and on underwater rocks wriggly tracks showed where turret shell molluscs had grazed. Small fishes such as *Pristella riddlei* congregated round my feet as I dip-netted in the leaf debris, small *Leporinus* dashing at stirred up bits of debris. But there were few fishes beneath the stones in these shaded pools compared with the rich algal-grazing catfish fauna in the open sunny pools.

What do fishes do with their time when not feeding or spawning? Life in these pools was very complex. One shaded pool watched for two hours one April afternoon had at least 12 large fish species, as well as small anostomines and cichlids, interacting but ignoring each other much of the time. Some 20 cuti hung just below the surface and dashed at any fruit dropping in from overhanging trees, deboru cichlids (*Acarichthys heckelii*) and the characoid yacatu (*Prochilodus*)

163

mouthed the muddy-sandy bottom, leaving neat oval patches cleared of algal debris on the rocks. One individual kamona (*Leporinus friderici*) spent nearly two hours mouthing and scraping pieces of wood off a stick, joined by another smaller *Leporinus* of another species which mouthed another part of the stick, leaving it temporarily when another *L. frederici* swam by, but returning to it almost immediately. There were at least three species of *Leporinus* in the pool. When, with a noise like an air rifle, a fruit fell into the water from an overhanging tree, a *L. frederici* seized it, chased by a cuti; the *frederici* retired under a rock with the fruit in its mouth, while the original *frederici* still scraped away at the stick and the yacatu continued to suck away at debris on a nearby rock. At one point four deep-bodied pacu (*Myloplus*) swam into view, follow-the-leader, and at another time two gold-flecked pirai passed by without much recognition from the other inhabitants of the pool.

It was in these clear savanna pools that the abrupt change-over between the day-active cichlids and characoids and the nocturnal catfishes and gymnotoids was first appreciated. Crabs and shrimps were active by night too, orange eyes gleaming in the torchlight, and some beetles also gyrated after dark. The sleeping behaviour of the cichlids and small chara-coids, hiding completely immobile behind the rocks, often led to them becoming trapped in small pools when the water level fell during the night. It was easy to see here which fishes were social and which solitary, single *Sternarchus* (= *Apteronotus*) *albifrons* pugnacious in defence of its crevice, but lugaluga *Eigemannia virescens* feeding four or six together all pecking at the debris on the sand or rockface. A nocturnal ballet of gymnotoids feeding, ethereal, almost transparent, unreal-looking fairy fishes, which moved backwards and forwards with equal ease, pecking at the bottom sand and shooting backwards to avoid the torch beam, for the nocturnal fishes were readily disturbed by the torch, whereas the diurnal fishes which appeared to be sleeping paid little heed to the torch light. Early in the night the nocturnal fishes did, however, seem less light shy than just before dawn, but perhaps they were hungrier early in the night and less easily put off feeding.

The stars lay mirrored in the calm pools where bats swept by with a swoosh of wings. Odd fish splashes showed where some predator was active; there was some evidence that huri were active part of the night, and many skinfish are nocturnal predators. The dawn came suddenly. At 5.30 am the gymnotoids were still feeding but very light-shy; the dawn chorus of birds did not start till about 6 am and lasted only half an hour, kiskadees and parrots greeting the day.

Fish Poisoning

Fish poisoning was a sore subject. How much did it deplete fish stocks by killing off all the small fish? Ought it to be completely banned? It is very difficult to extract fish from stony streams without it, but several different kinds of poison were in use in Guyana. The most lethal, the prussic acid extracted from the poisonous cassava grown here, would poison cattle and other animals should they drink from poisoned ponds, and there was a temptation for locals to use this in isolated places in very dry years as a calabash full could be carried easily and used to poison a whole large pond. This needed to be roundly condemned. But poison beaten out of 'bush ropes' grown locally seemed to affect the respiration of the fish and not to poison other creatures. Fishes that could use atmospheric air, as so many of the Rupununi species could, were not killed by this poison, and in rivers those fishes that were not removed from the water often recovered from this type of operation.

In the south savannas the first demonstration of a local fish poison, 'ishal' after which the village of Ishalton was named, a kind of 'haiari' (*Lonchocarpus*?) species, was used in a small tributary creek of the upper Rupununi river. Only the small species were taken here; the 'scale fishes' small characoids and cichlids were affected first, and those which were swept by the current out of the poisoned water recovered. Plecostomines and gymnotoids hidden in rock crevices only appeared later. Large-scale fish poisoning operations were undertaken by

165

whole villages, first building a dam across the river to isolate the pools for treatment. As the Administration frowned on poisoning, this I was never able to see. But I arrived just after one such affair near Dadanawa and collected the fish left behind (which included the maddest-looking catfish, *Surubim lima*, seen here for the first time), and in many places in the south savannas we came on poisoned pools in the river bed. These were easy to spot as they were bright green with a rich algal soup resulting from the decomposition of any dead fish not taken away and the excreta of birds attracted to the pool by the small dead fish floating after the Indians had departed. The flax of the bush rope and the wooden clubs use for beating it, could generally be found on nearby rocks. The bush rope is beaten to macerate it and then dragged through the water. Such brilliant green pools lay alongside crystal clear pools of unpoisoned water in the river bed.

In the north savannas I was taken to see the results of poisoning Maracuba pond near Karanambo in May 1961 before the rains arrived. This pond was then the concentrated remains of water drained from a very wide area. A red brocket deer bounded away as we approached it. The down-wind shore was deep in dead fish dried out by sun and wind. We counted 84–85 fish per square yard along a 50–100 yard long shore. The best-eating fish, arawana and lukanani, had been taken away; even the carrion crows choose arawana according to Tiny. Dead fish left behind here included a few arawana and lukanani, but large numbers of red pirai, hundreds of huri, cichlids, catfishes and some ten or so other species. Still alive in the pond were fish which could gulp air, arapaima, yarrow (*Hoplerythrinus unitaeniatus*) and hasser, all gulping at the surface, where there were over 30 small caiman and turtles. Carrion crow vultures (*Cathartes*) and caracara patrolled nearby. As we examined the dead fish some young blue herons (still at the white stage) flew up into a tree; they had one cattle egret with them, the first we had seen in the Rupununi district though this cattle country seemed an excellent home for them, and where they then very quickly became established.

166

8

To the North-west District, Visiting Amerindian Villages

Very soon after our arrival in Guyana Jack Holden, Rural Dean of the Anglican mission based at Kabakaburi on the Pomeroon river, very kindly invited me to accompany him on his visits to the Amerindian villages as far as Kokerit on the Barama river. This suggestion was inspired by Jack's knowledge of Richard Schomburgk's travels on much the same route 100 years previously and a desire to see how much conditions had changed in the intervening time. Schomburgk's *Travels in British Guiana During the Years 1840–1844*, carried out under the Commission of His Majesty the King of Prussia, are relatively unknown outside Guyana. Of the three volumes of detailed records of his extensive travels through Guyana, the two volumes on natural history were translated by Walter Roth, (father of Vincent Roth, Director of the Georgetown Museum) and published locally in Georgetown, 1922. I am still the lucky owner of a copy, albeit very damaged and travel stained. The object of our journey was also to collect information on fish ecology. However, Schomburgk, in his 40-foot canoe took several years over his explorations; his accounts are punctuated with 'we had a short stay here of eight days', whereas our journey took only two weeks. Furthermore he was an excellent naturalist, steeped in knowledge of the South American biota, whereas I had only recently arrived in South America from Africa, at very short notice and hideously unprepared. Also space was very limited in our 20-foot ballahoo and some of the collecting gear had to be left behind. But opportu-

167

nities to make such a journey are rare, and it is described here as a record of a time when conditions were changing rapidly and the Amerindians coming into increasingly close contact with the modern world, which was moving in to meet them as the interior was opened up.

Our journey took two weeks in July 1957, a time of year when the water level was high. This meant that fishing was not good as the fish are then scattered over a wide area, but that it was possible to travel farther in the time available, as with our Seagull outboard motor we could travel over dry-season water falls, some seven feet high, and the many fallen trees lying in the river. Photographs showed how greatly the aspect of the river changed with the seasons. An Amerindian from Kabaka-buri, Christopher Williams, a good naturalist (like most Amerindians encountered at that time) and Jack's dogs Teddy and Wasp accompanied us.

It was a complex journey calling at many Amerindian villages hidden up side creeks. The coastal villages were mainly of Arawak peoples, cultivators, with the exception of Waramuri, a Warau village of coastal boatbuilders and swamp dwellers, and Kokerit which was a Carib village. Our route, as numbered on Map 3, was across the sea from the Pomeroon river mouth to the entrance of the Moruca river (1), through mangrove forest and into open freshwater swamps to the District centre at Akwero, then crossing a 'watershed' and through forested creeks (Baramanni river) into the broad open, here tidal, Waini river. After a night at the Waini resthouse (2) we continued up this river to the Barama sawmill (Santa Cruz mission site) (3), then southwest up the Barama river to overnight at Weicawaba mission (4), before continuing up the Barama through high rainforest to Kokerit (5). On the return journey, at the Barama junction we turned up the Waini to Kwebana mission (6), then downriver to stay at Warapoka mission (7), before travelling through the Moruca again en route to Waramuri mission (8), up the creek to Manawarin mission (9), then through the Koria Itabu (10) to Wakapau mission (11). From here to Hackney on the Pomeroon, then up this river to Kabakaburi. The origional intention was to return

168

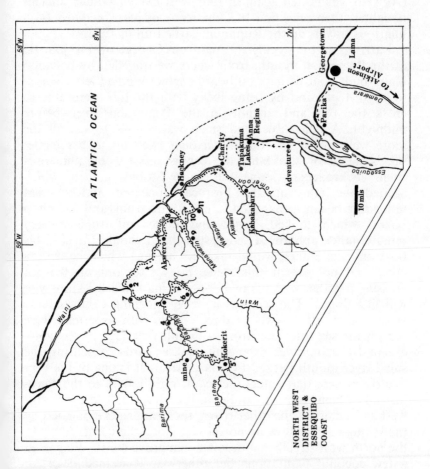

Map 3 Travels through the Northwest District (numbers denote route described in Chapter 8) and to the Essequibo coast (Chapter 9)

169

to Georgetown via the Tapakuma lakes and Anna Regina, but for various reasons this part of the trip had to be postponed. (Akwero was visited again in 1962 with Evelyn Waugh and his daughter, then revisiting BG, the scene of his *Ninetytwo Days* hilarious travels up the Rupununi cattle trail in 1933/4).

I arrived on the weekly steamer from Georgetown to join JH at the Pomeroon mouth, from where we travelled by ballahoo plank-built boat with an outboard engine. We had left Georgetown at 4 pm and by being lucky with the tide were able to cross the bar and anchor in the Pomeroon river before midnight. A delectable land smell wafted out to us, all the more welcome as the *Cainji Pheasant* lived up to her namesake's name of stinkbird, the cabins infested by numerous small cockroaches. Soon after dawn Stoby's launch, which carried the mail up the Moruca, appeared and a great unloading began. I managed to get my tin trunk and two chop boxes, which looked larger and more unfortunate every minute, taken aboard. JH suggested that I should travel in his boat and the launch would take the luggage which he, to my relief, did not see at this stage. So we set out on the sea crossing together with his two dogs ('being English I know you will like dogs'). The sea was its early morning calm and the voyage uneventful. Two or three corials with fishermen were out on the sea too. The Moruca mouth was hard to recognise except by mangroves extending out seawards, obscuring the small river mouth backed by a large river. It is one of the very few rivers here that enters the sea at right angles to the coast, instead of being almost parallel to it and opening to the northwest as in most of the other rivers, their sandspits elongated by the strong current flowing north-west along the coast. Away to the north-west stretched a desolate mangrove coast. We passed a few coconut plantations but otherwise it seemed deserted. Further to the north were the beaches where the large purple bunduri crabs (*Cardisoma guanhumi*) would begin their march in about another month's time, and the Amerindians go there to harvest them.

We entered the Moruca when the tide was low and the whole world a tangle of mangrove roots. The trees almost met overhead. At intervals we passed canals leading off to coconut estates; cut originally by the Dutch, they had cunning kokas made out of hollow mora tree trunks to control the water flow. After several hours' journey, during which the mangroves were gradually replaced by muka-muka arum palisades, we suddenly emerged into more open country, swamp areas with an entirely different smell.

That day everyone was coming to Akwero, where the District Commissioner had his office and there was a rest house, to meet the fortnightly mail launch. There were no roads, everyone travelled by canoe, even small children paddling themselves to school at the mission on one of the small patches of higher ground, like their 'farms' – small patches of land which surrounded their homes – on small islands. After a brief exchange of news at Akwero we continued along the river through the water savannas to the 'watershed', where we suddenly noticed the water lilies and other water plants had changed their slant, showing that the water was now flowing in the opposite direction; this was all the watershed there was and even this was variable, as although the water here was completely fresh, the backing-up effect of the tide was noticeable, and since tidal water entered the system at two widely separated river mouths, with something like a three-hour difference in time of high water, the 'watershed' changed with tidal states.

At intervals along the banks springhooks were set for fish, cunning devices to lift the hooked fish clear of the water before the pirai or other fish could damage the catch, very necessary if anything was to be left for human consumption. From the sunny open savannas we entered dark riverine forest, a sudden profound change after the bright savannas. Here in the shadow of the trees lived large water skaters never seen on the open savanna waters, where they were replaced by smaller species. The black water was overshaded by trees, but in a sunny patch golden-shower orchids sprayed over the stream from their perch on a riverside tree, golden flowers reflected in the black river. The manicole palms also threw lovely reflections into the water and showed their ability to keep the crown vertical even

171

when the trunk was leaning at a crazy angle over the river. It was another surprise to emerge suddenly into the large Baramanni river and then into the relatively huge, broad Waini. It was dark when we reached the rest house at the junction of these two rivers, frogs 'tink tinkling' and the smell of woodsmoke from the watchwoman's fire. Like most of Guyana's rest houses, instead of beds this had hooks for hammocks, as travellers 'walked with' their own hammock. We slung ours and slept soundly.

We awakened to a sunny day. The rest house looked out over the calm Waini river with its still reflections and rafts bringing timber downstream. Some of the heavier BG timbers, such as greenheart, have to be rafted as they are too heavy to float. Sometimes men travelled with them, even managing to sling hammocks on the rafts by using crossed poles. The rest house, like most BG rest houses, was on stilts above the river flood level, so the rooms looked out over the tree tops, where brightly coloured tanager birds were busy removing grass from disused hangnets in a large kamaka silkcotton tree. We collected small fish; had the watchwoman's husband been here he would have set hooks for morocot, a deep-bodied characoid fish, for us to see on our return.

We continued up the beautiful broad Waini with its relatively low bush walls rising 20 to 30 feet high above its tidal water. The flora and fauna of these coastal rivers have to cope with great variations in salinity, fresh in flood, seasonally salt, and perhaps exceptionally salt once in 20 years or so. We called at Warapoka mission to say we would be staying there on our return; this involved turning down a side creek of great beauty, trees arched overhead and below a tangle of roots on which the tide line was clearly marked. As usual in such places we had to keep a constant lookout for tacubas, those slowly rotting logs that can so easily hole a boat. At Warapoka there were high granite blocks around the landing, several covered with hollows where stone axes had been sharpened in days long ago. The Amerindian teacher Sam Bennet and his children were at the landing to greet us, having heard the outboard engine while we were still far away, as the creek winds so much. Returning to the main river the creek looked even more lovely, gleams of sun catching a large brilliant blue morpho butterfly against the tree buttresses and hanging plants.

We continued to chug up the seemingly endless Waini, the noise of the outboard engine echoing off the forest walls. We called at the Barama river-mouth sawmill for gasoline; its presence made known to us some way down river by orange-red crabwood sawdust floating downstream. It had been raining and looked drear and sordid in the extreme. Wednesday was a half-holiday and faces watched us from the windows through the rain. We climbed the 60 steps to the manager's house on the steep hill behind the mill for Teddy to see his mother, an aged white bitch which showed no sign of recognition, or joy in seeing her son. But Teddy was good with the cats. The manager's wife was away with the children at school in Georgetown, but we met his mother, of Portuguese extraction. She evidently did not like it much here. The house had religious pictures; outside a few hens scratched among the tin cans. The view was expansive both up and down river on a clear day, but today it was drizzling. Below us lay sodden shacks on wooden silts, and how sodden unpainted wooden buildings can look! Through the rest house windows we could see pools on the floor where the roof had leaked. In a window was an Ameridian girl JH knew, face supported on hand gazing at the sodden world; she had 'gone wrong' with a man of Afro descent. JH went to greet her but she disappeared.

I was taken into the mill while they were getting the gasolene. To enter we had to brave clouds of steam from a seemingly explosive and alarming engine chugging away driving a saw. We squeezed past saws, the dogs racing round with the local dogs. It gave us the creeps; death by saw or steam explosion? JH said that whole families of Amerindian women and children used to camp in here before he pressed for a shelter to be built for them. The saw was cutting several planks at once. Another device in operation was a mechanised claw for turning the logs prior to trimming off the rough outer

173

part before feeding them to the planker saw. The piles of wet sawdust were orange-red and there were rafts of crabwood logs along the river's edge. I wandered out to look at the election notices on the door (for this was before the 1957 elections) and workers came to peep at me to see whether I was Janet Jagen, one of their candidates who was expected to tour the district.

The store was closed as it was 'half-day' (and this at Barama miles from anywhere!) but they kindly let us into the shuttered shop; the smell from barrels of pigtails (supplied to prospectors known as pork-knockers) knocking us back. All manner of goods were sold, hurricane lamps, patent medicines, clothing, mirrors and combs, sweets for a penny each. Several friendly people appeared and one kind man (half East Indian) lent us a tarpaulin to cover our loads – we could return it on our way down river. He was one of JH's flock but had married the RC schoolteacher – 'the one caught making icecream from the children's milk'. Another friendly man, of Afro descent, was busy cleaning a cylinder block ('trying the compression') in a bucket of petrol as he talked of the fish in the river and the tangle nets they use here.

Finally we got away and leaving the broad now black waters of the Waini, through the mixed waters of the junction, we turned west up the white waters of the Barama river, and on and on. It was almost dark when we entered Weicawaba creek, a beautiful but narrow creek with tortuous turns, intertwined branches and black water, night noises and smells. Bats flitted ahead of us and nightjars stooped to drink, but suddenly the full moon appeared ahead of us through the trees. The village was in darkness when we arrived, but gradually a few people appeared, first recognising Teddy who had leapt ashore, barely able to wait, trembling in agitation. The rest house was up a hill – with the same set of propaganda Commonwealth pictures as in almost all of them, which included a picture of the Nile dam at Jinja Uganda. I made for the Little House with my torch and there oh joy met a moonshine uwari – a little opossum with large dark marks under its eyes – which gazed at me before disappearing into the night. I followed and met a forest swamp full of frog noises where the torchlight caught a

174

crab and a very strong cobweb caught my throat. We crowded round the kitchen fire trying to get warm and dry; it had been very very wet in the boat, the rain appearing with a tearing noise and the drops raising great spouts from the river, like slow motion pictures of splashing milk, then rolling on the water surface due to the differences in water temperature. Drip dry clothes were a great help on this trip. It was impossible to keep dry; we were wet through about three times a day and the best hope was to wear clothes which dried quickly. Finally there was hot soup, a full moon and a lovely hammock.

In the morning I explored the forest swamp while the village people were at church. A woman carrying a child appeared and I followed the path, balancing along tree trunks over the swamp, accompanied by Wasp who found this very slow and fell in at intervals. With the tree trunks lying in the swamp and the cycad-like palms it was rather like being back in the Coal Age and I felt I now knew why 'Uncle' George Carter from Cambridge University had come to BG in the 1930s to study conditions under which the fish, evolved to live in the deoxygenated waters of such swamps, were pre-adapted to breathe air and move out onto land, on the long road of terrestrial evolution. Carter had thought these swamps the nearest approach to the Carboniferous swamps. It seemed not inappropriate that the hymn floating out over the swamps was 'O God our help in ages past'. But life had evolved a good deal since then and birds now abounded. A bittern rose from the water and gazed at me from a tree; there were some noisy red-headed woodpeckers and a humming bird buzzed my face. Further on I came to a house; the people were all in church but the dogs barked to raise the entire neighbourhood. We retreated through the forest and tried another route. The path went right across graves in the graveyard; this seemed odd. Would it have happened in Africa? People would have been much too frightened. Up the hill were more houses, their hammocks surrounded by clay pots and gourds, dogs and tame parrots.

I had been asked to buy a parrot for a Georgetown friend. Had they one for sale? Yes, two. So we aquired a hawkheaded sun parrot (*Deropterus accipitrinus*) in which the head feathers

175

are raised into a crown above its face, and hannah, a seven-coloured parrot (*Touit* sp), which then travelled in a quake under the boat seat, cheering our remarks with squawks of 'hear, hear' at frequent intervals. The smaller seven-coloured looked after the sun parrot, fed her, chased away the dogs if they came too near, and preened her joyously until she raised her red and blue headdress – very like the crown of feathers worn by the toushau Amerindian village headman. These parrots were brought to me by quite a young man who said they belonged to his wife but she would sell them. I wanted to see the wife to make sure, and seeking her out in her house found her to be a very old crone, more like a grandmother than a mother. So the custom of a young man marrying an old woman and thus receiving tribal lore was still continued here, although it was said to be dying out. After she died he would marry a young wife and pass on the knowledge to her and have children. A useful overlapping of generations. In many parts of Africa, among the Kikuyu for example, the women who are the beasts of burden generally age fast and die first. What was the relative life expectancy of male and female among these Amerindians?

Next morning we returned down the creek to the Barama river. We were still below old St Bede's mission at the top of the tidal limit; this mission had been moved from the main river to the side creek after it was wrecked by pork-knockers years ago who tore up the church floor. We chugged on upriver, and at the site of old St Bede's, now barely noticeable except by a few congo pump (*Cecropia*) trees, a swirl in the river showed we had crossed the fall at the top of the tide. Above this the vegetation changed, and birds hawking the river were noticeably more abundant. The same thing had been noticed in the Bartica area; the rise and fall, even when totally freshwater, does not seem to allow the same aquatic insect fauna to develop; small fish are also noticeably absent from the shallows and fish-eating birds scarce, whereas there is an immediate change above the tidal limit.

What a long day it was, chugging up river all day. Never had I seen such tall trees, mainly mora (*Mora excelsa*) which grew up to over 160 feet high, along the banks. These seemed to carry the eye up about three times as high as any forest I had seen in Africa. We must have crossed about seven falls, only possible when the water is high and now only noticeable by the swirl in the river. Nearly all of them were below a river bend and a lake-like swelling formed above each. About every hour we had to fill the gasolene tank. For this the motor was stopped and in the sudden silence bird calls rang out, the 'pipyo' calls of the greenheart cotingid everywhere. Lovely perfumes came to us from white orchids and red bromeliads perched on trees fallen into the water. Not a soul did we see all day. JH said he usually met Amerindians coming down with rafts of crabwood for the mills, but now they had gone to work with the new manganese mines being opened up to the north-west. At Tassawini, the landing for the manganese mine three miles in from the river, we put ashore. The only sign was a benab temporary shelter and remains of a wooden box labelled Manganese Mine.

As we continued upriver we passed some deserted lumber camps, clearings, huts and deserted fields made visible by the inevitable congo pump and short vegetation. There was intermittent heavy rain. On and on, the dogs getting really impatient. Dusk came and stars, then a mist rising from the river obscuring the moon. JH says this *must* be rock point 'so called because of the ugly and dangerous rock' (encouraging) and 'very near'. He told of an Amerindan farmer from here dying of TB in a sanatorium in Georgetown who had begged JH to take him home to die, but there was the problem of infecting others. It was pitch black, and Wasp, unable to contain himself any longer, fell out into the river. Luckily we really were at last within reach of the landing. The teacher and schoolchildren were there to greet us, having heard the engine but not known whom to expect. There was half a mile of mudsplash to the village balancing on logs and wading through mud. The village was chaotic. The teacher's house was being rebuilt, and he and a puppy and a cat had moved into JH's rest house, but he asked us in too and we squeezed in among the boxes and piles of kokerite palm nuts. There was hunger

177

here as their cassava was finished and they were now feeding off the bush. Kokerite palm nuts (*Maximiliana regia*) had been their main food for some weeks. The teacher had been here for three years. JH told me that he had a very pretty sister who married an army officer and was settled in England. We slung our hammocks in the school while nightjars called their eerie 'who-are-you' outside all night. The school was approached by an avenue of coconuts planted by JH, who was doing quite an agricultural officer's job on his rounds. (By 1993, when this was part of the Barama Company timber concession, Kokerit had lost its Amerindian population.)

I awoke to see a girl sweeping hens out of the church prior to service, and slipped off into the bush to watch birds, set a fish trap and bathe. Later we walked through the village where three women were pounding up the leaves of a fish poison (kunaparu). We watched them poisoning the creek, scattering the pounded leaf on the water, but the catch was pitiful, mainly tiny *Corydoras* catfish, aquarium size. We walked to a second creek too deep to poison, but which had large pomacean water snails, and on through the village where women were preparing cassava bread, watched by a tame kibahee coatimundi and parrots. It rained heavily. Later in the day we explored the high forest on the other side of the creek. Here oligochaete 'earthworms' were wriggling up tree trunks along the rough wet bark, away from the waterlogged ground. Razorgrass (*Scleria*) grew where the ground had been culti-vated; this seemed to be particularly abundant on badly drained soils – we rarely saw it on sandy soil; the long green leaves look innocuous but leave a red slash wherever they touch the skin. The complexity of the whole forest community was so staggering that the only way to study it seemed to be to sit on one spot for ten years (as Beebe had done at Kartabo).

Under the bamboos were phallus-like stinkhorn fungi with delicate pink veils, one of which unfolded in the hour I was down at the river. At dusk when I returned from the forest through the bamboo grove, a veritable cathedral of arched bamboos, it was full of twittering green caiques preparing to roost for the night. The women of the village came to meet me

178

with a torch, as they had hollered and got no reply and feared a kanaima (bogey) might get me (or them) if we were out at night.

Our hammocks were slung in the school and next morning I woke to find myself right by the altar, moved in because the church roof leaked, and the congregation arriving for church. Have you ever found yourself in bed and everyone arriving for service? It was a 'She dreamt she was at the races in her maidenform bra' kind of situation! I slid down the hammock's mosquito net tube, grabbed my clothes and beat it for the bush, leaving the congregation quite unperturbed.

Next day we returned down the Barama, glad of the current's help, for petrol supplies were running low. En route we collected orchids from fallen tees. The Barama river-mouth residents were spending Saturday afternoon drinking neat rum out of cups and tin mugs in the manager's office, together with a few visitors. We escaped up the Waini, the channel of which was soon narrowed by beds of three-foot high wild guava bushes projecting into the river from both banks. As darkness fell this made the bank hard to see, until we found that a torch shone at the bank gave a double circle of light, the second reflected from the water except at the edge of the river where the two circles met (reminiscent of the dam-busters' wartime exploits).

We arrived at Kwebana after dark to be greeted by Mrs Jackson B.E.M. The rest house which overlooked the river I shared with a large brown bird-eating spider and a frog, while JH and Chris swung in the school. We had meals in Mrs Jackson's house with her daughter where she passed on all the local gossip as she spun local cotton for a hammock. Next morning Theodore Jackson rose at 3 am to go and lift morocut fish hooks some way down river. He returned at 5.30 am with one morocot; he had caught two but the piranha had eaten all but the head of the other one.

That afternoon we moved downriver to Warapoka. On climbing the hill there one looked over a sea of cassava, large areas having been cleared for gardens. Planted on fairly steep hills in a relatively quartzitic sandy soil, how long would it

179

grow here? Toucans and monkeys were common in the forest round the clearing, and roraima toucanets, like slim toucans but with long tails, preened in a leafless tree showing their bright colours to best advantage. The school teacher produced a figurine head found by her to be taken to the Guyana Museum, and spoke of others and stone axe heads from here given away to casual visitors. Amerindian babies were brought to be christened, charming babies with big dark eyes and black hair, which smiled readily and were rarely heard to cry.

We were due to make an early start on the long trip to Waramuri the next day but news came that a tree had fallen across the creek so we were imprisoned. Falling trees are a real hazard to life in these forests, for many of the trees are very shallow-rooted in the waterlogged soil. Without any fuss a party went from the village to clear the tree away, organised by an efficient village captain. The leafy branches had completely obstructed the creek but men with four or five corials soon cleared a path through it for us. Our escape was helped by the water level falling, for we were back in the zone influenced by the tide, allowing us to pass under some of the branches. But this delay meant that we missed the tide. The journey back was through the interconnecting water ways of the Moruka (see map 3).

Beneath the trees the still water had a pollen-dusted surface film. Ants walked on the water surface, also spiders – a large white and green-backed one running on the water surface in many parts of Guyana, a fauna that would repay study. Gyrinid beetles gyrated here. Lovely savanna smells met us as we emerged from the dark wood and the light became golden as evening approached; sedges with golden flower heads and white spider lilies (*Crinum commelyni*) dotted the water savannas. Springhooks to catch fish were set from tall stakes along the edge of the channel. Canoes were more frequent here, men and women travelling together, often with children and nearly always with a thin short-haired hunting dog on the prow, which barked at Wasp and Teddy. The people carried quakes, open-weave baskets, full of yams and cassava sticks ready for planting, travelling from island to island where they had their homes, surrounded by coconut palms, and their farms. At intervals the narrow channel was blocked with lumps of floating muka-muka and sudd and we had to pole the boat over these. At one place the dogs, impatient for dry land and a 'lamp-post', were put onto the sudd, but merely regarded this as an opportunity to hunt and got their feet wet which made matters worse.

We were too late to call at Santa Rosa RC mission where they generally gave JH tea, but we had to call at Stoby's store. He had acquired two sheep (the dogs had never seen one before) to 'try out', a ram had died as they 'did not know about these animals and what they should let them eat'. Stoby spoke of a new road being constructed which 'collected' another one, a terminology born of the watery channels of the area and universal water transport, where paddles were carried into church and cinema alike. As the light faded we were running between dense walls of muka-muka; fireflies haunting the banks were reflected in the black waters. It was quite dark when we reached Waramuri. The beach was almost deserted and the landing devoid of corials. We later heard that a cinema show in a nearby village was responsible. This was the only mission where the teacher (here of Afro origin) did not come down to meet us. Three assistant teachers (one Afro, two East Indian) were in residence in JH's house, but turned out to sling their hammocks in the school. The most lovely moths came to our lamp as we awaited our meal and chatted with the teachers. Lepidoptera, night-flying marabuntas (hornets), praying mantis and terrestrial hemiptera were the commonest visitors to the lamps throughout this trip, a great contrast with Africa where numerous aquatic insects – mayflies (Ephemeroptera), caddis (Trichoptera) and many others – would have visited the lamps under similar conditions, but these rarely came to the light here. The teachers' main news, heard on the radio, was that an RC teacher in Charity had been 'stuck' by his wife and died. Jealousy they said. This tragedy appeared like a Greek chorus at all subsequent missions; we even met the dispenser who attended to the man, and his story was that the teacher had been drinking and tried to put his arms round

181

his wife and persuade her to 'come upstairs' while she was killing and cleaning a fowl in preparation for an outing the next day. She, the mother of four by him, pushed him away with the knife and stuck his lung. She was horrified and fainted on hearing of his death.

Waramuri was a Warao village, a small tribe of coastal Amerindians found only around there and with a language of their own, distinct from the two great language groups of the Arawak and Carib tribes found elsewhere in Guyana. Here was a huge shell mound which had been excavated, yielding bones and bits of pot among innumerable black and white striped winkle shells (*Nerita*, as found living in the *Batis* off Georgetown), some shells whole and good as new, others becoming a kind of shellcrete. The mound was now surmounted by a cross. This was a very old mission and used to have a white resident priest – the school bell was dedicated to his little daughter who died here. From the mound we had a good view down the village. The houses were all on stilts and very open, the sides completely open or with a 'half-way' of palm leaf matting fence some four feet high. The village was on white sand with the palm shadows thrown in strong relief when the sun was out.

I had been told that a 'Mrs Booker' had a tibisiri (ite palm fibre) hammock to sell, so I wandered through the village looking for her. I found one Mrs Booker, but Booker's was a large and prosperous concern in BG (often called Bookers Guiana on this account) and it was evidently a popular name. She directed me to another Mrs B further down the village. The rain had almost stopped but the women were still in their houses, instead of under the great mango trees. I called from house to house asking for Mrs Booker and had a very varying response. An old crone busy eating was not helpful and did not know such a Mrs B, but the woman in the next house heard our conversation, called me and directed me on down the village. On the way (next door) I passed a house with palm screens around the area under it and a crowd around this screen. I had a glimpse of beds and the most awful groans issued – a woman in childbirth? No, it was a man's voice. As I

182

passed another house with an inadequate screen an old woman was being 'potted'. How public these open houses are at times like this. On past a glorious deep blue morning glory convolvulus creeper and a house where a group of women were pounding cassava in a corial-like hollowed out tree trunk, ready for a spree. As usual they were surrounded by children playing in hammocks and dogs which yapped at my coming. Then on to a house with a line of fish hooks and gourd floats slung over the 'half-way' screen at the side of the house. The village here was a single line of houses, and having reached the far end I returned. An awful wailing, a woman's voice, now came from the house with the screen, and JH was there with the other old woman. Chris appeared and told me that Dixon, a churchwarden and the man I had been chatting to about the hammock, had just died very suddenly and unexpectedly. It started with a pain in his leg and spread to his belly. Of course a kanaima would be suspected, particularly as there were village feuds here – schoolteacher, village warden and captain being involved in some row over pinching school milk. JH looked horribly shaken and a gloom was cast over the day. The son called and asked JH to take a photograph of the dead man. Later when we passed the house, the body was upstairs and the children were around it having a last look at grandpa.

Mrs Booker was eventually located next door to the corpse, sitting at her sewing machine chatting cheerfully to her friends, seemingly oblivious of the happenings a few yards away. It would take some time to make a coffin and we had to move on. So we escaped from the pall, the sun came out and we had a truly fairytale ride up Manawarin creek.

Under other conditions Manawarin creek with its dead trees, many destroyed in a vast fire of an exceptionally dry year (1926), and some more recently as many stumps were still blackened, might have been a sombre sight, but today the creek seemed delightful. The sun shone and every bird made the most of it. We first chugged through water savannas with occasional ite palms, then a patch of low bush with muka-muka along the river's edge. Cormorants, generally two at a time, perched on the dead tree trunks, their reflections superb in the black water. We passed within a few feet of a glossy purple and green ani sunning its wings and tail, every detail reflected in the water, Christopher flipped water at it but it did not move. Then in a patch of thin bush, in a leafless purple-flowered jacaranda-like tree was a golden red howler monkey, gleaming in the sun, with a baby on its back, and another three-quarter grown one with it; they watched us then climbed off, the baby clinging on for dear life. The stream opened into lagoons with water lilies, jacanas and wild muscovies, the drakes much larger than the ducks. Then the stream narrowed to little more than boat width, running quite swiftly between grassy walls, while great areas of green and uniformly flat bisiwisi sedge (*Eleocharis*) swamp led away and away to horizons of ite palm forest. Why were these swamps so different from the golden-headed sedge swamp of the Moruca water savannas? What factors controlled these differences? Was it length of inundation each year? Soil? Fire? Proximity to the sea? Finally on one of the first islands we came to, quite a small island, was Manawarin misson.

We disembarked and climbed the 50-foot hill glistening with large mica flakes to the rest house. The teacher here was Oswald Jackson, son of Mrs Jackson of Kwebana; the other teacher was out fishing. I liked the place with its wide views over the sedge swamp to the palm forest on one side, dead tree and water lily area below us, and another kind of sedge swamp the other side, with innumerable birds including macaws on their evening flight. A real island in the swamps, gloriously open after the forest. At night it seemed remarkably near to the stars, both Southern Cross and Plough visible above us. I always sympathised with Thurber's moth who tried to fly to a star. Surely from here we might see a tropical aurora, a rare phenomenon we had been asked to look out for at this time in connection with International Geophysical Year.

We stayed at Manawarin two nights. The first morning the dispenser arrived at 4.30 am to de-hookworm the entire population. JH was afflicted with most painful 'sore-eye' endemic to these parts, but alleviated by penicillin eye ointment. We set the fish trap. Next day one of the villagers,

Matthew, took me fishing in his dug-out corial among the blackened tree stumps. First he dug for worms on the hill. Then we went out through the rush swamp in a track only the width of the corial. On the way he collected some bisiwisi sedges and stopped below a tree to axe a termite nest into the boat. Though this looked spongy it was very hard, made of sunbaked clay. The water fern *Salvinia* covered the sides of the channel through the dead forest and Matthew arranged rings of bent sedges to keep areas about one foot in diameter clear of this floating weed. Into each cleared area he knocked some termites. This he did at a dozen stations along the channel and then returned to fish each in turn with a worm on a hook at the end of a very long rod. As he was preparing the last one there was a very loud snort, like a hippo, just behind us and a huge otter, its curiously cut away lower jaw giving it a shark-like appearance, put his head out and gazed at us. This was the river wolf, *Pteroneura brasiliensis*, the giant otter; they are said to travel in parties but we only saw one here. (Later these were studied by Keith and Elizabeth Laidler and in the Rupununi by Diane McTurk.)

It was beautifully quiet in the corial and we were silent as we fished. The sun shone and jacanas squabbled on the lilies between the trees, flashing their yellow wings as they moved. Occasionally there was a plop and splash, perhaps a hasser catfish or *Crenicichla* pike-perch sunfish breaking the surface. Dragonflies and water skaters abounded. I found a large hairy caterpillar swimming like a small snake, 'rescued' it and put it on a bush, but Matthew said it was a creature of the water. I found several more in the beds of cabomba water weed, the yellow flowers of which had opened at the surface as we fished. In a plastic jar I soon had a small aquarium of caterpillars crawling down pieces of cabomba with an air supply tangled in their long hairs, eating and defaecating prodigious amounts of the water weed. Given floating salvinia to climb on, they continued to climb down the cabomba. Larger specimens were brown on the sides and yellow along the back. (I later learned from Vide Graham that they were the caterpillars of a moth (*Maenes laboubeii*) and found them elsewhere.) In Africa, aquatic lepidoptera caterpillars cut thumbnail-sized pieces from water lily leaves and live in these glued to the under-surface of the lily leaf. I never found any like this here. In Guyana water snails, large dytiscid beetles, tricoptera and ephemeroptera were all noticeably scarce compared with comparable swampy habitats in Africa, but the surface film fauna seemed richer here than in Africa.

Matthew caught about 20 common patwa (the cichlid *Cichlasoma bimaculatum*) from the prebaited areas, all very dark in colour as fish often are from dark swampy water, swinging them into the corial before they fell off the hook, and one sunfish (*Crenicichla*). He considered this a poor catch, saying he would have had two or three hundred patwa like this in two hours' fishing a few weeks back. Gonad examinations showed that the main breeding season was over, and indeed we caught half-inch long young by lifting water plants into the corial. A wire trap set on the bottom of the four-foot deep channel caught nothing, merely bringing dead leaves and deoxygenated debris bubbling to the surface.

Matthew asked if I liked pawpaw and took me to his fields on the next island. He showed me a hasser nest near the landing. This was against and half surrounded by the buttresses of an aromata tree whose roots were growing in the water; the nest consisted of froth beneath some dead leaves. He brought me three leaves, on the undersides of which were irregular patches of about 1000 eggs, the eggs from each leaf in a different stage of development – one with dark eyes which promptly hatched, one with eyed ova, and one with newly laid yellower eggs. This supported the general belief that the male hasser attracts or drives several females to lay in his nest. The floating nest is a cunning device to keep the eggs buoyed up near the water surface but protected from the sun. This was different from the hasser nest in coastal trenches (where *Hoplosternum littorale* lays eggs in a nest of grass and bubbles), and next day we caught some local hasser which were all of another species (*H. thoracatum*).

Matthew's garden was rambling and overgrown with razor grass. The house was deserted as he no longer lived there. He was 'living in other people's houses on the mission' but visiting his garden every day. Perhaps he left when he lost his child, a girl, recently. I later heard that he and his wife were very upset; they thought that a kanaima was responsible and trussed up the child to catch the kanaima. Then in the night they thought this unchristian so disinterred the child and untrussed it; then both got very ill and thought the kanaima had them. Thus lies christianity on pagan souls. While in the garden he cut pineapple and sugar cane and we knocked down ripe pawpaws and red malacca pears (French cashew, an *Anacardium* sp). Bananas, cassava and the cotton tree which produces the cotton from which hammocks are made were also growing in the garden.

Next morning huri (*Hoplias malabaricus*) as well as hasser and imere catfish (*Trachycorystes galeatus*) were brought for sale. The fish trap set in shallow water by the shore caught many patwa. The effects of the hookworm medicine were such that Matthew felt unable to set hooks for hasser and other 'night fish' as we had planned to do. We left Manawarin later than intended. We had decided to try to cut through the Koria Itabu to the Wakapau river, although the water was not very high and this cut, marked equally with great rivers on the map, was only passable in a small boat and at high water. This would avoid the journey out to sea and the sea crossing, where with our heavily laden small boat we might have had to wait a long time for calm enough weather to cross to the Pomeroon mouth – I later met the widow of one of many men drowned on this crossing. But this short cut entailed press-ganging some extra paddlers and a corial to lighten our loads and reduce our draught. This took some time. Even Matthew did not appear to say farewell. When the press gang is at work it is wise to be absent. I chatted to the women and visited their houses while waiting. The great advantage of missions was that we had a common language in English. The women everywhere seemed to like to talk. How many children had I? Did I like their village? One carried a tiny skeleton of a baby recently very ill from whooping cough.

Finally we departed downstream and soon came to the cut

which lay through dead forest, over fallen trees (the boats were rocked over), under fallen trees and in and out. As we had to paddle and pole the whole way there was time to see and hear more, as there was no engine running, and even to scoop up the abundant water skaters and small fish. These included the pretty marbled hatchetfish (*Carnegiella* – well known to aquarists) which lived in small schools in these small side streams (its place in large rivers being occupied by the more robust 'freshwater flying fish' *Gastropelecus* which used to skitter along the river surface ahead of the boat). In one place I idly dipped the net onto the waving tail of large black electric eel below the boat, outlined against the sand in two feet of brown water. After this I was more wary of stepping out to push the boat over tacoubas. Unfortunately it rained hard most the way.

After the wood we came to savanna but still had to pole. Very gradually the stream opened out as other channels joined it. Then we met a few corials, men fishing and later school children paddling home, the boys all stark naked and a lovely bronze, having removed their clothes to keep them dry, the girls in blue gymslips. Side channels led from the main channel to houses on different islands, each house thatched with palm leaves and surrounded with coconut palms and a productive garden, for the soil was good. Corials with sails were later seen and in the distance the mission buildings as the light failed.

We stayed at Wakapau several nights, slinging our hammocks in the school as an East Indian teacher and his wife and baby were in the rest house. The school was brightly painted, its walls covered with pictures and eveything labelled; there was cheerful hanging notice saying 'Today is ... (nobody's) ... birthday', a nature corner and strings of brightly painted cottonreel counters in lots of ten. Some enterprising soul evidently guided this school. The whole compound was clean white sand, painful in the glare of the sun except where the palm trees threw their black shadows.

Here I went fishing with the Catechist Mr R who told me much about the ways of fish. First bait was collected by holding a basket over the side of the canoe and spitting chewed cassava into this, whereupon small characid fish swarmed over the basket and were caught by lifting it suddenly. We hooked three fish, but fishing was poor at present. As we fished a corial paddled by two men and with a sail came by laden with sea fish and a few large crabs 'pulled from holes'. Mr R bought three sea catfish from them. So much for our fishing effort!

Mr R told me of the effects of the great fire of 1926 and how much bush had become swamp savanna, indicating an area which had remained savanna since then. Another effect of very dry years is that when the river is very low salt water comes right up here, the fish fauna changes and the people 'punish' for drinking water and have to dig for it.

There were other fishing activities here, a long line set overnight caught a characoid foxfish (*Acestrorhynchus*). The school teacher and his brother-in-law, a goldsmith on holiday, tried a cast-net, and by day caught *Curimatus schomburgki*, a characoid not caught on hooks, which 'runs' in schools and has large eyes on the sides of the head each covered in a beautifully streamlined spectacle. And by night, cast-netting among the star reflections and frog noises, we caught gymnotoid electric fishes (*Hypopomus*). While looking for bait we walked on the swamp savannas now covered by two feet of water over which innumerable spiders had slung webs from the emergent water plants. White water lilies grew at the river's edge.

We heard howler monkey choruses at many places, by day and night as well as at dawn and dusk. One mid-morning I landed and stalked them, racing up under cover of the noise, then creeping through the dappled sun and shade and cobwebs. Two howlers crawled away as I sat on a fallen tree. Humming birds buzzed my face and black and red heliconid butterflies floated by while lizards rustled nearby in the dry leaves. Suddenly a large golden male howler was sitting at the top of a nearby tree, his golden mane framing his face, till he walked away with his slim chestnut red hindquarters fitting in below the hairy front half of his body, his beard hanging forward as he walked along a branch.

Visitors to Wakapau while we were there included the dispenser, of Afro origin, on his weekly visit in his well-equipped launch with its red cross on the front. He provided

Howler monkeys

gentian violet for my ground-itch toes, result of ever-wet feet, having first suggested the universal cure, penicillin eye ointment. White flags were hung out where his attention was needed. Few were needing him at present, said to be an improvement largely due to the school feeding scheme whereby milk and vitaminised biscuits (supplied from United Nations funds) were supplied to the children. Another visitor was Nurse Jones, a health visitor of over 20 year's experience and a very sensible body, one of the few of Afro origin to like working in the bush and getting on well ('getting an encouraging response') with the Amerindian women. She visited some of the 30 or so widely scattered homes a day to see if conditions were hygienic and was now in her launch, drinking tea and chatting with the boat crew. Her work was also financed by United Nations money. She had an Afro friend with her at

190

one stage – the friend she had matter of factly asked us about at Akwero: 'Was there another black person like me travelling first class on the boat? I am expecting a friend'. Nurse Jones was a sensible well-padded figure who wore wellington boots to wade ashore. She spoke of conditions in the new mining areas where houses could not go up fast enough and 'women arriving on every boat', prostitutes descending like harpies, attracted by tales of sudden wealth. The church was tumble-down but she had 'kept service there'. She was very much in control of her job which she liked; the 'most encouraging response' was a tribute to her good sense and way of approaching people.

The DC's launch also appeared and several visitors present without permits (necessary as this was an Amerindian reserve) thought of slipping away into the bush. The new DC, a young man of Afro origin on his first station, was making himself unpopular by trying to apply the letter of the law to generally ignored measures, such as having riding lights and life-saving devices in corials. However he was not with the launch. Instead Rambally, the Pensions Officer, appeared, a cheerful soul who bantered with Nurse Jones; we had met them both previously in Akwero rest house where Nurse Jones parked her parrots while travelling around. Their robust laughter contrasted with the very quiet Amerindian voices and smiles. Another visitor was the owner of the mail launch who arrived with letters, for there was a red postbox here.

On Saturday JH took me upriver to visit some of his par-ishioners on their islands. Fork-tailed flycatchers (*Muscivora tyrannus*) were hawking over the swamp. Several corials passed us paddled by a boy and girl, or two girls in gaily coloured clothes. Near the islands were three corials each with a small boy fishing in the lilies at the side of the stream. Going ashore we were greeted by the mail launch owner, of Boviander (Afro/Amerindian) descent, and met his Amerin-dian wife who produced a tibisiri hammock for us. Tibisiri fibres, rafia made from ite palm leaves, were drying in bundles on a clothes line. The garden had coffee trees planted higgledy piggledy, and large green calabashes hung on a calabash tree,

191

but the tangerines were unfortunately not in season. Round the house, where the ground had been kept 'clean' from weeds and grass, erosion of one to two feet showed round the coconut trees. On we went by another house, greeting the owners, women taking cassava rolls out of the matape long platted tube used to squeeze out the highly poisonous prussic acid juices prior to making thin rounds of cassava bread. We continued to the home of a young girl sadly crippled with arthritis – unusual in an Amerindian and which she had had since she was a young girl. She sat on the steps, with neatly braided hair and smiling, but her knees were very swollen. Here, too, was a naked small boy who yelled at our approach (most unusual) and went to a pile of kokerite nuts and ate some; he did not raise his eyes and it seemed that he was blind. His parents said he could tell night from day, but could see nothing except a lamp in front of his eyes. These cheerful and hospitable people loaded us with bananas, pineapples, kokerite nuts and pieces of plants including a root of a fish poison plant cultivated in their gardens. The golden evening light faded and dusk fell as we went home with an unbelievably huge Venus hanging in the sky mirrored in the calm river, and other planets appearing long before any stars were visible. There were lovely sunset cloud effects; we were travelling west towards the last beams arching over the sky to a point in the east opposite where the sun was setting. The outlines of the muka-muka fringing the river were mirrored too, though the originals were hidden against the dark background of the swamp. Behind us the Southern Cross appeared, here said to be a hunter shooting an acouri, and ahead was the handle of the Plough. The firefly reflections were disturbed by gentle ripples from rising fish.

The next morning, Sunday, the landing was alive with people arriving in corials for 6 am church. Many must have set out at 4 am. I went to church too, sitting in the back row with Wasp at my feet. It was a very long service with many hymns 'giving them their money's worth for coming so far'. The Catechist sang bravely at a rollicking speed, but was defeated by the slow drawl and loud voice of the African who was the 'choir'.

The service was followed by the marriage of two Amerindians. The bridal party carried somewhat withered bunches of variagated leaves (after JH's battle against artificial flowers which were then in vogue). The bride, heavily pregnant, looked glum throughout, as also did the smaller groom. I think they thought that they should look glum. They came across to the teacher's house to sign the Register. Here a crowd had gathered to buy prayer books etc, and the noise of cooking, eating, feeding dogs and parrots, packing etc was deafening. They stood glumly for a photograph, then proceded to a large corial, being greeted and accompanied by two fiddlers, one with a bought and one with a homemade violin, playing a jolly little air. Still unsmiling the bride (plus rouge and ear rings) and groom sat side by side on the front seat of the large corial and departed.

Judging by the wavy course we followed when we left next day it seemed that Chris must have been at the wedding spree the night before. We left the savanna and passed between dense walls of muka-muka, then through bush where parties of small monkeys chattered at us, right down the Wakapau river to its entry into the Pomeroon river. So this was another river encountered on this trip down which we travelled without first going up it, though travelling continuously by water. There must be few parts of the world where this can happen.

We had to collect my large tin trunk from the solitary store near the mouth of the Pomeroon river, seemingly built on a pile of coconut husks and steeped in the sickly-sweet smell of drying copra. Then up river to Hackney, where JH put his shoes on for the first time this trip, as this was rather a 'shoes congregation'. When they emerged from church I saw what he meant. Mainly of Afro descent, the women were resplendent in best dresses, shoes, hats, and even sunshades and handbags – a contrast from the bare-headed, generally pigtailed, one dress, barefoot Amerindian women, suckling their babies, of prevous congregations.

I escaped into the bush which here was mangrove swamp backed by corkwood trees, their flat buttresses used for making paddles. Numerous fiddler crabs scuttled away as I balanced

on the roots to avoid sinking into the mud; the great prop
roots of the mangroves had a regular pattern of branching,
their hoops making a kind of table four or five feet above
ground. Even here humming birds appeared, heliconid butterflies and small lizards, and the loud tattoo of a carpenter bird
red-headed woodpecker rang out. There were many
woodpeckers here, black and white with red heads busily
climbing the trees, always climbing. On the way back I glanced
up and there swaying at the top of a nearby corkwood tree was
a three-toed sloth just below the leaf canopy, the dappled
sunlight pouring through onto him, his head resting on his
arms as a child's head would do. Every so often he lifted his
face with its crewcut hair and ridiculous expression and
regarded the flies buzzing round his head, slowly raised an arm
and wiped the flies from the back of his head with his forearm,
then settled his head on his arms again. Overhead large
buzzards wheeled, I could see them through the broken
canopy. The wind was quite strong and the slender branches of
the sloth's eerie waved wildly at intervals but he took no
notice.

Being in this bush was like being under the sea, the light
filtering through dimly and many of the creatures red in
colour. Noises from the outer world reached us at intervals,
the chug chug from a boat's engine on the river, singing from
the church, the staccato tattoo of the woodpecker, cries from
the buzzards wheeling overhead. Time stood still while I sat on
the corkwood buttresses and watched the sloth through
binoculars, which showed every fly worrying him, and oblivious until later of the hordes of mosquitoes which sucked my
legs as I watched. Finally I crawled around to see him from a
different angle and even my crashing below did not disturb
him. So much for careful and noiseless stalking! I could see the
black patch on his back, but no yellow; the male three-toed
sloth has this characteristic diamond-shaped yellow and black
patch in the middle of his back. Were there others nearby?
How in this world of endless trees would one find a mate? Did
they cry out or smell? In Georgetown zoo I had heard one
utter a small cry when it stuck its head right through the

expanded metal mesh of its cage to have a better look at us, an act facilitated by the head being but little larger than the end of the neck in this species; we had a job to push it back, having to hold the slashing claws as we did so. As this species feeds 'only' on cecropia leaves it is hard to keep it in zoos. Cecropia grow mainly in abandoned clearings. Is this perhaps why the distribution of the three-toed sloth in Guyana is more restricted than that of the two-toed sloth, being confined to the coast, though the two-toed is found in less cultivated country of the interior? I did find some cecropia festooned with creepers nearby, which looked a more likely place for a sloth than the wildy swaying top of a swamp tree.

The gentry were chatting outside the church when I returned, and seemed rather aghast at my rolled-up trousers and muddy boots. I chatted to the teacher's wife about the school fish pond. We lunched with the head teacher's wife in a closed stuffy house with suburban furniture, yapping dogs and five children, beneath wooden roof joists with black marks round them which must have been made by rats. At 3 pm we were away upriver and continued solidly till we arrived at Kabakaburi at 8.30 pm having passed Charity on the way. It seemed a long way; as usual the tide was against us and the dogs impatient to be home.

A few days were spent at Kabakaburi, sorting out specimens and trying to catch fish. The children part-sang for me, very well indeed and unaccompanied. I was roped in to give a life-saving demonstration to the girl guides, during which I nearly drowned JH. We went upriver to St Monica's mission where pots and hammocks were being made. A local highlight was the government's film on How to Vote, shown with other films at Pickersgill sawmill – the faces of the audience silhouetted against the afterglow in the darkness as the film was fitted; most of audience came late and all carrying their paddles. I was shown the new 'aided self-help' houses going up, Chris's father, Captain of Kabakaburi having the prototype. The handicraft teacher from St Monica's, mother of a Carib boy scout on a trip to England, came in with two letters, one from him the other from his hostess, and asked JH to read them to

195

her. The boy's letter was of international frame, 'please send some more money' adding that 'serge is here very cheap'; he also asked for two good sets of bows and arrows and added that English boys cannot climb trees. The other was a sweet note from his hostess saying how much they had enjoyed having him to stay for her son's birthday party and at which his bow and arrow shooting had been a great thing. I swam in the river while Chris's wife Olive, a charming girl, washed clothes nearby. How many children had I? And finally she could resist it no longer, how old was I? She guessed 28 which was very flattering!

The mission was dominated by a vast kamaka (silk cotton) tree, full of epiphytic plants and hangnests, and the source of many legends and stories – it seems that the Dutch had a boom across the river from it many years ago (sadly it blew down in July 1961). When I crawled inside its hollow trunk and stood on the hushed soft carpet of dead wood droppings and beetle elytra and stretched out my arms I could not touch either side. The hollow stretched up as far as I could see with the torch (70 or 80 feet). At the top were some bats, said to be vampires which live here. Trickles of water flowed in a few places and a phosphorescent glow came from the dead wood. Odd peepings came from tree frogs that we could not see. I said that, with luck, I might meet a vampire.

It was 3 am when nature called me to wake. There was a slight noise and I recoiled into my sleeping bag, that blessed guardian of toes in vampire country. Something was scuttling about the room, while puppies squeaked under the house below. My blood 'ran cold'. Where was the torch? In the welcome beam of light reason returned and I searched for the bat and regretted that I had not had the presence of mind to stay still and let myself be bitten – surely a necessary experience for a neotropical biologist and better here, where the bats were said to be free of rabies, than in the Rupununi where they carried the dreaded paralytic rabies among the cattle and to be bitten entailed painful anti-rabies injections. It was several minutes before I found blood on my sleeping bag. So I had been bitten after all. But where? Nose and ears seemed intact, so were hands and arms. Then I found blood dripping from my elbow, the very tip of which, merely shaved by the bat's teeth, is one of the most difficult parts to see. So tales of vampires not disturbing the sleeper are true. In this case it was bad luck on the bat that it had chosen a victim who had drunk too much tea before retiring. The blood ran very freely and in the morning the wound had still not properly coagulated. The bat evidently used some very efficient kind of anticoagulant on the wound. Surely a medical use could be found for this? (One has since been developed.) With all this commotion the boy sleeping outside lit the lamp which they generally kept burning to keep the bats away. I lay awake hoping the bat would return, and listening to 'owls' making the most weird mammalian noises in the great tree outside. No wonder the Amerindians are superstitious about them.

Vampire bat

9

The Essequibo Coast and Electric Fishes

The coastland west of the broad Essequibo to the Pomeroon River was another world (see Map 3). I first went there with members of the Fisheries Department in April 1959 to collect electric eels which, for some unexplained reason, were abundant here but not found in seemingly similar waters east of the Essequibo. Journeys to the west coast were always governed by frantic drives to catch ferries across rivers, first the Demerara then the Essequibo, which at its mouth is about 20 miles wide. The drives were made more exciting by the driver's belief that if he waved his hand the cow or donkey, sheep or goat about to step on or off the road would move away in time; one climax came when a surprised cow removed the car door handle in its whisking tail as we passed.

In Essequibo everyone asked 'Is this your first visit to Essequibo? How do you like it here?' adding 'We like it, but feel a bit cut off'. Maybe I was influenced by the hair-raising ferry-catching journeys, but I was quite glad not to live there; one felt that old wrongs lay heavy on the coastal lands, 'Kaywana-blood' type of country, with large decaying estate houses, such as the one where a gaga old lady relative of a friend lived out her days in reputedly appalling squalor surrounded by ever-multiplying dogs and cats. Even the Anna Regina rectory drinking water – a trench with a notice 'This trench is to be used for drinking water only' – had a large drowned pig floating in it. The rectory was a dilapidated old house near a vast church, relic of sugar estate days. In 1959 instead of sugar it was all rice growing here, with a new BG million-dollar rice mill – one of the two belonging to the Rice

Development Corporation. In the rest house the wind soughed in from the sea through a broken window. Frigate birds (*Frigata magnificens*) in twos and threes, and up to a dozen sailed upwind. The sea beat against the sea wall which was being raised as at high tide it flooded the community centre. The contractors we noticed were using child labour to build the wall.

To get to the Essequibo coast we had embarked with the Landrover at Parika on the Essequibo, the point to which the road and railway ran from the Demerara river. All manner of agricultural needs were loaded with us: boxes of day-old chicks, a large pig, a bull, the green cold box containing artificial insemination serum for stock improvement, fish and blocks of ice. From here the daily ferry carrying cars made a three-hour crossing to Adventure, of Gerald Durrells' *Three Singles to Adventure* fame.

The Essequibo river was here mud-laden, carrying cloud shadows. Not unlike the Mersey in colour, it looked about the width of the Mersey at Liverpool but here this was only to one of the islands. These islands are densely populated; with binoculars one could see the red-roofed, white-painted houses amongst coconut palms and trees. Upriver belts of grey rain blotted out the shoreline, sun patches yellow and silver on the river. The channel was marked by buoys on each of which sat large-billed terns with their bright yellow beaks and striking black and white wings. The channel wound between various islands with lush vegetation coming right down to the river, trees and a tangle of vines sending sweet smells out over the water. Passing near them one could see stilt-rooted mangroves, with bromeliad epiphytes like small pineapple plants perched on them, and palms including the lovely slender manicole and more robust ite and others, legumes and wild cocoa with huge pods, and even bamboo which may be a sign of old habitations. Many of the mangroves were hung with young ones ready to plummet into the mud below to start independent existence, but others were in flower – individual trees seemed to have their own seasons.

Fellow passengers included East Indians who were the

dominant section of the population among the rice farmers along the coast. On the deck below us, by the Landrover, two East Indian men were arguing, one appeared to be deaf and many gestures and touchings of his arm were necessary; 'You Promise...' came up on the breeze, and the bargain appeared settled when one man kissed the other's hand. There were visiting government officials from Georgetown, and a cheerful Afro girl came round selling soft drinks and channa nuts which she bantered many passengers into buying. There was also a mysterious Archbishop Makarios-like character and a missionary lady. Also the owner of the Essequibo coast hearse (an East Indian girl) which had recently turned over and killed a policeman who was being taken to catch a taxi reported to be illegally carrying a 'dead' (local paper headlines 'He sought a dead and found it').

We called at a small settlement on Hog Island, a few houses in bush, where a ballahoo boat came out paddled by three men bringing an East Indian girl passenger and into which we offloaded an old East Indian woman who refused to be helped and clambered onto the boat with some difficulty – also a cheerful man with a beard, perhaps the father of one of the paddlers? Outside one of the shack houses was an imposing red letterbox.

Rounding the south end of Wakenaam Island, with its pimpler bushes and muka-muka palisade, flower perfume and a large butterfly wafted out to greet us, accompanied by bursts of cicada noise. A sandpiper flew by, then a bright yellow orial, a green parrot and an ani jumbie bird all flew out of the greenery and back into it again. Pools of yellow petals lay on the water in sheltered inlets below flowering trees. We called here too, a large island with coconut groves and a considerable population. On the stelling stood a bright red, white and blue taxi covered with Union Jacks in which a local worthy had persuaded the Governor to travel when visiting the island, in preference to the more sober (and reliable?) vehicle laid on by the District Commissioner for the occasion. We next called at the small privately owned Tiger Island to put off the owner, an East Indian lawyer; this island was said to be good for the

201

large tree-living iguanas which are considered a great delicacy in Guyana 'tasting like chicken'.

At midday we disembarked at Adventure where many people gathered by the large warehouse on the stelling to greet the daily steamer. Outside the DC's office was a notice inviting tenders for clearing water weeds from the dams and drainage channels. About BG$ 5000 a year was being spent on these operations, for when the banks are cleared of bush the sunlight gets in and the weed grows very fast. We were here to discuss the use of fish and manatees to clear weed. But there was much unemployment along the coast and it seemed a little hard to put the trench-clearers out of work – the old problem of 'industrial revolution' but in this case involving fish and manatees as machines versus men. We were asked how the manatees would react to the numerous electric eels in the trenches, a question we could not answer. The men clearing the trenches get shocks. To kill an electric eel they said they had to make one very quick slash with a very sharp cutlass, otherwise they got 'knocked'. And would not the manatees be eaten by the local inhabitants?

There appeared to be little fishing here and a real fish shortage along this coast. The river is too big for their small boats. Over on the Pomeroon river which is a more manageable size, we saw several landing places for pinseine boats, the tarred nets drying on racks, and occasional Chinese seines. We were told that marine turtles (of several species) come into the Essequibo Island beaches to lay their eggs from high tides at night in June–July. This is well known to the locals who 'take all the eggs', making no attempt to conserve any.

We called at a rice mill to see their fish ponds stocked with tilapia (an introduced African cichlid) and armoured catfish hasser (*Hoplosternum littorale*), the water fertilised by mill waste. A donkey dragging a board pulled the drying paddy into piles. The banks of the ponds supported a rich growth of sweet potatoes, cassava, bananas, pawpaws and mangoes. The hasser pond had morning glory *Ipomaea* covering most of its surface and the water was fairly clear, the other ponds stirred by drinking sheep and white geese; turkeys and fowls wandered

202

on the piles of rice debris. Guineafowl were also kept as domestic birds.

We continued to the home of the man who had collected 50 electric eels for us. These he had in tubs and barrels round his house, a small shack bursting with numerous remarkably neatly clad grandchildren. As electric eels gulp and use surface air, they can be kept in small amounts of water, though he said the big ones 'fight' in confinement. In a tank in his house he had the smallest eels we had yet seen. He also had shocking cages full of small squirrel monkeys, packed tightly without food or water, a dead baby on the bottom of one cage, and 'three and a half pairs' of dejected white-faced capuchins ('sakiwinki' *Pithecia*), which he was selling at BG$ 25 each. The male is black with a white face, the female brown; we had watched wild ones when exploring a creek near Saxacalli on the west bank of the Essequibo. The collector had the skin-tight face and thin body of a fanatic, and he thoughtlessly banged the cages causing all the creatures to jump with fright. Here was a real need for RSCPA activity. But his daughter-in-law seemed sensible when he 'blew his top' as we tried to talk with him. One of his troubles was evidently that he needed what he termed a 'convenience' to transport his creatures to Adventure.

As we raced along the coast road I tried to take in the flat open land with its numerous trenches with patches of *Salvinia* and *Eichhornia* water hyacinth, ducks dabbling in the sunlight in the vivid green water, sheep with ragged coats, cattle 'punishing' because of the drought, East Indian women in their brightly coloured cotton dresses sitting on boards over the trenches washing clothes in the very green, evidently very phosphate/nitrate rich polluted water, beating at the clothes with wooden paddles. Rice paddy was dried on mats alongside the road when the sun was out. By many of white houses Hindu thanksgiving flags fluttered on long sticks, red when new, white when sun-bleached and rain-washed, and not to be confused with white flags tied near the road when the travelling doctor's services were needed, or the green flags used to request the artificial insemination service.

At one point we met a ten foot long anaconda snake (here called camoodi) and a smaller caiman tied up with string as they had been caught 'fighting' by an excited crowd. The camoodi broke loose as I tried to photograph it and escaped back into the trench, the terrified onlookers only grabbing at its tail when it was safely out of reach. We tried to catch it in the seine but it escaped under the net and we only caught a snook (*Centropomus*) fish instead. The camoodi is not poisonous but kills by 'wrapping' (the colourful local term) and constricting its prey. It is said to be the largest snake in the world, officially attaining a length of 'over 30 feet long', a very conservative estimate if there is anything in travellers' tales. It matures early, 17-foot specimens are said to 'bring forth more than 30 young' for it is viviparous. The camoodie is widely distributed in Guyana. Some splendid specimens caught when swimming a river or curled up on logs being rafted down the rivers, were brought into Georgetown zoo. It is mainly aquatic, adapted to water life by having its nostrils directed upwards. The usual prey is said to be birds which are constricted and swallowed under water, but small mammals and fish are also eaten. In the zoo they were fed on rats. There were occasional stories of small children being crushed by this snake. This caiman was smaller than the camoodi. Is the caiman a regular part of the camoodi diet? Which one would have won this 'fight'?

The main coast road runs right to the lower Pomeroon, an area of good soils where many fruits and vegetables were grown for Georgetown markets. Wooden houses on stilts lined the road almost continuously until we swung away from the coast to cut across to the Pomeroon river. Here the sea defence was mangrove and courida (*Avicennia*) bush with an osmunda-like royal fern.

Above Charity on the Pomeroon river, boat building was in progess, the pools of rain water in the half-built boats supporting vigorous mosquito larvae. Here were productive gardens, lush, leafy, twittering greenery with abundant bright orange and red flowing spikes of heliconia, sakki birds and swallowtailed urania skipper moths; old orchards, with very

204

tall orange trees up which we had to climb to get the fruit, grapefruit, limes, rough-skinned lemons, bushes of coffee, cocoa, pawpaw, red peppers, 'sorrel' (the rosella used to make a very refreshing drink), mangoes and mamee apples ('eat this and drink alcohol and you die'), coconuts and bananas, and dragonflies everywhere.

But this highly populated zone was only a thin strip along the coast. Old sugar estate roads, at right angles to the coast ran through resettlement areas but soon reached white sand country, and very few of the local inhabitants penetrated more than about four miles in from the coast, being in the main terrified of the bush. One met an occasional surveyor, carrying a gun, and tracks in the sand showed that game was still fairly abundant. Back of the coast this was pleasant country. Our electric eel hunts described later were mainly near the road into the Tapakuma lakes, a sandy track between high trees for part of the way, along which blue and black-winged large *Morpho* butterflies flapped slowly. At Tapakuma there was an Amerindian mission with a school, and delicious pineapples grew here. These lakes provided an inland waterway from the coastal trenches to the Pomeroon river, with locks on the coastal trenches and a 'haul-over' enabling boats to be pulled across to the lakes. We were to have returned this way to the coast after the Pomeroon trip (described earlier) but the outboard engine broke down.

At the haul-over numerous aquatic caterpillars were swimming in the clear black water among the lily patches, tail ends out to the air, unwettable hairs keeping this air passage open. They swam with waves passing forwards along the body – making them look as though they were swimming backwards. The visiting professor Hans Lissmann later told me that physicists had predicted this would be the most efficient way to swim in calm water, though they did not then know of any creature that did this. A nice example of 'nature did it first'. In rough waters it is evidently more efficient for body waves to pass backwards in the more orthodox manner.

Returning to Georgetown, loaded with electric eels sloshing around in the canvas pool slung from the hood frame in the back of the Landrover, we had the usual race to catch ferries, arriving at the Demerara river as legal chaps in pinstripe trousers, arguing finer points of law, were disembarking after their day's work in Georgetown's law courts. It was dark when we crossed the river to the bright lights of Georgetown. And then we had the jolly job of unloading the electric eels in the dark, rubber-gloved but balanced precariously on the edges of the lab troughs, holding torches in our mouths. So ended another trip.

Electric Fishes

The electric fish hunt really started earlier than this. In December 1957, when camping in the south savannas of the Rupununi District on a small river then dried into a series of clear pools, I had been intrigued by the change-over between the day-active and night-active fishes, and quite intoxicated by the nocturnal ballet of the ethereal gymnotids in these pools. Slim knife fish (*Eigenmannia*), seven or eight inches long, almost transparent except for a black line down the side of the body, fed in small schools, pecking daintily at the bottom litter and swimming backwards out of the torchlit circle by undulations of the long ventral fin, darting backwards as swiftly and easily as forwards, retreating backwards into crevices in the rocks with unerring aim. In the same pools the yellow forehead of the shorter, thicker-set black-bodied *Apteronotus albifrons* would appear from a rock crevice, only to disappear quickly as it shot back into the crevice, for this species seemed very light-shy and solitary. I wrote to tell Hans Lissmann of Cambridge University of these fish and out he came to BG to study them, making two visits while we were there.

Hans was an authority on electic fishes and had developed a marvellous gadget for picking up the signals made by different species, for each species had its own frequency which could with the aid of a tape recorder be heard as a low buzz or high-pitched whine. This gadget had worked very well in laboratory tanks in Cambridge, but how would it work in the wild waters

206

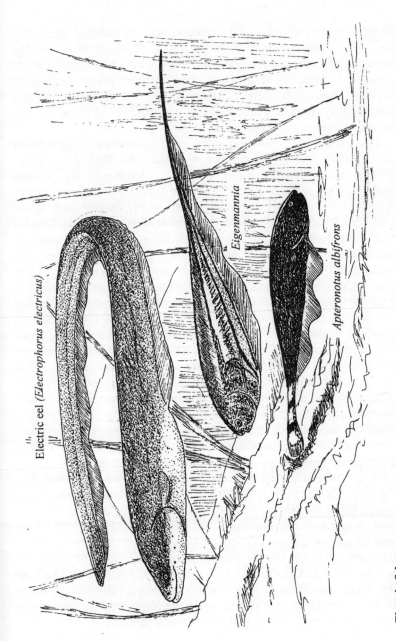

Electric eel (*Electrophorus electricus*)

Eigenmannia

Apteronotus albifrons

Electric fishes

of BG? Hans arrived at the weekend and on Sunday afternoon we had a ceremonial visit to the back of the botanic gadens armed with a long electrode on a stick which he dipped slowly into the trench. As it touched the water we reeled back with surprise, for 'Eat more Marmite' rang out loud and clear, followed by Indian music. It had picked up the local broadcasting station!

The gadget did, however, also pick up electric signals from the fish. It was a great moment when the first was heard. Shortly after this we made a visit to Atkinson, BG's main airfield. This was one of the bases leased by Britain to the Americans during the last war in return for 50 old destroyers, and here a maze of concrete roads enabled one to visit delightfully secret streams in the jungle, favourite picnic spots at weekends but quiet on weekdays when golden-footed tamarins and armadillos went about their business undisturbed, while toucans called overhead. The clear streams here seemed a likely spot for gymnotids so we set out for Redwater creek. We lost our way in the maze of roads but were overtaken by a School Feeding Van, a curious and unlikely thing to see in this seemingly uninhabited spot and the presence of which was never really explained. The school-feeders volunteered to lead us to the creek, and once there 'helped' our activities. We picked up several different frequencies and were able to dip-net out the electric fishes producing them. Having this device to guide us to fish made it almost too easy. The school-feeders were fascinated and wielded the dip-net. Then we heard one of a different frequency, 40 or 50 cycles a second below a tree root submerged at the side of the pool. But we could not find the fish. 'Boiled rice is the thing', said the school-feeders and produced some which we spread as ground bait along the tree root. Some bathers then appeared and splashed the pool, so we had to retreat awhile. When all was clear, despite the bathers the noise was still there and yet no fish. 'Strange, they seem to be all along the pool under this root.' Finally we yanked up the 'root' and there it was – a live electric cable, still emitting 40 or 50 cycles a second and quite unresponsive to the boiled rice fed to it by a distinguished visiting professor.

As this pool was used by bathers we thought that we should report the live cable to the Electrical Inspector at the base. The letter received in reply was, we felt, a complete short story:

Dear Sir or Madam,
We thank you for your public-spirited action in drawing our attention to the live wire in the Redwater pool used by bathers. On removal this was found to be a telephone cable. Nevertheless, we are still grateful for your public-spirited action.

This was about the time that the Mackenzie airfield telephone line was suddenly and mysteriously out of order.

The ecology of gymnotoids studied with this detector has been described in scientific journals by Hans. Each species produced electrical impulses of a different frequency which bear some relationship to the habitat of the species, those living in fast-flowing water using higher frequencies (up to 1500 cycles a second). The device showed how these fishes hide away by day, under a bridge or culvert, in weed or crevices, and how suddenly they emerge in the five minutes or so after sunset and spread out feeding. Their electrical impulses are involuntary and produced throughout the life of the fish; they seem to be used primarily to detect positions and to find food. Later work has also shown their role in social communication. Hans's gymnotid detector found small gymnotids, including the yellow-faced *Apteronotus albifrons* that he particularly wanted, in the tiny holes of the Rupununi stream laterite, but it was oh so difficult to extract the fish. Finally with the help of the ever-ingenious Tiny McTurk, the pieces of rock in which a fish sat buzzing away were levered out, placed in a mosquito net and slowly hacked to pieces with a coal chisel and hammer until the fish could be extracted or wriggled into the net – surely a new fishing method. Later we discovered that we could bolt the gymnotids from their crevices with rotenone, and that provided we caught them immediately and transferred them to clean water they would recover and live in captivity. Actually the *Apteronotus* proved to be most pugnacious and would attack one another. In the plastic bags into which we put them we had to make fold crevices; each fish would then take refuge in some crevice, shooting out at intervals to attack the others.

The electric eel, which is not an eel at all or even related to them, but is one of the group of gymnotoid fishes found only in Neotropical freshwaters, also produced an involuntary disharge throughout life. But in addition this fish produces a large voluntary discharge used to stun prey fish and frogs on which it feeds, and to deter its enemies. (I once saw an otter swimming round a very dead electric eel – do they often meet in life?) Another visitor from Cambridge University, Richard Keynes, wanted electic eels for experimental work so we used to collect these whenever we could and they entered very much into our lives. In spite of the enormous amount of physiological work then in progress on how the electric eel produces its discharges, being carried out in laboratories in the UK, USA, Europe and Brazil, very little was known of its life history or ecology. How it breeds was not known until decades later (and that the parents guard their young). We had great excitement in the fisheries department when a collector brought in two large eels together with some eggs he said he had found with them. Alas these proved to be reptile eggs. The smallest electric eels then on record were those found by this same collector who had them in an aquarium in his home where we saw them in April 1959. There were ten of them, six to eight inches long, which lived together in a tight bunch in one corner of the aquarium. The collector said that 34 had been brought in with the 'mother' and 'father' (said to be four or five feet long) but the little ones died off one by one. We took those still alive back to the botanic garden laboratory. Eight were then sent to Cambridge where they were immortalised in scientific study, the others lived on with us and grew rapidly, feeding on fish and growing to at least three feet by October 1961. Even these small ones gave quite a good shock, a sudden sharp jolt. The collector used to look for bubbles rising near the lock gates at night to lead him to the eels, for like so many of Guyana's fishes, electric eels gulp and use surface air, the lining of the mouth being raised into ridges as an accessory respiratory organ.

In the Rupununi the electric eels lived in holes in the laterite cliffs at the edge of the Rupununi river, where a curious booming sound was heard when they were disturbed. Hans was not anxious to meet one at close quarters as the sudden large discharge might damage his delicate instrument tuned for the small involuntary discharges of the other species. So when the slow tick of the involuntary discharge signifying an electric eel was heard, he tended to move away. A small one which could not do much damage might, however, be rather interesting, particularly as we were anxious to find out more about the life history and no-one had ever reported one smaller that about a foot long at this time. Such a one we thought we detected under a large boulder in the Rupununi river near Dadanawa, in a stony-bottomed pool less than a foot deep. Just then some vaqueiro cowboys appeared on horses to ford cattle across the river as it was the time of the annual round-up. They splashed their way across to our side of the river, and here we felt was the perfect opportunity to try out Humboldt's time-honoured method of catching the electric eel. For Humboldt, who described the electric eel in about 1800 from Venezuela, was told that the way to collect them was to drive old horses into the pool until the horses fell down exhausted and it was then safe to collect the discharged eels. We suggested this to the leader of the round-up, but his reply was to say that he would come back in the afternoon with the tractor and remove the boulder. So have times changed, and with the aid of a tractor, a wire cable and about eight brawny cowboys, who had come mainly to see the fun, we caught the eel that was then the smallest on record, slightly less than a foot long.

Other things that we know about the gymnotoids are that they are nocturnal, the eyes are poorly developed, and indeed nonfunctional in adult electric eels. Cunning experimental work by Lissmann showed that they have a very accurate awareness of their surroundings from the electric field around themselves. They probably use this to locate food and to communicate. Among the African mormyrids which have similar electric organs and which we used to keep in aquaria in

211

Uganda, one would attack the end of a wire leading to an individual in another tank. Gymnotoids also have remarkable powers of regeneration; they can recover even when badly damaged by a predator, of which there are very many in South American freshwaters. Many prey fishes living here have spines but the gymnotoids manage without them, even though they are evidently liked by other fish as pieces of 'lugaluga' (the common name for the smaller species such as *Eigenmannia*), are said to make very good bait for larger fish. Their nocturnal existence means that they have to hide away by day. Some gymnotoids have elongated snouts which parallel those found in certain mormyrid fishes in African rivers, 'elephant snout fish'. The parallellisms of the convergent evolution between fish of such unrelated groups as the gymnotoids and mormyrids is astonishing. Gymnotoids are considered to be an offshoot of the characin fishes, whereas mormyrids are thought to belong to the Osteoglossomorpha (bony tongues, along with arawana and arapaima), but both are nocturnal mainly insectivorous fishes.

Electric eels were not found in all of Guyana's freshwaters. Their absence from the water conservancies behind Georgetown was puzzling as they were abundant in the water savannas and lakes on the western side of the Essequibo, where we went to collect them. Seining in a trench some eight yards wide and five feet deep among water weeds and water lilies over sand and clay, we caught four large (3–4-foot) electric eels, and another escaped through the net, in the first haul. Black of body, they were all red below the head, reputedly the male colour compared with orange in the female, but I could never see that these colour differences were really allied to sex. The men said you always found three or four eels together, never singly. Like Gilbert and Sullivan's Duke of Plazatorro, this seining I would lead from the rear, and the 'it knock you good man' was hardly encouraging. The eels were poked with sticks whilst in the net and we could see by the special jerks of their bodies when they were discharging. This they would do perhaps five or six times and then lie quiet and could be manoeuvred (with a certain temerity and much

212

banter) into a round fish can. These cans were metal, but from which, by action of Faraday's principle the current going round the path of least resistance, one never got a shock. This seemed mysterious as one got very conscious of having to avoid any metal objects when working with these fish. We wore rubber gloves and boots, for the voltage had been measured at up to 550 volts in air, but one got less careful by the end of the day. We carried the eels back to Georgetown in a large canvas bath fixed from the roof frame in the back of the fisheries department's long-wheelbase Landrover, a system originally devised for carrying tilapia and other fish to stock farm and school fish ponds, and later to carry manatees.

Electric eels were easy to keep. Many could be kept in one tank as they used atmospheric air; they would drown if not allowed to gulp air. They were fed on dead or live fish or on frogs which they stunned before eating them. Sending them to the UK was not quite so simple. Some were shipped by air; it was then thought it might be cheaper to send them by sea and a large tank was made especially for this purpose. But something always seemed to go wrong. The large tank was lost when the customs shed in Georgetown burned down. So we were asked to send the next lot by air as 'perhaps safer from fire'. This seemed a possibility for, unknown to the writer, the air control tower had in fact just been burned down as a plane was coming in and the men directing operations had to leap from the control tower. In the event the shipping office was the next to be burned down and all the shipping papers were lost. Why did the unexpected always seem to happen?

10

Rivers and Waters of the Coastal Plain: The East Coast

The coastal road running east from Georgetown to the large Courantyne river, boundary between Guyana and Surinam (see Map 1), crossed many east coast rivers, making it relatively easy to visit them. Travels up these rivers provided a picture of how the country was being opened up; we also saw how the herons and manatees lived in the wild, and were introduced to many other creatures. We visited the water conservancies behind Georgetown with their long man-made canals and locks leading through to the Mahaica river, up the Abary river where the bush was being cleared for rice cultivation, and on geological survey visits to the Berbice and Courantyne rivers where bauxite was being mined. Another road north from Georgetown led to Mackenzie (now Linden) on the Demerara river, where large ocean-going steamers went 60 miles upriver to fetch bauxite.

The Lama Water Conservancy

Inland of the botanic gardens was the Lama or East Demerara water conservancy, 360 square miles of swamp country bordered by straight canals, one eight, another eleven, miles long all constructed by hand labour in bygone days. This area supplied water to irrigate the sugar estates and for Georgetown (which by then also had artesian wells), a sluice through the dam wall taking water from the canal to each estate. We embarked in a small launch at the back of the botanic gardens and, with the aid of two locks, travelled 36 miles across the conservancy to the Lama rest house, situated where the conservancy abuts the Mahaica river and a sluice controlled water intake from this river.

The conservancy dams holding the water were largely made of pegasse, fibrous material derived from the mats of floating vegetation which rise and fall with the water level in these swamps before falling to the bottom and there resisting decay in the acid water. Local fishermen visiting the conservancy were tempted to light fires to keep away the mosquitoes and as such fires eat their way right down into the pegasse, destroying the dam wall, visiting fishermen were not encouraged. However I made two visits, in January 1958 when the water was fairly high and in November that year when the canal was exceptionally low and the conservancy dry and burnt, both with Mr Schneidersman who travelled through the waterways and stayed at the Lama rest house during the week to oversee the gangs of men clearing the canals of water weed, such as the rapidly spreading *Leersia* grass, an endless task. A gang of these men lived in a large Noah's ark on a dredge for two weeks at a time, truly cut off in the swamps.

Mr Schneidersman, who had formerly lived in Southwest Africa, had been in Guyana for many years working in the conservancy. He told us of the droughts and devastating fires of 1911–12, and of floods in the 1930s, the time when he thought that the pirai (*Serrasalmus*) first gained access here. Large cuffam, as tarpon (*Megalops atlanticus*) are called in Guyana, were formerly plentiful and grew large in the conservancy, as testified by the old photographs adorning the resthouse walls of whiskered visitors proudly displaying their catches, but now tarpon were no longer found there. Why?

The journey to the rest house took nearly all day, but they were lovely trips, chugging along slowly with white herons and innumerable other birds rising ahead of us from the sweet-smelling water lily swamps through which we passed, with occasional clumps of palms, the clouds reflected deep in the canal – a river scene not unlike the swamps over so much of

216

Africa, except for the straight lines here of the man-made canals. The first leg of the journey was along the backs of the estates where coconut palms hung out at crazy angles over the canal, their reflections diverging from them as they somehow always managed to keep their feathery crowns upright. Little river bats disturbed by our passage flew out from the banks, where grew *Heliconia*, like miniature wild banana plants with bright orange flowering spurs. After passing Nancy Lock the canal ran along the open swamp, flooded in January but unusually dry on the November trip. In January on a day when the world seemed mostly sky, we passed through sweet-smelling fields of *Alisma* growing from a mass of pegasse, ite (*Mauritia flexuosa*) palm swamps, and parts of the river bounded by palisades of muka-muka. In November when the water was low the muka-muka stems revealed huge 'anklet' growths of pungently-smelling freshwater sponges at the water line. Yellow-flowering spikes of bladderwort (*Utricularia*) rose into the air from their filmy whorls of submerged leaves, and there were patches of white-flowered water gentian (*Limnanthemum*). Strangely, we saw no water hyacinth (*Eichhornia*) in the water conservancy – was the water here too acid for it?

Where the channel was narrow the waves of our passing sucked the white water lilies momentarily under water, as though drawn down by a giant hand. There were many kinds of water lilies, flat green leaves spread on the surface, others with crinkly-edged leaves standing up from the surface. The flower of each kind was open at a certain time of day. A large white flower starred the swamps from early morning but closed at midday; was this the species also open at night? Water lilies and lotus flowers were often used as house decorations for special occasions in Guyana, but the gorgeous pink lotus, so beautiful by day when the flowers were being arranged, shut at dusk just as the party was about to begin; the white water lilies tightly closed in the afternoon, would open into white stars at dusk, cycles probably adapted to the active times of the creatures which pollinate their flowers, about which we knew so little.

Manatees we saw not at all, if present they would have been shot we were told. At Nancy Lock we met a large salimpenta lizard (the Guyana dragon, *Dracaena guianensis*, very like a varanus lizard in Africa), said to prey on caiman eggs. Little spectacled caiman (*Caiman crocodilus* = *sclerops*), mostly 2–3 feet long, swam away from our launch, leaving a disturbed wake through the water lilies. At night round the Lama house the torch beam caught the orange gleam of their eyes at the water surface. One we dissected had stones in its stomach (as in African crocodiles, thought to swallow stones for ballast).

In Africa I had dug up crocodile eggs from their nests in hot sand on lake shores and heard the young squeaking audibly as they were hatching, while the mother, disturbed by our presence, waited nearby. But the female of these Guyana caiman makes a nest of rotting vegetation in which to lay her eggs. Hunters gather these eggs and hatch them to stuff the baby caiman as tourist souvenirs, so a good deal is known about their breeding habits, information collated by Beebe – though he called them alligators. He reported them to have a definite nesting season in Guyana, starting to mate in April and nests being most abundant in the main rains, May and June. The male caiman is apparently almost twice the size of the 3–5 foot long female. Males are said to be outnumbered by 15–20 females and in the mating season to 'roar' (unlike the grunt of a female) which attracts many females to swim round him. After mating each female goes to her nest, constructed several weeks previously by gathering a two-foot pile of vegetation on the trench bank, in which she deposits a batch of 20–40 eggs in the centre of the hot steaming mass. The female stays by the nest except when away feeding. After about 75 days the eggs hatch into young eight inches long. By then the nest top has hardened in the sun; the female is said to bite into it to help liberate the young when their low squeaking grunts announce that they are ready to emerge. The young stay near their mother for some time. Recently it has become known that the sex of young crocodilians depends on the temperature at which they develop, influenced by how deeply the eggs are buried. (See Ouboter, 1993).

218

White herons rose at intervals, the large American egret (*C. alba*) which feeds while solitarily wading in the freshwater swamps, its very angular neck and deep breast keel showing well in its reflection. In the evening small parties of these flew west to a roost near the rest house, flying in a V formation with necks folded and long legs trailing. Great grey herons (*Ardea cocoi*) also fished quietly at the edge of the swamp. More than a dozen of these, not in a V formation, arrived in a red sunset to roost at Lama in January; it was unusual to see so many of these large herons together. Smaller Florida blue and chow (*Butorides striatus*) were also here, the chow lifting its crest as it alighted. Night herons and their young were here one November morning.

Jacana lilytrotters (*Jacana jacana*), locally called spurwing, were very common, leaping up with a shattering 'ek-ek-ek-ek' cry and a flash of yellow wings. In January we saw many together as they flew low over the water ahead of the boat with scolding cries, reflections flying below them, yellow wings flashing both in air and from the water beneath. With their brown bodies, dark heads and colourful red-orange forehead shields, they were strikingly handsome birds. Groups of them

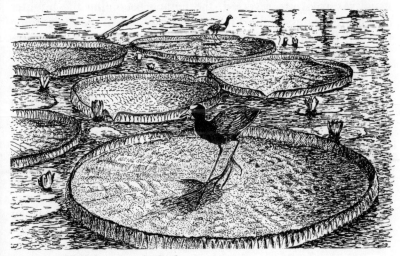

Jacana on *Victoria amazonica* leaf

stood on the lily leaves, raising their wings up over their backs and chattering at intervals. In January there were many half-grown young, but by November the parents were accompanied by two young. In July we had seen a jacana nest on swamp plants from the train window en route for the Abary, and in the botanic gardens very young chicks, like large bumble bees but with enormous feet, followed one parent over the lily leaves, the other parent clacking behind them. But one January day a pair in the botanic gardens put on such as impressive 'distraction display' to lead me away from a corner of the south-east island, that it seemed they must have a nest or young there at that time of year. Both birds made a continual fuss and noise, one wing-trailed (as plovers do), the outspread wings revealing the spurs, at that time a vivid orange-red. Are these spurs used in defence, or fighting between males? They are impressive objects nearly half an inch long, as we were able to measure when we later caught a spurwing in a cast-net one night on the Abary river. Both these displaying birds were the same colour, though one was slightly larger and this followed the other across the *Pistia* then carpeting the lake, at intervals slipping through the *Pistia* in their agitation. In this species the usual sex roles are reversed, the female becoming the brighter and more aggressive bird in the nesting season, the male doing most of the incubation and caring for the young (as in Phala-ropes).

Occasionally we saw cormorants (*Phalacrocorax olivaceus*) or an osprey (*Pandion haliaetus*), a sandpiper bobbing its tail, or a dabchick-like bird slipping away into the lilies. Collared and giant kingfishers were common. The snakebird, here called duckler (*Anhinga anhinga*) also fished here, spearing fish under water by a sudden outward jerk of its long neck; we saw these nesting at Crane pond in the Rupununi.

Parrots flew over at intervals, always in pairs. The ite palms were frequented by little flocks of small bright green long-tailed ite macaws (*Ara nobilis*) always in pairs even when banded together in flocks, flying two by two within the flock. New World vultures were at one time nearly always to be seen wheeling somewhere in the sky, but the black vulture

220

(*Coragyps atratus*), the species common around Georgetown and which scavenges dead animals, suddenly became scarce when the canefields were sprayed to poison rats. In November wild muscovy ducks (*Cairina moschata*) were here.

At the Lama rest house white-rumped swallows nested under the bridge. The house was more or less surrounded by water in which one could watch the fish, but near enough to the gallery forest along the Mahaica river for tree-living birds, such as woodhewers and carpenter birds – as the red-headed woodpeckers are here called – to be abundant. At 6 am one November morning when the sun was catching the tops of trees over the mist above the water, a kiskadee tyrant flycatcher was already hawking in the sun from the top of a stick above the mist. A pair of large red-headed woodpeckers were hollowing out a nest hole near the top of a fairly tall tree; the extremely staccato and rapid tattoo ringing out so loudly that it seemed to be a signal. The birds took turns to work at the hole, but only one bird (the male?) did the staccato drilling, the other bird took out the softer material during its stint. Everywhere the shafts of morning sunlight caught thousands of cobwebs. Guyana is a great place for spiders and from their webs they must be very abundant in the swamps.

In November the mango trees round the house were festooned with loofas, for the old-fashioned bath loofa grows like a cucumber on a vine here. One January evening I watched a pair of green parrots in the mango tree knocking down the fruit, green parrots with red wing patches, eating green mangoes in a tree covered with bromeliad epiphytes whose flowers were the same colour as the splashes of red on the parrot's wings. Two pairs of parrots suddenly flew away – however do they know so simultaneously that they are both going to leave?

Dragonflies of many kinds were very common, pairing ones reflected in the water. In the tropics dragonflies generally burst from their nymphal exoskeletons by night, avoiding the danger of the sun's heat drying the gauzy wings before they are properly expanded. The empty nymphal skins, undamaged except for the split along the back through which the adult humps its way when emerging, were found clinging by their claws to vegetation or posts a few feet above the water. The papery globes of praying mantis egg cocoons were also hidden in the vegetation. Swallow-tail butterflies and the large swallow-tail skipper (*Urania*) were common here too. At night the torchlight caught the orange glint of palaemonid shrimp eyes in the beds of water plants, and the brilliant eyes of large flat spiders on the water surface. It also caught an old sardine tin – picnickers had evidently been enjoying the same scene.

Rod fishing and trolling for lukanani, the large colourful cichlid (*Cichla ocellaris*) excellent to eat, was one of the traditional pastimes at Lama. There was even a special form of fishing for them, known as bash-bash, the rod being beaten on the surface of the water before casting the bait. The lukanani we caught here in January were all females containing almost ripe eggs, and in November they were males which had already developed the adipose hump on the nape that the males develop at the start of the breeding period. So lukanani evidently have a protracted breeding season here. In January we also saw small schools of baby lukanani, less than one inch long, and below the rest house a pair of about foot-long adults (the male, indicated by his hump, being slightly larger) guarding a hole several inches deep and four or five inches across. This hole probably contained their young, but the 'tide' then came in – for the water though quite fresh is still backed up by the tidal changes in the whole coastal area – the rising water bringing a scum that obscured the fish. There was a hard-surfaced log near the hole, on which the eggs would probably have been laid and the young then transferred in the parent's mouth to the specially made hole soon after they were hatched.

The Lama was a splendid place in which to watch fish behaviour at night. The cichlids stayed completely motionless though drifting slightly with any water flow, apparently asleep and unaware of the torchlight. But when awakened the immediate reaction was to shoot away in one tremendous spurt. A patwa (*Aequidens*) which awoke while being dip-netted shot away so suddenly that it hit a metal barge eight

222

yards away with a resounding clonk, showing a huge burst of speed – a device which must help it escape a predator. Gymnotoid electric fish were very active at night, *Eigenmannia* backing in and out under the jetty. Also at night, armoured catfishes (*Hypostomus*) emerged from their daytime hiding places and scraped algae from the wooden piles; they too were very light-shy.

Much experimental work has been carried out in laboratory tanks in many countries; field work here is an excellent supplement (and antidote) to work in aquaria where species are in artificial groupings. How do fishes interact under natural conditions? Have predators, which take large meals at infrequent intervals more spare time? Are they relatively inactive when not feeding and does this save energy and help them to achieve their larger size? We saw many examples of fishes simply getting in one another's way in the crowded dry season pools, one fish even flicked out of the water by another.

The Mahaica River

Some years later (Easter 1961) we saw the Lama stop-off again but from the other side, on a journey up the Mahaica river with the newly re-formed Natural History Society. The nine-hour launch journey took us 65 miles up river to St Cuthbert's mission where we stayed the night. With us were the Swedish conservationist Bengt Sjogren and the ornithologist Dorothy Synder from Boston, author of *The Birds of Guyana*. One of the joys of Guyana was that we had so many visitors interested in various aspects of South American natural history.

Mahaica was a name derived from the Amerindian name for the horned screamer (*Anhima cornuta*), now probably extinct from these parts. Nor did we see any hoatzin (*Opisthocomus hoazin*) along the river on this trip, though they were formerly found here. Most unexpectedly we met a red howler monkey, a male shining in the sun in a coconut tree on the riverbank. Suddenly a shot rang out, and this from a member of the Natural History Society. No wonder there is so little game left in these coastal areas – the immediate reaction seems to be to shoot. There was a really urgent need for education in conservation and protection for the game; always more people and more guns. Certain individuals, among them Vincent Roth, formerly director of the museum, and Tiny McTurk of Karanambo, had been battling for years to try and get protection laws enforced, but politicians were too afraid of offending voters by such enforcement. So the tragic situation exists that very soon there will not be any game for the voters' children to enjoy.

At St Cuthbert's, when we had slung our hammocks in the schoolroom we went fishing by night, but without success. As we walked back to the mission we hoped to see armadillos and other nocturnal creatures, but the Easter moon was so full that the white sand of which this part of the country is made shone like snow. Also we were joined by a piwarri-happy local, piwarri being a fermented cassava drink, so we were by no means a discreetly quiet mammal-watching party.

At 5 am while the moon was still shining and dawn coming very slowly I sat on the white sand surrounded by the early morning bush smells. It was very like being back in the Kalahari but reassuringly free from lions; the South American countryside is much kinder than Africa to naturalists who want to sit and look at things without having to worry too much about being charged or jumped on from behind by some large animal. Just before dawn there was a terrific chorus of hannaquois from the little chachalaca (*Ortelis motmot*) which sounded like three pairs of birds together at the edge of the forest clearing. A most musical 'klungalunglung' then drew me into the forest along a path festooned with razor grass – that reprehensible plant *Scleria* which drapes old gardens, innocuously green but the leaves leaving razor-like slashes, blood-trails, wherever they happen to touch the skin. The path led on across burnt patches of bush, past a travellers palm, where the loud whirr of a tiny orange hermit-humming bird made me duck, to a tall tree where a green oropendola (*Psaroclios viridis*) was displaying to two females which were building nests simultaneously near the top of a fairly tall tree. Another three of these woven nests, several feet long with an entrance hole at the top, hung from the other side of the tree, completed but with no signs of the owners – had these females built them too?

It was a rapturous and surprising display, the liquid 'klunga-lung' call, like that of a bell bird carrying half a mile or more over the forest. Only the females were nest building, each weaving grass into her own long hanging nest. Both females generally arrived together, each carrying a long piece of grass in her beak, and every time they arrived the male displayed above them, bowing down to the least finished nest. Each display started with a 'chuuurrrrrrr', as though he was getting up steam, then the bright green male suddenly upended, tail up revealing his vivid yellow underside with rich chestnut undercoverts, wings up over his head, the head with its red-tipped beak pointing down, almost overbalancing head first in a forward bow down to the female on the nest below. This display was repeated about three times at two-minute intervals, then he flew off but returned to the same place when the female fetched another length of grass, which she did every two or three minutes. How well the colours of the male fitted in with the green and brown leaves – always the need to be inconspicuous except to the mate, and they all had the cold bright blue eye found in other species of cacique; does this help them to avoid danger to the eye? The male's forward bow was very like part of the display of a lesser bird of paradise (*Paradisaea minor*) which we had seen many years previously in Little Tobago, where this species was introduced from New Guinea in 1909 when threatened with extinction by the fashion for plumes on ladies' hats. But the green oropendola lacked the long plumes which gave a golden shower when the bird of paradise lifted its wings.

The male green oropendola produced two other notes, a 'creer creer check' and a cluck when chasing a female, the 'klungalung' call was only used in his forward bow display. He was chasing one of the females through the tree when I realised that I had the only stove and the others would be awaiting breakfast, so I had to leave. But he was still displaying when several of us returned here about midday. One of the party happened to fly to Kaieteur the following day and found that the green oropendola males were also displaying, and nest building was in progess there too at that time of year.

There was time here too to look around the forest and watch the red-billed toucans (*Ramphastos tucanus*) in the tree tops. Down by a pool in a small stream running through a clearing large black water skaters (gerrids) cleaned their long legs, and red-orange velvetty *Velia*-like ones skated on the water surface. Ants crossed the stream on a stick bridge, while solitary black and red heliconid butterflies floated by. We found an unusual wasp nest covered with hanging wasps with silver abdomens. As the day warmed up skink lizards ran through the leaves with a tremendous rustle, and humming birds of various species sucked nectar from *Ixora*-like red flowers. We swam in the river, but the water was too darkly stained for goggles to be much use; one of the party fished with flour paste and caught long slender characid *Creatochanes*.

On the way downriver we called at two Amerindian settlements, where we were greeted by large numbers of Arawak children. At one they were making a dug-out canoe from a large tree trunk. It was already partly hollowed out (by termites?) and with woodpecker holes, and was being further hollowed using a long 'beef-eater' ceremonial type of axe. The family were sitting around the thatched open-sided house and swinging in hammocks amid a litter of household goods, bowls and strainers, large pineapples, a Hahn's macaw in a basket, a warishi woven cane rucksack for carrying goods through the bush. They gave us cassiri to drink, made from fermented cassava with a sour but cocoa-like flavour. They showed us a fish poison plant (*Clibadium*) growing here, also the large grains of 'hill rice' grown without irrigation, and a large native wild cashew ('hububi') the fruits of which they squeeze for a drink. They had a cunning sugar cane juice extractor fixed into the bole of a tree. On a nearby tree hung nine nests of the red-rumped caique (*Cacicus haemorrhous*) which were still building nests, black birds with the yellow bill and blue eyes of caiques and vivid scarlet rump flashing as they flew. We were also shown a violaceous euphonia's nest (*Tanagra violacea*) about 20 feet up an aquari palm where the bark had split, the youngsters' heads peeping out from the nest. The colourful parents coming to feed the young were together in a nearby palm, the male two-coloured, upper parts metallic blue under parts rich orange yellow, and the female olive green and yellower beneath. As these are in much demand as cage birds for their bright colours and sweet canary-like songs, the Indians sometimes catch the young and cage them near the nest where the parents continue to feed them through the bars.

Along the river were many different kinds of palm: ite palms now heavy with fruit, those that had not already shed them, aqueru palms and thinner awawa palms, both with rings of spines round the trunks and both now in fruit. Along the river grew waterwallaba (*Macrolobium* spp) and dumbcane (*Dieffenbackia sequine*), one chew of which paralyses the tongue and makes speech impossible for some days, and which was reputedly once used on slaves.

As we proceeded downriver we chased many large kingfishers (*Megaceryle torquata*), the male and female differing in colour, the spotted tail cocked as they landed on a bush ahead of us. We also met an occasional canoe, generally paddled by a man at either end and loaded with baggage and the family. As we reached the Lama the moon came up suddenly, the river bending so the moon was first on one side then the other until on a straight stretch the full moon was dead ahead, the river a rippled silver trail into the distance, a second moon lying reflected deep in the calmer water just ahead of the boat. The banks were solid black silhouettes pierced by the outlines of trees; there was even a long-eared owl on a dead tree silhouetted against the moon, as though trying to be a design on a Christmas card, and moonlight glinted from the palm leaves as we passed. Ahead a silver trail, but upstream the river looked golden. So ended another journey. As I had been told before coming to BG: 'You go up the river and eat all your food, then you come down the river.'

227

The Abary River

The Abary was one of the coastal plain rivers in which the tidal rise and fall backed up the freshwater right to the head of the river, the 'creek hands' where the manatees lived. Ram Singh of the BG museum knew the river and its bird and human faunas very well and took many visiting scientists there. I went with them in May, July and August 1959 and again in July 1961. The Abary had the merit that it was easy to get there, by train from Georgetown, and then to travel up and down river on the milk launch or other boats. Taurakuli and Tiger Island where we stayed was an eight-hour chug up river.

BG had several railways, old ones along the east and west coasts of Demerara and more recently ones in the bauxite areas and in the north-west to carry the manganese from mine to shipping wharf on the Barama river. The east coast line between Georgetown and New Amsterdam on the Berbice river was said to be the oldest railway in South America. It was a friendly train in which one spoke with the driver before starting and asked to be put down where one wanted to alight if this was not at a station, and to be collected there on a later trip. The train coach made an excellent observation car, travelling high above the flat country along a raised embankment which formed a second line of sea defence when the sea wall was breached. Through the rice fields we went, and across grassland sadly overgrazed by innumerable scrawny cattle, sheep which were surprisingly aquatic creatures, paddling to find food in the wet season, and numerous rotund brown and white goats. The animals on the dry ground were mostly followed by two or three cattle egrets taking the insects disturbed by their feet. We travelled on through coconut groves, laced with the shadows of their delicately arching fronds; alongside swamps full of water birds and flowering water plants. At the small stations the train was met by vendors of refreshments, with bunches of large yellow or red bananas, mangoes in season and doubtful-looking buns, and all the hurley burley of passengers with large bundles, and often dogs and hens and cage birds, alighting or joining the train.

At the Abary bridge we descended and there awaited the milk launch returning upriver. At least that was the theory. The first time that I was taken there the owner of the launch went to the races instead of turning back upriver, so the launch never arrived. Being merely an unorthodox stop where the railway happened to cross a river, there was no road. But eventually we did get a lift upriver on a passing timber-collecting launch. In later years Lear and Margaret Grimmer from Washington zoo who were studying hoatzins on the Abary had their camp in a reputedly haunted house near this railway bridge, backed by a coconut plantation.

Delays at the Abary bridge did not matter as they were full of zoological delights. The river here was flanked with mangroves, the mud seething with fiddler and other crabs when the tide was out. Large tarpon (*Megalops atlanticus*) splashed at the river surface and from the bridge one looked down on to the riverine species of foureye fish (*Anableps anableps*) of various sizes swimming at the surface, head upstream to the current, staying in the same place for long periods except when frightened away by another fish or the shadow of a passing bird, then gradually returning. In the channels among the mangroves the dip net took the strange little one-inch long white ghost-like cyprinodontoid fish *Tomeurus*, a genus remarkable for its breeding habits; for after internal fertilisation, achieved with the aid of a very complex organ derived from the modified pelvic fins of the male, the female lays an egg which is almost ready to hatch into a small fish when laid. An adaptation to the rapidly changing water level in this tide-dominated world? This was a fish I had sought for zoological colleagues intrigued by its breeding habits in aquaria, envious of the opportunities we had to study it in the field. I also found *Tomeurus* about 70 miles up the Courantyne river, but whereas they turned out to be the known species, *Tomeurus gracilis*, this Abary one was a species new to science, as yet unnamed. Here they were living in small schools, the slender white fish given away by a shining spot on the top of the head (resembling the shining spot in some small characids due to a encysted parasitic worm). The males were larger than the females, as in egg-laying cyprinodonts, and unlike the live-bearing poeciliids such as the millions rainbow fish *Lebistes*, in which the female is much larger than the male.

Just above the bridge were the bundouri pimpler bushes *Machaerium* (*Drepanocarpus*) *lunatus* and other bushes lining the river where lived the hoatzins, otherwise known as canje pheasants, birds of zoological interest in the possession of wing claws and large and specialised crops, placed in a sub-order of their own. They had been described from such haunts by Beebe and at the time of our visit were being studied by Lear and Margaret Grimmer of Washington zoo with a view to conserving them in zoos. They were large beautiful birds, their plumage mottled in browns and greens, the back bottle-green with yellowish markings, the long green-black tail with a broad terminal band of buff, breast buff, with chestnut belly and flanks and a large ragged rufous crest over the red eye. But they were ungainly in their movements and flopped rather than flew from bush to bush as they fed on the pimpler leaves. Among their special characters part of the huge crop is used for leaf storage. They were noisy too, having a harsh cry. They never left these riverine bushes. Although I saw them sitting on nests I never saw the young dive from the nests into the water below to escape capture, then scramble back into the bushes using the reptilian-like claw on each bastard wing, as so vividly described by Beebe. The young are notable as being the only birds to have such a claw; the adults still scamble through the branches with wings outstretched 'oaring' their way along. It seems the claws are a secondary adaptation for the very specialised and localised world in which these chicks live. Although hoatzin have some pheasant and rail-like characters, they are unique in the possession of these claws and their large specialised crops. Theresa Clay, another of our interesting visitors, examined the bird lice frequenting their feathers; they have enormous numbers of such lice and carry six species of Mallophaga belonging to five genera, lice which suggest they may be related to the rails or other South American birds rather than to game birds.

In recent years hoatzin numbers had diminished rapidly,

mainly because their habitat was being drastically reduced, the bushes along the river disappearing as land was cleared for mechanised agriculture. Hoatzin have also been found to be edible by a hungry ever-increasing human population, though they are probably not very appetising – despite their other name Cainji pheasant. They too, like the rest of the Abary vertebrate fauna, suffered badly from trigger-happy weekend visitors who raced up and down the Abary in speedboats using anything that moved for target practice. Hoatzins are only too easy to spot and shoot, being noisy, bulky birds which never fly away from the riverine bushes. Also in dry years (as in one year we were there) the hoatzins may miss a nesting season, for like the indigenous herons they nest in the main rains, at the time the riverine bush grows thick and green, so a series of dry years is likely to lead to a further drop in their already depleted numbers. The Grimmers worked intensively to try to get some to take substitute foods such as spinach so that they might be saved in zoos, but they proved extremely difficult to keep alive away from their native haunts. Beebe mentioned a £5 fine for killing hoatzin, but there was no mention of this when we were in BG; perhaps it was still on the statute books but had been forgotten?

The Abary was an excellent river on which to study the effects of humans on this countryside. From the top of the milk launch one could look for miles across the open savannas beneath their wide skies; flat country with brown and white cattle dotting the grassland, swampy areas haunted by white herons which showed up from far away miraged to larger-than-life size, and a fast-growing acreage of rice fields increasingly worked with enormous agricultural implements owned on a cooperative basis. Here the river banks were only some two feet high, open grass with occasional patches of muka-muka where it was not too brackish – for this plant seems to die off rapidly in dry years when brackish water penetrates farther up river than usual, and occasional corkwood and *Macrolobium* trees, or bushes where night herons roosted by day and other herons by night. The mud-marked tree trunks showed the tidal rise and fall in water level.

231

Above the Abary Villa, which was several hours' chug above Tiger Island, the water became clear and dark, sparkling in the wind flurries, no longer silt-laden enough to hold the shadows of passing birds but clear with reflections of the muka-muka palisades; golden leaves floated on the black water, water with an acid taste. Occasional muddy bands showed where water from side streams entered the river and was blown upstream with the prevailing wind. A rim of trees appeared round the savanna ahead of us along the river; it was near here that we first saw a manatee rising to breathe.

Towards Taurakuli, which was some eight hours upstream from the Abary Bridge, we were suddenly met by the sweet smell of bush at the edge of the forest, here mixed with palm trees, and bird calls from the tree tops, the world of sight giving way to an enclosed world of smells and sounds. Living here in wooden shacks were a few farmers, mainly of Afro extraction, opening up new gardens for plantains or coconuts, with goats and a few cattle followed by cattle egrets even here. The clearings had a sour smell. The forest edge was here being attacked by every means – huge orange flames leapt against pale blue smoke; the whine of a sawmill dealing with the larger timber; goats at the forest edge helping the process. The parastic plant dodder (*Cassytha filiformes*) had arrived here from the coast, festooning bushes around the clearings. This plant, which spread enormously while we were in BG is rather surprisingly a member of the same family (Lauraceae) as the lofty greenheart tree, one of Guyana's main exports.

Thus were the coastal savannas being enlarged, and doubtless this was one of the factors which enabled the cattle egret to get established in the New World. Similar processes in Europe and Africa, above all the introduction of mechanised clearing, may have helped cattle egret numbers to build up till they needed to spread to new worlds, but at first failed to find enough suitable country there to allow them to become established; or perhaps they came in too small numbers. Now these coastal savannas had become excellent country for cattle egrets, thanks to man's activities.

In 1959 there was a large cattle egret night roost opposite

232

Tiger Island, empty by day, but they nested in a large heronry a few miles downriver from Tiger Island. Here there were hundreds of cattle egret nests in which the birds were sitting and young birds present in July–August 1959, together with a few Florida blue and with a few hoatzin nesting on their flimsy stick nests in the tops of the bushes, and grey herons around. But in 1961 this heronry was no longer in use – perhaps the target practice along the river was too much for the birds and they had moved away from the river.

Before the coming of the cattle egret the boat-tailed carib grackle (*Quiscalus lugubris*) and the icterid military starling or red-breasted blackbird (*Leistes militaris*) and the common ani (*Crotophaga ani*) followed cattle here. Even now these species could be seen around the livestock, and they still had this role in the Rupununi where the cattle egret was not established until 1961, though by 1966 Tiny McTurk reported they were plentiful at Cajueiro his Karanambo outstation. The cattle egrets were not established in the New World when Beebe visited the Abary and many other changes had occurred since his day. Capybara and giant otters commonly seen then, as well as the horned screamer, were no longer to be found. Beebe wrote that these savannas were densely wooded jungle until a great dought in 1837 was followed by devastating fires and floods. He described vast flocks of wild fowl, mainly greynecked tree ducks there at the time of his visit.

The kindly and observant Mr Reid, who lent his house at Taurakuli to ornithologists visiting it with Ram Singh, had been farming here since 1937 and had a fund of observations about opening up this land on the Upper Abary. As we travelled down river by launch he talked of the savanna spreading particularly on the down-wind side, one bank of the river fires more easily than the other and some types of bush once burned disappeared completely. East of the river the cattle came here in about 1909, on the west side some years later. Tree roots found in the savannas when digging drains told of the forest's retreat. Early-maturing cattle did best here. Herefords had been tried but were not very satisfactory as they needed shade and tended to calve in the wet season, a disadvantage as they dropped their calves into the water or mud. The wet season, when so much of the savanna is flooded, is the hungry time for cattle here; farmers have to grow and cut 'paragrass' to tide the cattle over this period. Goats were no good here as they do not like water. He thought that the game and fish around Taurakuli had decreased sadly, even the night herons being shot for food. But there had been an increase in the numbers of manatees there, which he thought was due to the increased cattle downstream taking the riverside grass, so the manatees had had to move up and now fed on water weeds in the headwaters. When I wondered why these savannas get two rainy seasons a year whereas the Rupununi savannas have only one, he observed that the 'big rains come from the land, the short rains from the sea'.

At Tiger Island we used to sling our hammocks in an old barn belonging to Ram's friend who ran the milk launch. It was a huge barn. After our hammocks were slung we discerned in the gloom of another corner a large double bed complete with sheets in which two of the farmer's sons were sleeping. But it was rather a ramshackle barn and when we arrived on another trip it had just blown down. So that particular night was not a very comfortable one. Some of us 'slept' on the launch, plagued by mosquitoes and drenched for good measure as there was a violent thunderstorm. The others tried to sleep on the woodpile, which was at least dry, but they first had to shoo away the hens. We arrived late (1 am) and those on the woodpile described shining a torch towards dawn to find themselves encircled by eyes – of numerous toads which had been out hunting when the party moved in and now wanted to get back into the woodpile but were suspicious of the strange bodies that had suddenly appeared. Tiger Island was also very rich in bêtes rouge, those tiny mites which crawl up legs until they meet an obstruction, such as an elastic band round a waist, where they dig in and attach themselves. We itched for a very long time after walking in the grass there. The island had an interesting history, being built up, a mud hummock above the surrounding swamps, by runaway slaves in the long ago (as described by Beebe in *Our Search for a Wilderness*).

234

There was never much time for fishing on these Abary trips, though cast-netting at night from Tiger Island we caught a long-bodied armoured catfish (*Loricarichthys*), here called 'smoke fish' as a demonstration showed it would puff a cigarette if one was put into its mouth, and skinfish catfishes such as larima (*Pimelodus*) and kumakuma (*Brachyplatstoma*). Local residents set hooks in the river for these skinfish. A six inch gill-net used in the river here caught cuffam (*Tarpon*), bashaw (the sciaenid *Cynoscion acoupa*) and the skinfish duwala (*Ageneiosus*).

We were generally travelling with ornithologists on this river, which was very rich in bird life. Swamps off the river had a large variety of water birds. In addition to many heron species, in August there were many waders here of various kinds, feeding yellowlegs (*Tringa*) were common, the beautiful slim black and white black-necked stilts (*Himantopus*) flew over us trailing their very long red legs, black skimmers (*Rynchops*) skimmed the river where large-billed terns (*Phaetusa simplex*) with their huge yellow bills were busy diving. Tiger Island had noisily chattering kingfishers, black and white pied water tyrants (*Fluvicola pica*), the marsh tyrant or parson bird (*Arundicola leucocephala*), and many other flycatchers as well as numerous seed eaters, mangrove cuckoos, mocking birds, even a Venezuelan horned owl. In August the boat-tailed grackles (*Quiscalus lugubris*) were displaying, the boat tail spread right over the head of the displaying bird, and at this time grey-breasted martins (*Progne chalybea*) were congregating. High overhead vultures (*Cathartes*) were nearly always to be seen, as were caracara falcons stalking the savannas. Upriver Hahn's small green red-shouldered macaws were common at the forest's edge, where mocking birds and bunya hangnets had their colonies of woven nests, generally near human habitations. One of the comic sights was two ducks sitting high up a dead tree, admittedly they were tree ducks (*Dendrocygna*) but this looked an abnormal place to see upright ducks perched; they nest on the stumps of the ite palms and the parent duck is said to solve the problem of getting the young down by carrying them in its beak, but this alas I never saw. The large muscovy ducks were not nearly so common as they evidently were in Beebe's time – they are much too good to eat.

Along the river numerous caiman, mud-coloured and immobile as though carved out of wood, sunbasked on the banks with open mouths, not even bothering to move into the water as we passed; others swam by the launch. Descending the Abary on the milk launch we stopped at frequent intervals for the milk to be collected to go to the government-run pasteurisation plant in Georgetown. Perhaps it was just as well it was pasteurised, for the cows were milked in the fields and the milk brought to the launch in an assortment of old biscuit tins and cooking pots. At the launch some of the milk was tested with a hydrometer to see how much it had been diluted with river water – sometimes brackish at that. It was then strained through a flour bag into large churns. In dry years brackish water penetrates far up river and the cattle 'punish' for lack of 'sweet' water.

The Berbice and Courantyne Rivers

Geological visits took Richard to the bauxite mining areas on the white sands 60 to 80 miles inland from the coast, at Mackenzie on the Demerara river, Kwakwani on the Berbice and Siparuni on the large Courantyne bordering Surinam. I sometimes went too, which was a great opportunity to look at creatures in the surrounding seasonal forest.

The Berbice is a longer river than the Demerara, New Amsterdam at its mouth was once a busy port, but the mouth had silted up and large ships could no longer enter the river. The cattle trail from the Rupununi district ended in the Ebini savannas on the Berbice, a white sand area that I only saw from the air as we flew to Kwakwani for a few days in February 1958. Although 80 miles from the sea, the tidal rise and fall here was still about four feet, but this part of the Berbice river was rich in bird life. Hoatzin were still fairly abundant in the pimpler trees by the river. Fishing along the river were tiger bitterns, the beautiful capped heron *Pilhero-dius*, a clean yellowish-white heron with a black crown and two long white plumes on its nape, and we met a sun bittern. We also came on a family of five waterdog otters (*Lutra*) draped on a log two feet above the water; the small ones slipped into the water at our approach, their flat heads (pink tongues and white of chin and teeth) appearing above the water as they watched us, while the large male stayed on the log, the sun gleaming on its dark grey glossy pelt.

Kwakwani was right in the forest, with toucans and green-heart birds calling, and alarming screams from a cotingid bird high in the canopy, sun parrots and macaws flying over. We saw our first labba by the river, being skinned after a night's hunting. Tapir, caypybara, two kinds of sloth, two kinds of anteater, and spider monkeys were all still found in the bush here. Fishing was a favourite pastime. We heard much of the haimara (*Hoplias macrophthalmus*) said to reach 20 pounds in weight. I had caught a small one in the dip-net by torchlight. It had been questioned whether this species is distinct from the widely distributed smaller huri (*H. malabaricus*), but here there seemed little doubt that they were distinct, the larger-growing and bigger-eyed haimara living in the forested rivers and having different habits from the more ubiquitous huri found in shallow water. Haimara were said to be the only fish here full of eggs in February and to lay their eggs in a nest in the grass in shady places where there are sand banks at high water. They were generally hooked at night (in contrast with lukanani caught by day). I later heard that Amerindians catch haimara when they are sleeping in the morning by tickling them and putting fingers in the eye sockets to lift them from the water, which seems quite a feat, for haimara have formidably sharp canine teeth.

The Courantyne is the large river forming the boundary between Guyana and Surinam, but unlike other rivers used as international boundaries, here the boundary was the highwater mark on the Guyana side, so Surinam (formerly Dutch Guiana) had all the fishing rights. These it maintained, patrolling the river with a launch. In Guyana this was thought to be an anti-smuggling patrol, for tales of drug smuggling were told. We made a trip up the lower reaches of the Courantyne in July 1958, to Siparuni where bauxite prospecting was in progress 70 miles upriver, above Orealla mission.

Our journey was full of incident. First along the coastal road, by ferry across the Berbice river at New Amsterdam, through country now very green, the young rice plants six inches high. En route we visited the Black Bush Poulder project or Torani scheme where 27,000 acres were being cleared and irrigated to settle 1600 families on two-and-a-half-acre plots; a scheme involving considerable capital expenditure.

We were to be met and taken up river by speed boat, but our guide had a 'better idea' about where to meet us, so we did not find one another until dusk, We started upriver by a sliver of a moon, hoatzin crests silhouetted against the evening sky, and huge flocks of parrots, as always in pairs, flying to and settling down in their night roosts on islands in the river. The speedboat was a frail aluminium craft, 12 feet long and open to the heavens. Then there was a sudden squall and it poured. Waves rose slapping into the boat and we were jolly nearly pooped in the utter darkness. After the squall had subsided, a light which had been glimpsed away on the bank mysteriously seemed to have changed sides of the river. Our guide assured us it had not, but we insisted we make for it to investigate. It seemed that we were landing on the Surinam side of the river, and mindful of recent shooting incidents I clambered ashore, calling out in a high falsetto (to show I was a harmless female) that we were friends. It was Orealla mission on the BG side; we had turned right round in the squall and were now going downriver again. Had it not been for the light we would have continued till the petrol ran out. It was no use trying to get dry, and we left again shortly afterwards with a guide, but soon met a sloop with a very worried geologist coming to look for us. We eventually made Siparuni at 3 am and spent the rest of the night in sopping plastic raincoats trying to keep warm, for everything, including all our bedding, was soaked.

By day, with the sun shining again, we found we were in a

charming spot, high on a sandy bluff in wallaba forest, looking out over the Courantyne river where dolphins came up on the flood tide and played around, even though it was 70 miles from the sea. There was still a six-foot tidal rise and fall, but high tide was three hours behind its time at the river's mouth. Tree tops with brilliantly coloured trogons were below us, and the whole area was rich in bird life.

It was here that I first saw *Tomeurus*, the little white cyprinodont fish with the puzzling breeding habits in which the female lays an egg that is almost ready to hatch; we dip-netted them from the sides of the river below the sandy cliffs, where they lived with the small characin *Pristella riddlei*. Here there was a remarkable butterfly migration, innumerable pale yellow butterflies, and some other species, all crossing the river east to Surinam, passing us a rate of about 100 a minute. Here too I met the rattling butterflies (*Ageronia.* sp), also seen in the Rupununi and New river, though possibly of another species – grey and white butterflies with a fluttery flight, quite unlike the floating flight of the heliconids so common in Guyana; they rattled particularly loudly when they met and circled one another, and at rest they faced downwards on the tree trunks (unlike most others which faced upwards) about eight feet from the ground.

Male manakin birds – later studied by David Snow in Guyana – had a lek display area near the house, zipzipping across it to attract a female. I spent a lot of time looking at the invertebrates: cockroaches under leaves, small crickets and beetle larvae, innumerable springtails. Lizards, large green and very noisy, especially in the dry leaves round burnt trees were common, and I found a legless lizard (*Amphisbaena*). Millipedes were legion, and there were scorpions under some logs, but on the whole few ants – why was this? I failed to find any *Peripatus*, though I was always hoping to do so; maybe it was not damp enough. A nightjar disturbed by these log-turning activities flew off with a liquid 'phut', while a howler monkey chorus floated over the forest.

We were taken to visit a 'bush negro' village on the Surinam side of the river here, notable for the splendidly carved wooden houses made by the bush negroes, descendents of runaway slaves, whose language is still pidgin English, though the architecture of their houses looked as though it had been influenced by Indonesians living in Surinam.

11

The Half-way World and Fishing the Mudflats

Scissors crab

The vast expanse of tidal mudflats along the whole length of the Guyana coastline is a half-way world of reflections and images, seemingly suspended between sea and sky, half sea half sky, the waters changing with the seasons, half salt half fresh, home of the foureye fish (*Anableps*), itself rather a half-way creature, its eyes with a double lens to look both up into the air and down into the water. This is an ever-changing world, in quiet weather with a dreamlike quality of soft greys and blue sky reflections. On calm days mirages magnify the wading herons a mile or so away, lifting their image into the sky. But on boisterous windy days the waves come in from the Atlantic uninhibited by land nearer than the coast of Africa 3000 miles away. Always the tide washes and ebbs remorselessly, day in day out, aeon after aeon; an ancient world populated with fiddler crabs and wading birds long before man arrived here, or even evolved, but always different with changing weather, light and tides.

As we were tied to Georgetown for much of the latter part of our stay in Guyana we frequented the shores and grew to love the mudflats. Gradually patterns unfolded. Daily patterns following the ebbing and washing of the tides, influenced by the height of tide at springs and neaps and the time of day at which high water occurred, with a tidal range here of about nine feet at springs, four feet at neaps. Seasonal patterns following the wind and rains were reflected in the movements of birds, fish and other creatures. Superseasonal patterns followed bands of erosion moving along the coast from south-east to north-west leading to accretion in other places with associated changes in the shoreland vegetation.

The slope of the land is so gradual that the tide floods – 'washes' as the local expression has it – and ebbs ('falls') over a mile or so of semi-liquid mud. This mud is so characteristic that people born in Guyana were locally called 'mudheads'. Since the building of the sea wall, started by the Dutch, the shore has built up and at high tides the sea is now considerably higher than the land behind the sea wall. At high spring tides with a strong wind waves dash over the sea wall, flooding the land behind it with brackish water. Bands of erosion move along the coast and every so often the wall is breached and the sea comes pouring in. Watching it one can understand stories of little Dutch boys sitting on holes in dykes to prevent the gaps from widening in desperate struggles with the sea. In our time there the railway line embankment provided a second line of defence.

242

The grey-brown water of the sea is here so mud-laden that shadows, not reflections, are cast on it by passing birds and ships. On windy-blue days the sun strikes golden brown through the little waves on the cream-capped choppy sea, the angles of the waves holding the blueness of the sky. The waves look so solid that the view from the sea wall resembles a relief map of a highly eroded country, a model with ever-changing mountain slopes. The scene is not, however, devoid of reflections, for as the tide ebbs the polished steel-grey surface of the liquid mud reflects every wading heron, white or blue, and the little pools left behind by the tide among the gradually drying mud hummocks clear rapidly and hold the blueness of the sky. Among such pools the blue herons are well camouflaged, but the young ones in white plumage stand out clearly; why this change of plumage? In the pools the mud settles almost immediately, the clear water then revealing crabs and small fish.

The master factors controlling the seasonal cycle appeared to be the strong onshore north-east tradewinds which blew strongly from January to March, and the rains which generally started about April or May (though in one year delayed until June) and lasted until September. These were the calmest months of the year and as the rivers swelled pouring their dark brown waters out to sea, the edge of the shallow sea became increasingly brackish. The coastal district of Guyana also had a second rainy season, the 'Christmas' rains about November to January; one year (1958) these failed, but in some years they were almost as heavy as the main rains.

Except during the calm months of the year, June to September, when the sea lies opalescent the tide washing and ebbing very gently, there is generally a good onshore breeze. The prevailing wind is north-east, sweeping in from the Atlantic. Cries of birds come in on the wind. Shorewards of the lagoons which develop along much of the coast, the sea wind also brings in the acrid smell of the brilliant yellow-green batis (*Batis maritima*), a samphire-like plant growing along the brackish pools, and the honey smell of courida (*Avicennia nitida*) courida mangrove bushes when these are in flower. This world is populated by herons which are here in varying numbers all the year, by waders – some resident, others on their long migrations north and south – by terns of many kinds and skimmers, while overhead sail frigate birds and brown pelicans. Below are vast armies of fiddler crabs, small mullets and catfishes, and in the February–March windy season the iridescent blue and pink floats of Portugese-man-of-war jellyfish colonies (*Physalia*), sailing in so confidently on the breeeze, to lie stranded on the shore, the end of their long journey.

Kitty jetty in Georgetown, where Jocelyn Crane, a zoologist from New York, had studied the behaviour of the several species of 'scissors' fiddler crabs which lived here in such numbers, was one of our favourite haunts. The jetty was a 100-yard long stone wall projecting out to sea at right angles to the shore, providing a harbour for wooden fishing boats. Steps led over the sea wall and the first part of the jetty traversed 'toplands' of tussocky grass and batis; at the seaward end it projected out above the mudflats covered at all tides. At very high tides the sea washed right over the wall and covered the toplands, but at neaps the upper shore remained dry.

On a visit here on New Year's morning 1960, when most of the toplands had been flooded and water was pouring back to sea eroding a new channel as it did so and the ebbing tide had retreated to the base of the three-foot high mud cliff at the lower edge of the toplands, on the higher ground a party of fishermen were mending their nets near the Lonetree, a landmark useful to fishermen from far out at sea. A saffron robe had been left on the ground by a party of East Indian women in bright cotton dresses who were along the jetty taking a baby to cast its hair and flowers upon the sea and ask blessings for it, for Kitty jetty was a favorourite spot for this 'mooran' ceremony performed when the child is about one year old. Despite the humans present, parties of little blue herons were feeding in the batis on the toplands, an area now alive with little white-clawed fiddler crabs (*Uca pugnax rapax*). Snowy egrets were the first to alight on the lower beach after the tide fell, paddling in the gently ebbing tide, picking their glistening yellow feet daintily clear of the water as they moved, their clean black legs and yellow feet matching their black and yellow beak which gleamed in the sun, their snowy plumes startlingly white against the brown-grey water, their crests and aegrette mantle plumes blown sideways by the wind. Soon they were joined by a few tricolor herons, but as the tide ebbed the snowies followed it seawards, continuing to paddle, whereas the tricolors snooped along the channels running out to sea among the mud hummocks. The blue herons remained on the toplands among the batis until the tide had retreated much farther, apart from an odd blue which landed with a harsh 'kakaka' on the mud.

The wading birds appeared too. A ringed plover arrived on the sandy beach at my feet, then six Hudsonian curlews (wimbrel), large waders with a very decurved and top-heavy beak compared with wimbrel seen in England, then several golden plover in winter dress. A small semipalmated sandpiper landed in a tuft of vivid green rushes. Further out to sea, mirrored in the silver-grey mud, small waders, knots and grey and golden plovers and other Hudsonian curlews were feeding.

On the toplands the water was clear in the pools where sheriger swimming crabs (*Callinectes bocourti*) were hunting, looking like personifications of evil, their flat bodies gliding over the bottom, paddled along by their green legs, their purple and yellow pincers claws held outstretched ahead of them, wide open, inert but ruthless, their antennae and mouth-parts vibrating rapidly, presumably sensing food. I saw them leap at small fish (*Poecilia vivipara*) and even at other sheriger. Here a large one seized the claw of a dead companion. I tried to photograph it but taking photographs through water is always tantalising, and having waited for the wind ripple to cease and sun to emerge, the horrid beast sank backwards into the mud at my feet. Little puffs of mud showed where it and several others had done so.

As the tide withdrew very gently, the fiddler crabs emerged. First the white-clawed species on the toplands where they fed and the many males beckoned with their one enlarged claw – as though to the sea to return, but in reality each to mark his territory round a burrow and persuade a female to visit him. Then the larger orange-clawed fiddler crabs (*Uca maracoani*) which live farther down the beach, where the freshwater has less effect, emerged, their claws washed by the sea a vivid orange against the brown mud, first appearing as periscope eyes pushing up through the mud.

The fiddler crab parades down the beach were spectacular. One October midmorning when the tide was dead low and the rich algal growth lifting off the bottom mud in the clear pools, buoyed up by the bubbles of oxygen produced by photosynthesis, on the hummocky mud many large fiddler crabs were beckoning with their orange claws; six or seven would be in the binocular field at once, all standing on the tips of their legs. But at the east side of the jetty a file of crabs followed the leader out from the shore to the mud seawards, 16–20 crabs in single file, all *U. maracoani* (there was no sign of white-clawed *U. pugnax* that day). Medium-sized males were in the lead, but sizes varied and females were moving too. Over the drying mud they went, splashing through the pools quickly, the vanguard now 20–30 yards farther out than the main mass along the shore. Some started to feed as they went, so at intervals the file was broken up, but more followed. Two other such streams were moving seawards 50 yards or so eastwards along the shore, the large ones in the van, moving fast without feeding. In the manner of all crabs they walked sideways, but large claw forward whether this be right or left claw, which meant that they faced into, or had their back to sun and wind depending on which claw was enlarged. All sizes, males and females, were moving, but the main enormous mass was concentrated along the shore. There was a good breeze and bright sun. The crabs scuttled or sank into the mud if the shadow of a flying egret or gull passed over them, and darted into the mud as a sandpiper moved towards them. Towards the end of the jetty they scattered feeding, females using both claws, the males only the small one. The trek continued for over an hour. Despite this dispersal the main concentration of crabs was still along the shore, some very large individuals were waving on the toplands bank, and others were crawling up from the shore to the toplands. There were many small ones, too, lower down the beach.

So many things happened as the tide ebbed. The barnacles attached to the jetty wall closed, one could hear them doing so, a gentle shushing if one passed a hand along the wall several inches in front of them after the tide had just gone. Click-shrimps (*Heterchelis*??) could also be heard in the pools by the jetty. One evening a rat appeared to catch fiddler crabs, knocking each down and biting off its large claw before carrying it into the upland vegetation and then returning for another crab. In the Demerara estuary racoons (*Procyon cancrivora*) would emerge from the mangroves to feed on crabs, but none were seen at Kitty. Sometimes we saw a black and yellow snake, two or three feet long, moving out over the mud or swimming in the pools of liquid mud, seemingly retreating from the crabs. One October evening after a commotion in a pool the snake emerged with a six inch goby across its mouth, which it proceeded to swallow, surprisingly tail first.

Black-winged skimmers (*Rynchops niger*) would skim along the channels near the jetty, always into or slightly across the wind, never downwind. As they passed one could see how the elongated lower beak was kept in the water and the upper one shut to meet it. They would work a channel, then fly back downwind and start to skim again upwind, their long wings held up above the body in a V, only the outer third vibrating, the lower two thirds kept more or less still. Sometimes flocks of 70 or more would be here. They disappeared from the coast just after the main rains when we would find them in the interior, nesting on the sandbanks of the Rupununi river after the annual floods had subsided, where they laid two or three large mottled eggs and skimmed the river uttering their harsh cries. Skimmers are said to have a unique kind of slit pupil associated with crepuscular skimming, but in Guyana they generally seemed to skim in daylight. On the mudflats they sat near the edge of the tide in large flocks, facing into the wind, tidy black and white birds with bright red bills, their short red legs set far back on their long bodies; they seemed to find taking off a problem, and would often run along the sand instead of taking off if approached. Coming in from the sea, swimming, one could get quite close to them, though they watched one warily. The young birds were dark brown rather than black and white.

On the flood tide one March day the foureye fish, *Anableps*, came swirling into view at midday, when the fiddler crab males were waving or digging holes and one could hear the crabs and the mud drying. As the tide came in quite fast up the channels the crabs disappeared into their holes, sliding into them sideways, the large claw always down first, whether left or right, and the stalked eyes neatly folded down. The tide poured into the pools over little three inch high waterfalls into the mud cracks; the tide raced in with the wind behind, in a circling movement covered with bubbles and froth. A few herons were still out on the mud, but the sandpipers were becoming very agitated, wheeling in flocks nearly touching the water. The noise of ripples replaced the noise of cracking mud. Wind ripples appeared on pools and sparkling little waves, the shadow of a tern swept by on the muddy flood and the sandpipers went into the courida bushes. Then the foureyes (here *Anableps microlepis*) arrived, swept inshore and grounded on the mud, showing their side stripes and using snake-like undulations to get off the mud again. Jetsam wood came too. Swirling gleaming eyes and bubbles were everywhere – more than 50 pairs of grey-green eyes in a shoal. A cast-netting fisherman appeared and caught several foureyes and sheriger swimming crabs now active with the tide. As the tide flooded the pools the foureyes flopped and slithered over into them from the top of the tide. The tide came racing in until the whole world seemed to be swirling water with slithering fish and excited waders and schools of foureyes were stranded on the mud. The crabs had now all disappeared into their holes, herons gone and the waders sat in courida bushes, perched like songbirds.

What happens on the shore at night? We went to Kitty jetty one moonlight night to see if the crabs were active, but they were not. Kitty was rather a haunt for loving couples at night (as well-described by Gerald Durrell in *Three Singles to Adventure*), which rather interfered with other zoology. On the last night of the year (1960) when we escaped from Georgetown to Beterverwachting beach the full moon had just risen over the sea. The tide was out and a breeze blowing in from the Atlantic shimmered and rippled the pools left behind in the small parallel wind ridges on the damp sand, the moon's path a broad shimmering sea of silver, its reflection calm and clear only in very sheltered pools. As the moon rose higher, the silver reflections became more intense, the damp patches shining with an almost phosphorescent light. The shush of waves far out below the moon, and the twittering cries of waders came to us on the wind. Nearer at hand a black silhouette showed where a sandpiper was feeding in a shallow pool, darting suddenly here and there in the moonlight, probably getting small shrimps left by the retreating tide. Behind us were land noises, the 'weet weet' of a frog in a trench, crickets and far-away cars along the coast road. As we climbed the sea wall the smell of driftwood, mostly coconut husks and pieces of sugar cane, came up to meet us. Upturned boats lay at the top of the tide, below one on drier sand sang a cricket. The shore here was now sandy, but the empty shells of oysters scrunched below our feet with a hollow sound. On the seaward side of the courida bushes the torch revealed 'jumbie' ghost crabs (*Ocypodus*) scurrying into the protection of the mass of aerial roots which grew up through the sand like a mat around each courida. Along the seaward side of the wall in a pool left by the retreating tide strange plops showed where young grey mullets swam, and bubble eyes crossing and scattering the round reflection of the moon, weaving patterns on the water surface, showed where foureyes were swimming. They were very light-shy and in the torchlight escaped like aeroplanes out of a searchlight beam, plop plop across the surface of the pool. A visitor had asked whether anyone had looked at them as incipient flying fish? So this nocturnal visit showed that the fiddler crabs are not active even on bright moonlight nights (though males had been seen waving till dusk at Kitty on other occasions when the moon was full), that foureyes are very light-shy and that night herons are out near the edge of the sea, their calls carrying far at night.

The seasonal changes here seemed to be bound up mainly with the winds and by the rains which had such an effect on the salinity of the sea in the neighbourhood of the large rivers. This effect was particularly marked on the west side of their inflows into the sea, for the tides and currents sweeping north-westwards along the coast carried the freshwater from the rivers west of the river mouths. Thus freshwater-loving fish such as the large *Brachyplatystoma* catfishes (laulau, kumakuma and manari) were caught on the flats west of the Demerara river when the freshwater discharge was high. Similarly catches in a shore seine just west of the Mahaica mouth in May, when the water here hardly tasted salt, included freshwater fish such as the cichlid congo patwa (*Cichlasoma bimaculatum*). This fish was very worried by the waves; when returned to the edge of the sea it kept getting rolled ashore by them – it just did not know about waves.

The bird populations on the foreshore underwent very marked seasonal changes as this coast is on a migration route for many of the waders. Even the resident birds varied greatly in abundance with time of year, the herons and skimmers being most in evidence on the Georgetown foreshore in the wetter months. This was when the herons nested in the nearby botanic gardens and were busy feeding young; the plentiful supply of food in the sea at this time meant that they did not have to go far to seek food. Where did they disappear to in the very dry months? Just before the main rains, when the numbers roosting in the botanic gardens at night and feeding on the foreshore dwindled markedly, and in the year that the Christmas rains failed (1958), the herons vanished from their usual haunts. The skimmers left the shore after the main rains, the time when they nested on river sandbanks in the Interior.

The calm weather in the rains allowed a rich growth of algae on the mud surface, probably the food source for young mullets and other fish. Another well-marked seasonal event was the appearance each July or August of enormous numbers of courida (*Avicennia*) mangrove seedlings along the tidelines. Already sprouting root and shoot from their green cotyledons, these would be rolled at the edge of the tide, which did not

250

seem to affect their viability, and were eaten by the brown and white goats which wandered on the shore.

We saw superseasonal changes here too. In March 1957 courida mangrove trees lined the shore on the eastern side of Kitty jetty, and behind these grew batis and tussock grass. These trees were all cut down in December 1957 in connection with spraying against 'sandfly' (really an annoying *Culicoides* midge) and mosquito control. After the trees were cut, though whether as a consequence or coincidentally was debated, the shore east of the jetty eroded away. High tides then washed farther and oftener over the toplands; here the batis spread, presumably as the water and ground became more brackish. The white-clawed fiddler crabs became increasingly active, riddling the toplands with their holes, which made it very friable and erodable by rain and high tides. The action of the crabs was, however, complex in its effects on the shoreline. Vide Graham, one of Guyana's best naturalists, reckoned that the burrowing crabs may help to build up a beach by raising mounds on which vegetation becomes established. But here the crabs seemed to be helping to break it down. The tides gradually cut back to shelly sand on the toplands. Below this sand reef a lagoon formed, haunted by hunting sheriger swimming crabs as well as by innumerable fiddler crabs. On the western side of the jetty, between this and the pier at the mouth of the Demerara river half a mile or more away, cordgrass (*Spartina brasiliensis*) extended further out to sea at this time and the beach appeared to be consolidating. At certain tides and lights waves of golden light rippled through the cordgrass as the pliant stems bent in rapid succession, each holding the water and captured sunlight as they lifted from the water after the passing of each wave. Waves of erosion and consolidation moved north-westwards along the coast. These were studied by a team from the Delft Hydrological Laboratory who found that there is a 30-year cycle for a stretch of shore to pass from eroded to built up and eroded again.

The 'sling mud' evidently protects the shore from erosion. When the mud moves away and sandy shelly banks are exposed, beware and prepare to guard the sea wall against breach. We saw a dramatic example of this when the mud was peeled off from the shore off Buxton in the strong January–March winds of 1957. It seemed incredible that the shore could change so much in such a short time. The sandy beach at Buxton was partly flung over the sea wall and partly spread to the west, where one could then walk along a sandy shore half a mile out to sea for some miles, where formerly there had been soft mud. At Buxton the outlines and patterns of old cane fields outside the present sea wall were revealed, with bits of roofing slate, blue Delft crockery and old Dutch gin bottles showing their age. Behind the sea wall fiddler crabs and other marine creatures moved in and the vegetation completely changed. The muka-muka arum formerly growing here was all killed. There is thus much interchange between land and sea and from brack to fresh or salt water with weather and other conditions prevailing in different years.

Fishing the Mudflats

Pinseines were used on the tidal mudflats, walls of netting six feet high and 2000 yards long which were hung on sticks in a slight curve on a gently sloping beach. These rely on the tide to bring fish inshore of the net walls; the fish are then stranded in the net as the tide recedes. At low tide the owners scoot out over the surface of the liquid mud on a so-called 'catamaran', really just a board balancing a box to hold the catch, propelled by kneeling on the board with one knee and pushing in the mud with the other leg. The net may be fished for a few tides, but then has to be lifted and moved as the tidal height varies from day to day. This was done from pinseine boats, flat-bottomed plank-built boats some 12 feet long, with a gaffrig sail, often made of old flour bags complete with some advertisement such as a charging bull and 'Mexican mills are best'. These boats were generally fitted with an outboard motor.

The Georgetown fish market figures suggested that a third of the fish marketed in 1960 came from pinseines. Catches were highest in the wet months, June to September, which are also the calm months, and again in December, though the sudden increase in December landings may have been partly due to the fishermen being spurred on by the thought of extra money for the Christmas spree. Although many of them were probably Hindu, rum consumption increased at this festive season. The pinseine catches were mainly of queriman grey mullets (*Mugil liza*),one of the most sought-after fishes caught by this method and which formed nearly 5% of the pinseine catches purchased by the fish market. But large catches of snook (*Centropomus* spp) and pagee (*Lobotes surinamensis*) were also sometimes caught, and in the rains the highly esteemed characoid morocut (*Colossoma brachypomus*) was caught in the north-west. One fisherman said he would fish ten tides a week making BG$ 4–5 a tide. When visiting the north-west after morocut these small boats would be away ten days or so. It cannot have been a very comfortable life for the fishermen living in these small open boats and fishing every tide day and night, but it could be lucrative. One successful fisherman, an East Indian, proud that he had been a fisherman all his life and had 'never worked one day for another man', now the father of seven children, had two sons in the UK reading medicine at Belfast University. One of them had married a German girl there, and the father was now saving up to go over to Europe to meet this new part of the family. Since he did not trust the crews that he could get he always went along with the pinseine boat, and to this he attributed his success. Fishermen in country districts could be spiteful; 'they say your best friend is your worst enemy' he concluded, telling me how someone had set fire to his BG$ 1000 seine net; soaked in tar it made a merry blaze and they never discovered who did it. In another case two fishermen sharing a pinseine decided to end their partnership by cutting the net in half and keeping half each. These cases seemed strange, for these fishermen were very cooperative and friendly to us, but it is a hard life.

It is significant that this fisherman had worked hard so that his children did not have to be fishermen. Here is active selection in operation against the most successful fishermen passing on their knowledge to their sons. Only those who cannot do better stay in fishing, and so it is largely a hit or miss business. No proper study had then been made of the species caught in the pinseines and the conditions under which the best catches could be made. How did the pinseine come to Guyana? The nearest I got to finding out was to meet a fisherman who had an 'aunt-in-law who was the fastest net knitter there ever was, and daughter of Magobeer who introduced the pinseine to BG', he thought from Surinam. 'She could knit five to six fathoms a day and a slow knitter might take two days to do one fathom'. Who was this Magobeer?

Une Affaire de Boue

I always rather envied the boys scooting over the mud surface on their catamaran boards; it looked as though it would give a lovely sensation of flying along, with showers of mud each side. So when a visiting French fishery officer colleague wanted to visit the pinseines in operation it was not difficult to be persuaded to go as 'interpreter'. The correct dress required careful consideration; I eventually elected for my oldest paint-strewn slacks rescued from the rag bag for the occasion, with a plastic raincoat as it was raining and seemed so cold, over a bathing costume, with a cotton skirt to cover the worst for the return trip along the coast in the car. Mon cher colleague selected a vivid yellow oilskin. A kind East Indian fisherman was taking us out to his father's pinseine. The heavens opened, but as he so rightly said, we would get wet anyway. So off we set. Both m.c. colleague (200 + pounds) and myself (no chicken) perched on one catamaran pushed by the fisherman balanced on the rear end the board. Pushing along was no mean feat, m.c.c. perched on the box, enormous in his oilskin, and myself on the prow in front of the box, where I was soon sitting in, and travelling backwards through, three inches of soft mud. As we struck a wetter patch we submerged into the, luckily, warm water until I was sitting in the sea. The cold raindrops ran like quicksilver on the surface of the warmer water. But we got to the net where we were joined by four or five East Indian youngsters scooting fast on their boards and regarding our visit as a huge joke. I was trying to take photographs, despite rain and mud from hair to toes, dripping from eyelashes and nowhere to wipe one's hands clean, as that usually convenient place the seat of one's pants was definitely the worst of the lot. Three cadell (longline) fishing boats sailed in right over the net while we were there, their reflections in the liquid mud below them. The boys let the net down and the boats, powered only by their flour-bag sails, went right over the net without stalling, further evidence of how liquid the mud was, and how flat the bottoms of the boats. These boats were travelling right on the mud, as no water remained now that the tide had ebbed. Sometimes they stuck in the mud, their reflections below them, but soon blew free again. My excruciating French did not improve in translating under these circumstances, but the fish were extracted from the net by plunging hands into the mud. Borrowing a board from one of the boys, I tried out a little mud scoot on my own, '*C'est une bonne attraction pour les touristes*', and raced by the boys on other boards with encouraging whoops of delight we set off for home, this time on separate boards and with chattering teeth, across mud pocked with rain, while five brown pelicans sailed with majestic ease overhead.

The catch was a poor one, mainly flounders. The boys had great fun helping to splash the fish, and us, clean with freshwater emerging from a koka, water surprisingly much warmer than the sea. Alas I had forgotten to bring a spare shirt, so attired in a cotton skirt over a very wet bathing costume and plastic raincoat we made for Georgetown. Here I had to deliver m.c. colleague (who had managed to change into respectable dry clothes) to a French luncheon party given in his honour in a Georgetown home. We were already late so went straight there 'Come in' said our kind hosts, 'we are expecting you too.' 'But I cannot take my raincoat off,' was the weak reply. 'Never mind, my wife will lend you a blouse.' And it was a splendid lunch, complete with sherry, wine and most welcome hot soup, the conversation all in French. I managed to sit on a non-wettable chair, for by now the bathing costume was most definitely seeping through. So perhaps I could always go to special luncheons dressed like this? Postscript: my subsequent Christmas present from the brother of my host was a folding clothes brush, a special brand labelled 'suitable for clothes or hair'.

12

At Sea: Food Fishes and the Trawl Survey

Georgetown had three large municipal markets, huge covered halls jammed with stalls carrying all manner of things. There were special sections for meat, for vegetables, for fruit, for fish. Other booths were festooned with brightly coloured lengths of cloth, combs and mirrors, others with baskets of every kind, hurricane lamps and bicycle parts. Behind the stalls the vendors, men and women, generally of Afro or Indian origin, clamoured for custom: 'Wot you want darlin'?' Outside the market the pavements were gay with piles of fruit laid out on the ground, each in an area about six feet long presided over by a vendor. Oranges and grapefruit, pineapples and, in season, mangoes, passion fruit, red peppers, pawpaws, small tomatoes, beans and eggs, large purple brinjal eggplants, warty green soursops and many others. Piles of coconuts were presided over by a vendor with a large cutlass who opened them for the liquid refreshment of shoppers, for the sun and dust made marketing thirsty work. The side roads round the market were thronged with people, greeting and calling to one another, arguing vociferously but on the whole goodnaturedly, an unbelievable number of Georgetown's 70,000 bicycles, and carts pulled by small donkeys or larger mules. Donkeys, hitched to fence posts, braying at intervals added to the general clamour.

To get to the fish section of the Bourda market, which was nearest our home, one threaded one's way through the colourful crowds and piles of fruit, and past barrels of live crabs, a dozen or so tied together on a string. Most of the year these were locally caught buck crabs (*Ucides cordatus*), always

257

in great demand for 'crab-backs' are a Guyanese speciality. But about August when the great crab marches were on in the north-west, the larger purplish bunduri crab (*Cardisoma guanhumi*) was brought into Georgetown markets. Enormous numbers of these evidently undertake a mass movement to the sea at this time of year but this to my great regret I never managed to see. The fish section inside the market consisted of four or five rows of stalls covered with piles of fish, most, like the fruit, divided into 'parcels' of four or five fish for some suitable coin such as 25 cents (about a shilling – and English shillings could be used instead). The different stalls tended to specialise in fishes from different sources. Several stalls would be covered with red snapper (*Lutjanus aya*), bright red fish one to two feet long with cold glassy eyes, the fish which commanded the highest prices, with an occasional very large brown and spotted grouper being cut up into steaks, and sometimes a mariner's dolphin (*Coryphaena hippurus*), a colourful fish (not the mammal dolphin) some three feet long, the dorsal fin running like a mane along its back. These all came from the snapper schooner catches, caught on hooks on handlines fished near the edge of the continental shelf from small schooners which were generally away for about two weeks.

Other stalls would be piled with silvery grey mullets, the largest known locally as queriman (*Mugil brasiliensis*), a round-bodied fish some 18 inches long, with large scales and a streamlined clear spectacle over the eye. These were the next most popular fish. They came from the pinseine stake nets set on the tidal mudflats and were caught together with two other smaller species of mullet and large numbers of silvery grey sciaenids, particularly those known in the market as grey snapper (*Cynoscion acoupa*), table bashaw (*Cynoscion jamaicensis*), bangamaree (*Macrodon ancylodon*), and sometimes numbers of the small-eyed golden sciaenid the highly prized butterfish (*Nebris microps*) and the golden croaker (*Micropogon furnieri*) so common in trawl catches. Some very large fish were sometimes caught in these pinseines – five-foot long tarpon (*Megalops atlanticus*), that splendid silver leaper also known as a sport fish and which could be seen leaping from the surface of the coastal rivers of BG at certain times of year, also *Centropomus* species, here called snook, but very different from the South African snoek known in Britain during the war. Large pargee (*Lobotes surinamensis*), a very deep bodied laterally flattened fish, its size increased by the almost continuous dorsal, caudal and anal fins round the body, were sometimes caught in pinseines too; their juveniles look, and behave, like drifting leaves, a good disguise in the mangrove swamps where the young live. Another fish in a family of its own also caught in pinseines in numbers at certain times of year was the cobia *Rachycentron canadus*, here called 'cod', a black fish two or three feet long. Not much is known about the biology of this species, but the large catches inshore in the rains (June, July) suggested that this movement might be connected with breeding or feeding. Sometimes large jewfish, related to the grouper, were stranded in the pinseines. Smaller fish in these nets included the sea patwa moharra (*Diapterus rhombus*), a silvery deep-bodied fish some six inches long with wickedly sharp spines. As already mentioned 'patwa' is also used for the freshwater cichlids which also have strong sharp spines. Sometimes silver herrings, *Pellona*, appeared on these stalls and grunts of two species both included under the common name 'annafolk'. The confusion of these two not very similar species under one common name was surprising, for on the whole, the BG fishermen were very observant and had distinct names for most of the fish, including species which to my eye were very much less distinct than these two. Perhaps it is something to do with what the name originally meant – that annafolk is used as a kind of generic group name. Why bashaw or basher for all the *Cynoscion* and related scianids? Distinguished by adjectives such as rockhead bashaw (*Larimus breviceps* and *Stellifer* spp), guppy bashaw (*Plagioscion* spp). Renaming *Cynoscion virescens* 'seatrout' to enhance its market value parallels the story of the Amerindians forbidden by some missionaries to eat the much-liked labba, a rodent without a cloven hoof, caught baptising one to change its name into that of a food approved by their spiritual advisers.

259

The fish folklore of Guyana would make a fascinating study for it draws elements from so many parts of the world. Indigenous Amerindian names often include that useful word balli, meaning bastard, for something which is very like but just not quite something else, also found in plant names such as in mora (*Mora excelsa*) and moraballi. Besides different Amerindian names, names and terms were also brought from Africa (e.g. the congo patwa) and from India, from Madeira (the longline terms like skillick line are said to have come with the Portuguese immigrants) and from England. Names from Indonesia, too, may have seeped along the coast from the large Indonesian element in nextdoor Surinam, and Spanish names from Venezuela to the west, Dutch and French from Guianas to the east, while Portuguese names from Brazil were widely used in the Rupununi.

The pinseine grounds on the tidal mudflats and the red snapper grounds at the edge of the continental shelf were widely separated. The area in between was not fished at all until the introduction of trawling in 1957, when a two-year survey was initiated by the RV *Cape St Mary* financed out of Colonial Development and Welfare funds from the United Kingdom. The gently sloping shelf is here some 60 to 80 miles wide and along the 230-mile coastline of Guyana 16,000 square miles of potential trawling ground were to be explored. The only trawling done previously off BG was experimental hauls from much smaller craft which made their trials in inshore waters.

The RV *Cape St Mary* survey aimed to discover which parts of the shelf were good trawling ground and what kinds of fish could be caught in the trawl, which is fundamentally a large bag pulled along the sea bottom, how numerous the fishes were, and whether they could be caught all year round. Since trawling involves sinking a good deal of capital into a fishery, it was necessary to find out how large a fishery the stocks could support. This entailed finding out about the movements of the fish, how often they spawn and how fast they grow to replenish the stocks.

The RV *Cape St Mary* 100 feet long, 238 gross tons and

capable of ten knots, was originally designed and built for fisheries research off West Africa. When the various West African territories on the approach of independence no longer wished to contribute to an interterritorial research service, the *Cape St Mary* was offered to BG for two years. So she came to BG, complete with two West African crew members who stayed with her throughout the BG survey, one of whom married in BG and wanted to stay there indefinitely. In West Africa the ship had been attached to the West African Fisheries Research Institute, where she had four scientists working with her: a fish biologist, one to study the bottom fauna on which the fish fed, another to study the plankton, and a chemist to study the water chemistry which might determine the movements of the fish. Unfortunately the ship had spent much time out of action. Ironically, when she came to BG she behaved very well on the whole and spent little time in dock, but because BG was 'too poor' to afford it, the survey was carried out without any scientist attached to it in a full-time capacity. The local fishery officers were supposed to keep an eye on it, but were busy with other projects. The survey off Guyana was, in fact, only possible because the ship had a skipper of unusual experience in fishery surveys carried out in many parts of the world. He had taken part in Russia's first five-year plan, for at the time of the depression in England he had left his home in Lowestoft and conducted a herring survey in the Caspian Sea; he also knew tropical waters well, having skippered surveys off Ceylon and West Africa. The Fisheries Adviser to the Colonial Office, Dr C.F. Hickling, who came to BG to initiate the survey, went on the first trip, drew up plans for subsequent fishing and determined what records should be kept.

During the two-year period 35 cruises were made, each between four and eleven days long. Some 37,000 miles were traversed, fishing 12,070 stations, each station comprising one drag of the standard Peter Carey trawl used thoughout. Each haul was generally of two hours' duration, and as night fishing was not productive the usual procedure was to make five two-hour drags during daylight hours and then anchor for the

261

night. When fishing proved good a dhan marker buoy was put over the side and fishing continued in the area until catches started to decline before moving to another area. In the event, fishing was not evenly distributed throughout the whole shelf as far less was done on the hard bottom near the shelf edge which was strewn with old coral blocks which inevitably damaged the trawl.

In the hope that a full time scientist would be appointed I had kept clear of the survey in its first year, but when no such scientist had materialised the skipper asked me to help out, as the records they were collecting meant nothing if they were not interpreted, nor could they understand the fish movements until they knew what species were present, what food they were eating and when they were spawning, So I became biologist to the trawl survey. We then had to salvage what we could.

Skipper Bill, W.G. Mitchell, a white-haired fatherly figure with benign countenance but in firm control of affairs, was a Lowestoft man. He and the Chief Mate, Owen a Welshman, and the Chief Engineer, Frank from the north of England, who read classical books when off duty, had all been with the ship in West Africa, so were able to compare fishing on the two sides of the tropical Atlantic. The rest of the officers and crew were Guyanese recruited locally, apart from James and Amaduthe, the two West African greasers who had come with the ship from West Africa. Suleman the Second Engineer was a Guyanese of East Indian descent, shy and polite, crooking his little finger as he helped himself to pepper sauce at table with the tip of his spoon; the Trainee Mate and the Boatswain were Afro-Guyanese, and Wong my assistant was Guyanese of Chinese origin, straight from school, so we were a mixed gang, but all seemed to get on well together.

It soon became clear that the best trawling grounds were the sandy mud areas, out to about 40 metres in the south-east and 60 in the north-west, where sciaenid fishes predominated in the catches. Since the shelf sloped more steeply in the north-west, these limits were both at about 40 miles from the coast. Beyond this only small, generally very spiny and often red, species were caught and the ground became increasingly dangerous for the trawl, great lumps of coral, huge masses of sponge and sea fans coming up in the trawl and tearing the bag. Where the bottom was clean sand catches were also very poor, perhaps just a few flatfish – though from the green waters over such sand patches some pelagic fish were sometimes caught in large numbers, taken when the trawl was on its way up or down. These included various types of herring, shoals of small barracuda and Spanish mackerel (*Scomberomorus* species), with occasional catches of large numbers of latterally-flattened moonfish (*Vomer setapinnis*) or pomfret (*Peprilus paru*). All these fishes were silvery in colour.

The draught of the *Cape St Mary* precluded fishing in waters less than about 16 metres deep. The ketch *Arthur Rogers* had done much of her experimental fishing in about ten metres. These shallower waters were very muddy with shifting banks of sling mud moving north-west along the coast, horrible stuff to catch in the trawl as all the fish had then to be washed to rid them of the mud filling their mouths and gill cavities, which led to rapid spoilage. When there was a strong onshore wind, as was only too common in January to March when the north-east trade wind was blowing, this stirred up the coastal mud and many species of fish moved out from the coast and were only caught in the trawl under these conditions. These included, for example, the sciaenid Chinese butterfish (*Lonchurus lanceolatus*), many small *Arius* catfish, small stingrays (*Urotrygon*) and electric rays (*Narcine brasiliensis*), together with immature fish of species caught further offshore when adult – such as the young of many sciaenids and grunts (Pomadasyidae). These muddy areas appeared to be 'nursery grounds' for many of the commercial species. The catfish were a great nuisance as their spines became entangled in the net, which caused considerable delay in disentangling them before the trawl could be reset. So the catfish helped to protect the nursery grounds of more important commercial species. The electric rays provided incidents whenever some poor member of the crew shovelling the 'trash' overboard with metal spade got a good shock – to the great amusement of his companions.

We found that there were basically four fish zones, a 'brown' fish zone out to about 16–20 metres, with many small catfish and rays, mostly dark brown in colour, living in opaque brown water over soft mud. Then a 'golden' fish zone, populated mainly by sciaenids living over harder sandier mud, the main trawl zone. Here the golden croaker (*Micropogon furnieri*) made up over 40% by weight of all the fish caught during the survey, bangamaree (*Macrodon ancylodon*) 18% and the 'seatrout' (*Cynoscion virescens*) 11% of the weight of fish. Together with other sciaenid species, the sciaenid contribution was about 75% of the total weight of fish landed during the whole two-year survey. In this zone some grunts were also important, and at certain times some of the fishes generally caught in the brown and silver fish zones, for there was some interchange between the zones with weather conditions. Further out the 'silver' fish zone catch included more pelagic species, barracuda and Spanish mackerel. The 'red' fish zone was over harder coral and sand in water deeper than 16 metres, where lived many fish common in the clear blue water around the coral islands in the West Indies to the north.

As we moved out from the coast the bottom deposits became increasingly hard, the water changed from muddy brown to a green band of nutrient-rich water off the rivers' mouths in the rains when much freshwater was pouring out to sea (clearly visible from the air when flying over the mouths of the Orinoco), then to the clear sparkling blue of the Atlantic ocean. Despite very sharp interfaces, rapid changes in water types could occur at any one place. We saw a beautiful example of this in February when fishing round a fixed dhan buoy in the north-west in about 40 metres. We were fishing in light green water until 1 pm, when a mass of brown water, separated from the green by a sharp interface, swept by us on the tide travelling north-west past the fixed buoy; the water here remained brown for a day and a half, then became green again during the night. As the interface swept past the ship we saw what a busy place it was, flotsam from the rivers and sea accumulated on the drift lines, with innumerable Portuguese-men-of-war, large colonial coelenterate colonies suspended from the surface by their purple floats, which were very abundant at this time of year; Mother Carey's chicken storm petrels followed the line of drift and frigate birds flew high overhead. The skipper maintained that sharks haunted these tidal contours too.

Alas that we did not have a hydrologist or water chemist to study these water changes. When fishing off West Africa it had been found that the thermocline temperature discontinuity layer had a profound effect on the fish communities. Off Guyana we found well-marked seasonal movements among the trawl-caught fishes. The fish tended to move inshore into shallower water and into the estuaries in June to August when the rivers were in flood and the weather relatively calm, and at that time trawl catches were poor in the north-west and good in the south-east. Conversely the fish tended to move into deeper water during strong offshore winds, as in January to March, and catches were then best in the north-west.

What was it really like working at sea here? The Skipper summed up by saying that it was about the easiest trawling that he had ever experienced. Even the wrecks charted in the area gave very little trouble, it seemed that the soft sling mud and sand pushed by the strong tides and currents had smoothed out the bottom over such wrecks, and only once was the trawl fouled by one. The days were very full, from 5 am when the rattle and clank of gear announced that the first trawl of the day was being shot, until long after dark when we were still busy examining specimens, cutting open fish to see what they had been eating, and at what size they started to breed, and whether they were going to spawn at that time of year. Vast mugs of tea were consumed throughout the day, and there were brief meals, eaten with anyone who happened to be off duty and in the mess at the time, the opportunity to try new kinds of fish and invertebrates – cuttlefish or squat lobsters – all fresh from the sea.

Every haul was an excitment, for we never knew what would come up in the net. The trawl bag would be swung inboard, the cod end untied ... 'come on, get savage with it' ... and onto the deck with a great slither and slide would spill a streaming mass of croaking, grunting, flapping fish, all gleaming from the sea, gold and silver, iridescent sea treasure, the croakers keeping up a continuous purr for several minutes. But the lovely colours faded so rapidly. The sharks and barracudas were generally dead when emptied from the trawl, and the silver on the long ribbon-like bodies of the very common cutlass fish hairtails (*Trichiurus lepturus*) rubbed off like anti-fouling paint onto other fish, perhaps a nature-did-it-first device to keep these fish free from parasites? The sea catfishes came in very much alive, formidable spines jerking up and down and mouths opening and closing. Odd puffer fish (*Colomesus*) stayed alive a long time, as did the curious batfish (Ogocephalidae), with an opalescent blue-green fire in their eyes. The stingrays, very much alive and lashing their formidable and highly dangerous barbed tail spines, were flung overboard immediately before they could do any damage to the crew sorting the fish.

The trawl would be shot again immediately, and then the catch was sorted and stored in ice boxes in the hold, and the trash, which often included some of the most interesting specimens unless these could be rescued in time, was pushed overboard. Only the larger fish were gutted, the sea trout, Spanish mackerel, barracuda and any sharks, which provided an opportunity to see what these were feeding on and their breeding condition. The waxy swimbladders of sea trout were taken out to be dried, for these were exported as raw material for making isinglas, used in clearing beer or wine.

Meanwhile Wong and I selected any specimens we wanted to examine in detail. We were building up a reference collection of fishes from this area, and had nearly 200 species representing 70 fish families; some of the species were new to science. We also measured enormous numbers of the common species for growth studies, and examined the gonad states and stomachs of large numbers. We had a good little laboratory on deck, where we took the specimens for further study and preservation in milkchurns of 5% formalin. The state of our hands after a few weeks at this game, handling spiny fish on a heaving ship and plunging them into formalin, does not bear remembering. We had rubber gloves of course, but such was the spinyness of the fish that these soon pierced the gloves, the formalin got inside and this was worse than no gloves at all. At intervals the cook or some other member of the crew would poke his head into the laboratory to see what was happening and pass comments on the fish. It was all very friendly. It could, however, be pretty rough when the north-east trades had been blowing for some days and the sea had a good lop, and she was not a comfortable ship under these conditions. Even the Chief was regularly seasick. The laboratory had a very useful toehold under the work bench, by which one could anchor and steady oneself while trying to insert scissors into fish under these conditions, an operation requiring the use of both hands. Luckily we were south of the hurricane belt, so these were not threats. There was a comfortable two-berth cabin for the scientists, but on calm nights I often used to creep up and sleep on top of the wheelhouse, lashing my sleeping bag to the ship in case the wind blew up in the night and rolled me into the sea. It was so lovely up there on moonlit nights, the mast swinging under the Southern Cross, a huge orange moon rising from the sea, the moon higher and silver with a gleaming path of light, dead overhead and now mysteriously much smaller. Occasionally we trawled at night, generally when running out into deeper water.

Sharks haunted the interfaces and tore fish from the trawl as we brought the net alongside the ship when fishing some areas. Clean, swift forms, brown some with black fin tips, weaving through the green water, sometimes lifted in a wave and momentarily set as in alabaster with the sunlight glowing through the green wave – creatures of great beauty although so destructive. They came in packs of seven or eight at a time, and when they arrived the fish left the area and we had to move a mile or so before we had good catches again, then the sharks, attracted by the smell of the fish in the trawl – and what a smell it must be with all those different fishes jammed together – found us again. Sometimes the men hooked them from the ship, and it often required two men to drag one aboard, so powerful were their bodies, clean lines arching violently in the sun. I never liked to see them destroyed and degenerating so quickly into a lump of dead flesh on the deck. The marvel was, however, when they contained young, for they were ovoviviparous. There was something about unborn sharks to stir the roughest hearts to thoughts on 'being born a shark'. So clean and innocent they looked, perfect in every detail, like all unborn fish from inside the parent's body, unsullied by the world, guts free from food apart from yolk absorbed in the later stages of internal development, free from parasites, the skin scarless. In the small black-tipped sharks (*Carcharinus*) there were generally about four young, yolk sacs attached to their bellies. Baby bonnet sharks (*Sphyrna tiburo*) and hammerheads were charming, but perhaps the most delightful were young sawfish. One female *Pristis*, over nine feet long, contained 11 little ones, each about 16 inches long with a yolk sac containing a pint of batter-like yolk attached to its belly; each was complete including the saw, except that its small saw was in a sheath, so avoiding damage to the mother. Baby stingrays (*Dasyatis say*) like the young dogfish (*Mustelus highmani*, a new species) were born tail first, the rays sliding into the world with their wing-like pectoral fins folded over their backs, rolled round the body. Young butterfly rays (*Pteroplatea*) not yet ready to be born had a curious spiracular structure into which long filaments from the parent with a deep-red rich blood supply penetrated. In February many dogfish and rays were born on deck as the catch came in. These included large numbers of a small ray *Urotrygon microphthalmus*, previously known scientifically from only one specimen, a male from the Amazon delta; they generally had four young at a time, two in each of the paired oviduct sacs, often though not always two males and two females. The young could swim as soon as they were born, even if premature.

We occasionally saw manta rays around the ship and one February day caught one in the trawl. Ten feet wide from 'wingtip' to 'wingtip', this was a male *Mobula* whose stomach contained half a bucketful of small white shrimps, with two small jelly fish and one cutlass hairtail fish (*Trichiurus*). From the manta ray fell two albino sucker fish (*Remora albescens*) with wrinkled skins, both seven inches long, one male and one female, pigmentless except for the eye with its yellow iris and black pupil. This species lives in the gill cavities of manta rays and its dorsal fin is modified as a sucker for hanging onto its host. These two produced faecal pellets of shrimp remains and they were kept alive by feeding them on bits of shrimp. They lived, and fed, attached to the bottom or sides of an enamel basin, upside down or sideways on apparently indifferently, staying in the same position for hours on end. When the water was changed they would make a flying leap at the side of the bowl and hang on with the dorsal sucker immediately on contact, and often remained above the water for considerable periods. The short ventral pelvic fins, with their stout but well-padded spiny skeleton, were extended ventrally, suddenly and with great force if the ventral surface of the fish was touched, an adaptation which would ensure that the fish was not crushed by its host. After this trip I was persuaded to produce one of my pets at a drinks party, where it distinguished itself by leaping from my grasp and catching onto the arm of the nearest lady as it fell. It attached itself most successfully, but she was not amused. Do they catch leaping manta rays in this way? Work has been done on the intriguing problem of how male and female remora get into the same host, and it seems they probably get there as very young fish.

Since 75% of the trawl catch was of sciaenids, special studies were made of this family. Sciaenids are found in shallow seas of tropical and temperate zones throughout the world; many of them, such as the croakers and weakfish, are highly prized as food. Many species have complicated swim bladders used in producing loud sounds; some such as the croakers have special drumming muscles. We found 22 species in Guyana, of which 20 were taken in the trawl. One (*Cynoscion steindachneri*) was found mainly in brackish swamps and grew well in brackish ponds, and one (*Pachypops fourcroi*) was seen only in freshwater, far inland in the Rupununi district. Some ran up estuaries into freshwater, such as *Plagioscion*, being taken both in the trawl and in the rivers. Their food habits were diverse. The stomachs of the very common croaker (*Micropogon*

269

furnieri) and less common bastard croaker (*Paralonchurus*) both contained polychaete worms from the mud. *Menticirrhus* (a species without a swim bladder) lived on crustacea and sand eels from harder bottoms, *Larimus breviceps* with its upturned mouth and the laterally compressed *Isopisthus*, both contained small planktonic shrimps. Many species, including bangamaree and sea trout fed on penaeid shrimps, mantis shrimps and fish, overlapping in their food habits and sharing the same sources of food. The larger sciaenids ate smaller sciaenids; croaker and bangamaree were quite often found in sea trout stomachs, and the smaller *Stellifer* species, known as rockhead bashaw, provided a plentiful food supply for the large ones.

These predatory sciaenids which generally live in rather opaque muddy water, all swallow their prey whole, head first, which made it easy to identify the prey. But many of the clearer-water dwellers such as the barracuda and Spanish mackerel chop their prey into pieces before swallowing it, and sometimes several fishes in a school will contain bits of the same prey fish. The red snapper, which generally contained small fishes and invertebrates, chews its prey and it was often difficult to identify the mangled stomach contents. The size of the fish that a sea trout could swallow was amazing. On one occasion when they had taken to eating cutlass fish (*Trichiurus*) – for sea trout seemed to have crazes for types of food at different times, sometimes all being packed with shrimps, at other times fish – one sea trout stomach contained two cutlass fish 45 and 50 cm long, swallowed whole and each nearly as long as the swallower. Another 49-cm sea trout had a 45-cm cutlass fish curled in its stomach. However did they manage to get them in? Another large *Cynoscion*, *C. leiarchus*, contained many herrings, indicating that this is a more pelagic species, and its very silver colour and general shape backed this up.

Most of the sea trout and bangamaree taken in the trawl had quiescent gonads so it was hard to find out about breeding seasons. The only ripe fish were taken in very inshore catches, suggesting that ripe fish move inshore, so are not often caught in the trawl. The basket-toothed juveniles of bangamaree were common in the estuaries, where they were caught in the

Chinese bag seines used to catch shrimps; the only young sea trout were from the mouth of the Demerara river. Among the croaker on the other hand, ripe fish were taken in the trawl in every month of the year, indicating that their breeding is not seasonal. This was supported by the capture of young croakers entering brackish waters at Onverwagt in every month of the year. Ripe fish were taken at many different times of year in some other species, such as the table bashaws and non-sciaenids including moharra (*Diapterus rhombeus*) the grunts (*Genyatremus luteus* and *Conodon nobilis*) and carangid moon fish (*Vomer setapinnis*). This absence of defined breeding seasons is in marked contrast with the situation in temperate waters and means that small fish enter the catchable stock at all times of year. This also meant that it was very difficult to determine growth rates from progressions of length frequency modes. Croakers (*Micropogon*) grown in brackish ponds at Onverwagt grew to about 12 inches long and 14 ounces in weight in 12–16 months but did not mature. In the sea they matured when ten inches long and half this weight, but conditions for growth were very different in the two environments. Also, the croakers in the sea were always crowded with a stage of a platyhelminth parasitic worm in the gut mesentary, and these never occurred in the pond fish. Nevertheless, the pond rate did suggest that croakers in the sea probably mature within one year.

The trawl also brought up many exciting invertebrates, many of them of great rarity and interest to specialists in their particular fields. Sadly most of these were just pushed overboard with the trash. When we were at sea we tried to keep representative collections, but there was not much time for this. Vide Graham, an excellent naturalist and artist who was teaching biology in Georgetown, came with us on one trip to help collect them and record their colours while still alive. In the golden fish zone, brown rhizostome jellyfish (*Stomolophis meleagra*) were often very abundant, and could be seen pulsating by the ship, often seeming to travel against the current. On very soft mud, grey five-armed starfish (*Astropecten*) were brought up in thousands if the trawl dug into the

271

soft mud, together with polychaete tubes, sipunculids and sea pansies, and the curious 'purple-heart-shaped' sea pen *Renilla*. On the harder sandy mud, the best trawling ground, basket stars (*Astrophyton muricatum*) were abundant, also *Luida* starfishes and feather stars (crinoids) *Tropiometra carinata*. Multicoloured string-like hydroids came from the interface of mud and sand. Species of penaeid shrimp were common, but the trawl we used with its 2½ inch mesh cod-end did not retain many shrimps. The shrimp trawlers which came here from the USA later and fished mostly on the harder shellier bottoms off Surinam, for penaeids which were frozen and exported to the USA, used smaller-meshed trawls.

Hauls in the deeper water produced a wonderful array of brightly coloured invertebrates, corals and yellow sponges, sea fans (*Gorgonia*), sea pens (pennatulids), squat lobsters (*Syllarides aequinoctalis*) like minature armoured vehicles, and many kind of crabs with legs of brilliant hues – blue, violet, red – swimming crabs, neat box crabs (*Calappa*), spider crabs, also many brittle stars (ophiuroids), starfishes, some holothurians and molluscs. The fishes from the deeper waters were mostly small and spiny and not very edible – apart from lutjanid red snappers which were only once caught in any numbers; they included curious batfish (ogcocephalids) of at least four species, trunk fishes, porcupine and puffer fish, file fishes with elongated pectoral flaps, trigger fish, surgeon fish, flying gurnards, scorpaenids of half a dozen species, a few chaetodontid butterfly fish and occasional tile fish. They were all shapes and sizes and colours. This fish fauna was very reminiscent of that round the West Indian coral islands (many species seen swimming happily alive later when snorkelling off Tobago), though wrasses and parrot fishes were only represented by about two species of each, probably because the coral at this depth was dead, remnants from the approximately 100m lower sea level in the Ice Ages.

What happened to the *Cape St Mary* after the survey? She went to Hong Kong under her own power. This required quite some organisation. A surveyor flew from Hong Kong to examine her. Before he came he received a cable to say that she could not be slipped for at least two months, so he thought 'what busy yards BG must have, much busier than Hong Kong where they could have slipped her much sooner'. So are myths created. It was therefore a surprise to him to find on arrival in BG that the reason for the delay was one barge on the one slipway, and this was up the Mazaruni river, over a bar which the *Cape St Mary* could only cross at very high tides, about once a month. For the Guyanese crew who took her to Hong Kong, with a different skipper taken on for the delivery, this was a Big Adventure. They were only sorry that the authorities in a Hong Kong already crowded with immigrants took no chances and returned them to BG on the next plane before they had time to look around.

About this time we had been asked by the Royal Irrigation Department in Thailand to send them two manatees, one male, one female, and the possibility of shipping them to Asia in the *Cape St Mary* was discussed. What a formidable pile of lettuces it would take. But the project was abandoned when they said they were not taking any manatees.

So the *Cape St Mary* made Hong Kong and was refitted to enable her to carry out surveys in an area with typhoon dangers, and to carry several scientists. The next thing we heard was when they sent to BG for the insurance papers and we understood that she had exploded and gone to the bottom. Sad news. May her hull rest in peace, we said. But we later heard that this was not true, only another rumour.

13

Forty years on: subsequent research and environmental changes.

It took years to decipher the many notebooks and examine the collections brought back to the British Museum (Natural History) in London to prepare publications that others could then consult. I was very fortunate to be able do this in the BMNH Fish Section with its 'type' collections of fishes, excellent libraries, and colleagues with whom I had already worked on collections brought back from Africa. Visiting scientists also helped and some of the newly discovered fish species had to be sent to specialists in other museums to be described and named. As a BMNH 'Associate' – a scheme devised mainly for retired members of staff – I earned the princely sum of 7s 6d (about US $1) an hour – but this was a boost from my nominal salary in BG of $1 a year, incremental date April 1st ('April Fools' Day'), as at that time a marriage bar meant I had had to retire from the UK Overseas Research Service in 1953. Eventually papers were published in scientific journals, including ones on the trawl survey and fishes of the continental shelf (1962), the ecology of the Rupununi fishes (1964), Guyana's sciaenid and cichlid fishes (1966, 1969), the biology of the immigrant cattle egret (1967). Guyana observations were also aired at a British Ecological Society symposium on *Speciation in Tropical Environments* in 1969, and at the First International Congress of Ecology, on *Unifying Concepts in Ecology*, held in the Hague in 1974. Here discussions centred on categories of biodiversity, stability and maturity in communities, possible reasons for the great richness of tropical floras and faunas, and man's increasing influence on the environment.

The BM was an excellent base for visits to other parts of the world. From 1964–74 London was the HQ for the International Biological Programme, the main aim of which was to measure and understand the differences in rates of biological production in various parts of the world. The Scientific Coordinator was my old friend (and former Director) Barton Worthington, who had initiated many of the research organizations in Africa, and the delightfully eccentric distinguished Polish hydrobiologist, Julian Rzoska, was Coordinator of IBP's Freshwater Section. In 1968 Julian and I attended the IBP's Regional Meeting of Latin American Countries, held at the Santa Fé limnological laboratory on the Paraná River in Argentina. Here the life histories of the migrating fishes were being investigated, aided by tagging forty thousand fishes of 25 species. The most spectacular movements were of the characoid *Prochilodus platensis* moving 700 km upriver at speeds of up to 8.7 km a day, and of the salmon-like characoid *Salminus maxillosus* moving up and down river at comparable speeds and distances. A group of us were also involved in preparing an IBP handbook on *Methods for Assessing Fish Production in Freshwaters*, and eventually a 53-author tome summing up the IBP's work on *The Functioning of Freshwater Ecosystems*.

We met with many other biologists then working on the ecology of fishes in South American rivers. Amongst them Peter Bayley who was examining the abundances of young fishes in the Amazon and Miguel Petrere who was analysing the fish market statistics. Michael Goulding in a classic book on *The Fishes and the Forest* (1980) demonstrated the dependence of many Amazon fishes on foods from the flooded forests. He also studied the spectacular long-range migrations of the large catfishes, some species of which evidently travel from the Amazon estuary over 2000 km (1200 miles) upriver to spawn, the young then drifting downstream to estuarine waters. Angelo Agostinho and his students concentrated on the ecology of the fishes in the huge reservoirs created behind the new hydroelectric dams of the Paraná system.

276

Man-made lake studies were then very fashionable as hydro-electric schemes in many parts of the world were impounding large rivers, providing great opportunities both to investigate how riverine fish faunas become changed to lacustrine ones, and on how to develop fisheries in these new lakes to provide protein for the burgeoning human populations. In Africa the Zambezi River had been dammed forming Lake Kariba, the huge Volta lake had been created in Ghana and the Nasser-Nubia lake on the Nile in Egypt. South America aquired a large man-made lake in Surinam at Brokopondo. In Brazil the many large man-made lakes included the Sobradinho Reservoir on the São Francisco, the Tucurui on the Tocantins, and a whole series of lakes behind barrages on the Paraná River. In Venezuela the Guri reservoir was created on an Orinoco tributary, and in French Guiana a reservoir on the Sinnimary River. These all stimulated ecological studies of riverine fishes. But in Guyana plans for a large dam in the Upper Mazaruni, which would have meant displacing some 4500 people in 14 Amerindian river settlements, were discarded when finance from the World Bank was not forthcoming.

In 1968 I returned to South America for two very happy months in camp collecting fishes in the headwater streams of the Xingu and Araguaia tributaries of the Amazon, finding some species I had known in BG and others new to science. This was as a member of the Royal Society/Royal Geographical Society's Anglo-Brazilian expedition to the Mato Grosso in central Brazil. Designed as a study of the environmental effects of the long-distance roads then being created through the rainforest and Xingu reserve, this two-year expedition involved over 40 scientists in many disciplines – soil scientists and forest botanists as well as many zoologists. The ecology of Maracá Island in a tributary of the Tacutu River north of Boa Vista, on the same latitude but west of the Rupununi District, was later surveyed by another long RS/RGS/Brazilian expedition, (as described by Hemming & Ratter, 1993).

In 1977 after a Tropical Ecology Symposium in Panama I visited the Smithsonian Institution's laboratory on Barra

Colorado Island in the Panama Canal, where Tom Zaret was studying the effects of the introduced piscivorous lukanani (my old friend *Cichla ocellaris*). Introduced to a tributary stream as a sport fish, this had descended to the lake, where it multiplied, decimating the local fish fauna and affecting the whole ecology of the lake. Fish-eating birds left the lake and malaria-carrying mosquitoes increased as they were no longer cropped by native fishes.

Electric fish studies, initiated by Hans Lissmann, proliferated exceedingly in laboratories in many parts of the world, with field studies both on the gymnotoids in South America and on the ecologically convergent (but unrelated) mormyrid electric fishes in Africa. In 1995, when I revisited Brazil on an International Limnological Society (SIL) post-congress excursion to look at the classic Amazonian black and white water sites near Manaus, Cristine Cox-Fernandes took me trawling for zooplanktivorous gymnotoids in the running waters of the Rio Negro. Just before sunset the trawl was very dramatically jammed with a spectacular catch of over 450 specimens of one gymnotoid species (of *Rhabdolichops*). Meanwhile, another 1000 km (600 miles) up the main Amazon from Manaus, Will Crampton was studying the habitat preferences and electric signals of 64 species of gymnotoids, many new to science, discovered in the vast seasonally flooded white-water swamp at Mamirauá near Tefé.

I had fun collating Guyana observations with those from African lakes and rivers and other tropical regions in two books: *Fish Communities in Tropical Freshwaters* (1975) followed by *Ecological Studies in tropical fish Communities* (1987). The latter included comparisons with marine communities, aided by a passion for snorkelling over colourful coral reefs in warm seas. New information from ecological studies in neotropical countries continues to pour in at an accelerating rate, both from scientific expeditions from the developed world and from laboratory centres in South America, now fitted with sophisticated modern equipment; for example from INPA's laboratory in Manaus, initially associated with Dr Sioli's team from the Max-Planck-Institut für Limaologie in Germany.

In 1992 the United Nations Earth Summit Conference on Environment and Development held in Rio, Brazil was a landmark in alerting both scientists and statesmen to the vital importance of conserving the integrity of the ecosystems on which all life depends. A Convention on Biological Diversity was signed by over 150 nations which led to a programme of cooperation in scientific research between institutions (such as museums and universities) in the developed world and their counterparts in countries defined as rich in biological diversity but poor in financial resources (such as Guyana). This began a decade of studies on the importance and roles of biological diversity in conservation, (many from UK under the 'Darwin Initiative' scheme) to determine which ecosystems, species, and genetic material are in most urgent need of conservation. Ecologically we are all dependent on natural processes for air and water, food production, recycling waste disposal, health and happiness, so how can we value the ecosystems? The economic aspects of biodiverse organisms, for example in providing food, useful and potentially useful drugs, as well as in maintaining ecosystems, are being intensively studied. Even more important are the ethical and aesthetic aspects of nature, of incalculable value for the psychological well-being of mankind.

Environmental Changes in Guyana

Meanwhile what had happened in Guyana, as BG had become on attaining independence in 1966? Sadly, fisheries studies declined when for various (political and financial) reasons many Guyanese (including Bertie Allsopp) left the country during the severe economic depression in the 1970s. An estimated 200,000 Guyanese went to live overseas, but the coastal plain, comprising less than 10% of the land area, still contains 90% of the Guyanese population of 760,000. The majority of the country's 50,000 Amerindians still live in the interior, where extractive industries give employment to c 40,000 to 60,000 people, though to relatively few Amerindians.

279

The government of Guyana now has a Natural Resources Programme, aided by United Nations Development Programmes and other projects funded by various overseas agencies. The University of Guyana has expanded; its Faculty of Science had an Environmental Studies Unit established in 1993 which has now graduated its first intake of students. Its Centre for the Study of Biological Diversity is producing a series of publications in cooperation with overseas institutions, including the Smithsonian Institution. For example in collating data on Guyanese plant and animal material in museums outside Guyana, mapping where these were collected to indicate biodiversity in various parts of Guyana and suggest areas most in need of conservation or further study (Funk, Zermoglio and Nasir, 1999). The university's Amerindian Research Unit has studied the role of wildlife in the lives of Makushi people, excellent field biologists.

At the Commonwealth Heads of Government Meeting in Malaysia in 1989, concerned with the accelerating destruction of the world's rain-forests, Guyana donated one million acres (360,000 hectares) of its pristine forest to the international community. The objectives of this 'Iwokrama rainforest project' situated between the Rupununi and the Essequibo were: to create an Amazonian Wilderness Preserve for the maintainance and study of diversity and ecological processes, a programme for sustainable utilisation of tropical rainforest to yield economic benefits for the people of Guyana, and as an International Centre for Research and Training. Though initiated in 1990, plans were held up as this area was within territory claimed by the Makushi people, but after years in legal limbo the Iwokrama International Centre for Rain Forest Conservation and Development was formerly established in May 1996, with a field station at Kurupukari, where the Lethem road crosses the Essequibo (see Map 1).

Biologically the Iwokrama project is of prime importance for the whole region. A GEF-UNDP grant supported the project in 1993, but as the President of Guyana reported to the United Nations General Assembly in June 1997, assistance is needed from overseas donors, Guyana being 'a small developing state which must face the task of sustainable development against great odds'. In 1999 some international finance has been found, but much expertise is needed in carrying out the necessary studies.

Prior to the mid-1980s the interior of Guyana had remained virtually untouched, but with the advent of a new 'structural adjustment programme' based on logging and mining, the situation began changing rapidly. The resulting environmental changes were discussed at two workshops in London: in May 1997 on *Environment and Development in Guyana*', with an associated book on *Land Use, Land Degradation and Land Management in Guyana* edited by Patrick Williams (University of Guyana), John Parry (McGill University, Canada), and Michael Eden (University of London); in June 1998 at the '*Amazonia 2000: Development, Environment and Geopolitics*' meeting. The history of the logging and mining concessions, attempts to set up forest reserves, and the controversy concerning a plan to put a road from Brazil to Georgetown through the rain forest which would inevitably open up much country, was summarised by Marcus Colchester (1997) in *Guyana Fragile Frontier: Loggers, Miners and Forest Peoples*. The Guyana Review, June 1999 (on the Internet) devoted a section to threats to the environment, Iwokrama and the floral and faunal surveys in that area towards the preparation of field guides.

Briefly, the abyssmal financial situation in the 1970–80s led to selling off concessions to foreign companies (several from Southeast Asia) to clear large areas of forest, in most cases ignoring the impacts on the local Amerindian communities dependent on forest products for their livelihood. Mining developments for bauxite, gold and diamonds now involve huge 'missile-dredges' which gouge out and dig deep into river banks, resulting in sedimentation which prevents residents from getting fish for domestic purposes or for aquarium trading. Fallen trees and the creation of new sand banks impede river navigation. The use of mercury by gold miners endangers residents who depend on river water for all purposes, and mercury is building up in the fish foodchain, as

281

it has in gold-mining areas in neighbouring Brazil and Venezuela. Reports from the Upper and Middle Mazaruni tell of what were once clear rivers flowing between forested banks now become wide washes of mud and debris.

In the Essequibo system an environmental disaster struck in August 1995 at the Omai open-pit mine (star on Map 1), a Canadian Golden Star company enterprise which since 1991 had become one of South America's largest goldmines, when the tailings pond containing cyanide, other chemicals and mill waste, developed cracks and the contents cascaded into the Omai tributary and rushed in a massive plume down the Essequibo River. This meant that several thousand people in scattered communities along the river could not use the river for drinking, washing or fishing for a considerable period.

The coastal area is said to have undergone pronounced physical alterations from land settlement schemes, with clearance of mangroves which has enhanced coastal erosion and flooding of saline water into the rice-growing lands. Initially the extensive hinterland had remained largely unaltered except for areas exploited for commercial logging and mining or for subsistence purposes by the indigenous population. But large areas of the State Forests have now been leased to loggers, the most accessible areas immediately south of the coastal plain being the most heavily exploited - the hilly sand and clay region that carries dry evergreen forest, containing wallaba (*Eperua* spp) and mora (*Mora excelsa*), has become the major source of fuelwood and charcoal. Bauxite mining in this region has led to extensive forest clearance where regeneration on these sandy soils is slow, thus endangering the dry evergreen forest.

Selective logging need not result in deforestation, but forest monitoring is inadequate and more mapping and information on tree growth rates are needed. The construction of forest roads also leads the way for more destructive activities like mining and large-scale farming. The problems involved were illustrated in the Barama River project in NW Guyana, established in 1991 by a consortium of South Korean and Malaysian investors, which has a Timber Sales Agreement to extract timber from c 1.6 million ha, the harvested logs being processed into plywood for sale on the export market. An Environmental and Social Assessment was made by the Edinburgh Centre for Tropical Forests, but local environmentalists, Amerindian organisations and political activists reported that logging here was destroying habitats for wild animals on which local Amerindians depend for food, and the increased run off and erosion were damaging local streams and rivers. Many Amerindians (for example from the Kokerit settlement on the Barama River we visited in 1958) have migrated to other areas or become integrated into coastal communities.

The main trends now apparent in the mining industry of Guyana are the capital-intensive nature of local operations since the introduction of missile-dredges late 1980s, entry of highly capitalized foreign operators (in late 1980s), and the illegal entry of prospectors from Brazil. There is evidence of mercury pollution in Mazaruni and Potaro river areas where gold mining has lately increased, and of mining dredges damaging river banks and channels, polluting rivers with adverse effects on fish resources. Gold mining on a small scale widely distributed along rivers is difficult to monitor and the situation has been aggrevated by itinerant Brazilian gold miners (*garimpeiros*) invading Guyana. Furthermore, their open pits breed malaria-carrying mosquitoes. In the Upper Mazaruni Kamarang is now the hub of the mining industry, which has affected the social fabric of Akawaio life, with the school, rum shops and discos now located alongside the airstrip.

There has been however, mounting pressure from environmentalists and international funding agencies to ensure that commercial investment does not grossly degrade the environment. In the 1990s Government signed several international agreements, ratifying the International Convention on Biological Diversity, laying out a National Environment Action Plan to implement its new commitments, and setting up an Environmental Protection Agency. Since 1993 the development agencies have been sending in teams of environmental consultants to try to alleviate environmental damage. Obstacles to proposed schemes included delays in access to government offices, also government's reluctance to consider any region for protected status until exhaustive mineral surveys have been carried out - for under Guyanese law all subsurface resources are considered the property of the state. This law also delayed Amerindian land settlement claims. Guyana reputedly now has environmental consultants jetting in to study particular aspects of the country's situation, but lightning field trips can result in reports which then gather dust in government offices.

The only National Park is still the 11,600 ha Kaieteur Falls area, established largely for its scenic value, but this lacked a management plan; illegal miners working the Potaro river for gold and diamonds above and below falls were said to use the park buildings. Attempts to increase the size of the park to conserve viable populations of fauna and flora were fiercely resisted by the mining lobby. A WWF study recommended an expanded park of over 500 square miles, but a reduced version of half this area is now being discussed by government.

Among eleven priority conservation zones proposed for protected area status by biologists at the University of Guyana, the Kanuku Mountains have long attracted the interest of conservationsts, including Conservation International and the European Commission. The EC proposed the creation of a 'Kanuku Amerindian National Park' of some 290,000 ha as part of an integrated parks development that would directly involve the local people, for there are seven Amerindian reservations, including sixteen villages and 4,600 Amerindians living within the area of influence of the proposed park. Amerindians have a key role to play in development of protected areas and it is the Amerindian peoples who possess the biological knowledge of Guyana's plants and animals that sustain the ecosystems here on which human life depends.

The wildlife trade is another contentious issue. This has been a means of sustenance for large numbers of people for several generations, but has recently become more competitive and exploitive. The World Bank in 1995 reported that in 1992 about 153,000 wild animals were exported, including parrots, macaws, poison arrow frogs, and caiman skins. The declared foreign exchange income was US $1.9 million. But there is increasing concern that many species of wildlife are becoming endangered by the trade, particularly by export of endangered species and illegal shipment of animals. Guyana's wildlife is worth so much more than this. Apart from its incalculable aesthetic value, wild animals and fish are extremely important as food for the forest peoples. Furthermore the wildlife provides the basis for ecotourism, which is now being developed. And without forests and unpolluted waters this wildlife will vanish, and in many areas is fast disappearing. Management for conservation and sustainable use of wildlife is complex but is now being tackled by the government's Environmental Protection Agency and Wildlife Division.

The Iwokrama project and North Rupununi District Development Board are working together to develop a detailed information base on the wildlife and other natural resources. Floral and fauna surveys over the past three years from the Iwokrama International Centre, with technical cooperation from the Smithsonian's Biodiversity of the Guianas Programme for floral surveys, and by the Philadelphia Academy of Natural Sciences and the Royal Ontario Museum for faunal surveys, have now recorded more than 1175 plant species, with 114 species of reptiles and amphibians, 450 of birds, 127 of mammals and 320 fish species in adjacent rivers (Guyana Review, June 1999).

How much can the development of ecotourism help the country? Among other attractions Diane McTurk, who has been running the Karanambo ranch since her parents died many years ago, has been developing ecotourism facilities for fishermen and other visitors and is also looking after a group of orphen giant otters which recently became TV stars in widely shown television programmes. Rainforest 'eco-adventures' tours are now arranged to visit Kaieteur Falls, one of the wonders of the World, and other parts of the country. As the only English-speaking part of South America, and for many other reasons, travelling and working in Guyana is much easier than in adjacent South American countries. Visiting

285

biologists could contribute to the International Iwokrama Rainforest Project, which greatly needs specialist assistance.

Despite the degradation of some areas, most of Guyana still remains unspoilt, rich in orchids and other exotic plants, with a wonderful bird fauna and intriguing creatures about which so much remains to be discovered. But it needs much outside help to keep it so. Travelling in Guyana's forests, across the open sunny savannas and on the great rivers, is very reviving to the human spirit. So why not visit the Land of Waters?

BIBLIOGRAPHY

Attenborough, D. (1956) *Zoo Quest to Guiana*. London: Lutterworth Press.

Barrington-Brown, C. (1877) *Canoe and Camp Life in British Guiana*. London: E. Stanford.

Bates, H.W. (1863) *The Naturalist on the River Amazons*. London: John Murray (Reprinted 1969).

Beebe, Mary B. & Beebe, W. (1910) *Our Search for a Wilderness*. An account of two ornithological expeditions to Venezuela and British Guiana. New York: Henry Holt.

Beebe, W., Hartley, G.I. & Howes, P.G. (1917) *Tropical Wild Life in British Guiana*, Contributions from the Tropical Research Station of the New York Zoological Society. New York: Zoological Society.

Beebe, W. (1922) *The Edge of the Jungle*. London: Witherby.

Bertram, Colin (1963) *In Search of Mermaids*. London: Peter Davies.

Blackburn, Julia (1981) *Charles Waterton 1782–1865. Traveller and Conservationist*. Natural Trust Classics. London: Century.

Brock, S. (1963) *Hunting in the Wilderness*. London: Robert Hale.

Colchester, M. (1997) *Guyana Fragile Frontier: Loggers, Miners and Forest Peoples*. London: Latin America Bureau & World Rainforest Movement.

Durrell, Gerald (1954) *Three Singles to Adventure*. London: Rupert Hart Davies (1964, 1965, 1966 Penguin Books).

Eigenmann, C.H. (1917) *The freshwater fishes of British Guiana, including a study of the ecological grouping of species and the relation of the fauna of the plateau to that of the lowlands*. Memoirs Carnegie Museum No 5, Pittsburgh.

287

Emmons, L.H. & Feer, F. (1990) *Neotropical Rainforest Mammals*. A Field Guide. University of Chicago Press.

Fanshaw D.B. (1952) *The Vegetation of British Guiana A Preliminary Review*. Imperial Forestry Institute Paper No 29, University of Oxford.

Funk, V.A., Zermoglio, M. Fernanda & Nasir, Naseem (1999) Testing the use of specimen collection data and GIS in biodiversity exploration and conservation decision making in Guyana. *Biodiversity and Conservation*, 8: 727–751.

Goulding, Michael (1980) *The Fishes and the Forest. Explorations in Amazonian Natural History*. Berkeley: University of California Press.

Hemming, John & Ratter, James (1993) *Maracá Rainforest Island*. London: Macmillan.

Hingston, R.W.G. (1932) *A Naturalist in the Guiana Forest*. London: Ed. Arnold.

Humboldt, A. von (1852) *Travels to the Equinoctial Regions of America during the years 1799–1804, by Alexander von Humboldt and Aimé Bonpland*. London: H.G. Bohn.

Kricher, J. (1997) *A Neotropical Companion: An Introduction to the Animals, Plants, and Ecosystems of the New World Tropics*. (2nd Edn) Princeton University Press.

Lowe-McConnell, R.H. (1962) The fishes of the British Guiana continental shelf, Atlantic coast of South America, with notes on their natural history. *Journal Linnean Society (Zoology)* 44: 669–700.

Lowe-McConnell, R.H. (1964) The fishes of the Rupununi savanna district of British Guiana, South America. *Journal Linnean Society (Zoology)* 45: 103–144.

Lowe-McConnell, R.H. (1966) The Sciaenid fishes of British Guiana. *Bulletin of Marine Science* 16: 20–57.

Lowe-McConnell. R.H. (1967) Biology of the Cattle egret *Ardeola ibis* in Guyana, South America. *Ibis* 109: 168–179.

Lowe-McConnell, R.H. (1969) The cichlid fishes of Guyana, S. America, with notes on their ecology and breeding behaviour. *Journal Linnean Society (Zoology)* 48: 255–302.

Lowe-McConnell, R.H. (1987) *Ecological studies in tropical fish communities.* Cambridge University Press 3982 pp (Portuguese language edition 1999, University of Sao Paulo).

Ouboter, P.E. (ed) (1993) *The Freshwater Ecosystems of Suriname.* Dordrecht: Kluwer Academic Publishers.

O'Shea, T., Ackerman, B.B. & Percival, H.F. (1995) *Population biology of the Florida manatee.* Information & Technology report 1, U.S. Department of the Interior, Washington, DC.

Roth, Vincent (1943) *Fish Life in British Guiana 1907–1943.* Guiana Edition No 8, Daily Chronicle Georgetown.

Roth, V. (ed) (1950–61) *Timehri: The Journal of the Royal Agricultural and Commercial Society of British Guiana*, has many relevant articles by various authors. Georgetown: Daily Chronicle.

Schomburgk, Richard (trans W.E. Roth) 1922. *Travels in British Guiana 1840–1844.* Georgetown: Daily Chronicle.

Snyder, D.E. (1966) *The Birds of Guyana*, Salem: Peabody Museum.

Swan, Michael (1958) *The Marches of El Dorado, British Guiana, Brazil, Venezuela.* London, Jonathan Cape.

Wallace, A.R. (1853) *A Narrative of Travels on the Amazon and Rio Negro.* London: Ward Lock & Co.

Waterton, Charles (1826) *Wanderings in South America: in the years 1812–1824.* Suffolk: Clay & Sons (New Editions: with Biographical Introduction and Explanatory Index by Rev. J.G. Wood, 1905, London: Macmillan & Co.; 1981 National Trust Classics, see Blackburn).

Waugh, Evelyn (1934) *Ninety-Two Days. A Journey in Guiana and Brazil.* London: Duckworth. (Part reprinted 1951 in *When the Going was Good.* Penguin Books)

Williams, P.E., Parry, J.T. & Eden, M.J. (1997) *Land Use, Land Degradation and Land Management in Guyana.* London: Commonwealth Geographical Bureau.